SELECTED REPRINTS a project of the AAPT Committee on Resource Letters

Reprint books in this series are available at $2 each, or any combination of 3 for $5. Single orders to one address for any combination of 15 or more reprint books, $1.50 per copy from: Department BN, American Institute of Physics, 335 East 45 Street, New York, N. Y. 10017.

SMALL AMPLITUDE WAVES IN PLASMA

1 Resource Letter PP-2 on Plasma Physics: Waves and Radiation Processes in Plasmas --- G. Bekefi and Sanborn C. Brown

5 Waves in Anisotropic Plasmas --- W. P. Allis, S. J. Buchsbaum, and A. Bers

46 Plasma Oscillations (I) --- I. B. Bernstein and S. K. Trehan

85 On the Vibrations of the Electronic Plasma --- L. Landau

95 Landau Damping of Electron Plasma Waves --- J. H. Malmberg, C. B. Wharton, and W. E. Drummond

108 One Dimensional Plasma Model --- John Dawson

Resource Letter PP–2* on Plasma Physics: Waves and Radiation Processes in Plasmas

G. Bekefi and Sanborn C. Brown

Department of Physics, Massachusetts Institute of Technology, Cambridge, Massachusetts 02139

Prepared at the request of the AAPT Committee on Resource Letters; supported by a grant from the National Science Foundation.

This is one of a series of Resource Letters on different topics, intended to guide college physicists to some of the literature and other teaching aids that may help them improve course contents in specified fields of physics. No Resource Letter is meant to be exhaustive and complete; in time there may be more than one letter on some of the main subjects of interest. Comments and suggestions concerning the content and arrangement of letters as well as suggestions for future topics will be welcomed. Please send such communications to Professor Arnold Arons, Chairman Resource Letter Committee, Department of Physics, Amherst College, Amherst, Massachusetts.

Notation: The letter *E* after the item number means that the reference should be mainly useful for *elementary* courses. In view of the complexity of the subject, *elementary* will normally imply junior courses. The letter *I* indicates *intermediate* (senior and first-year graduates) and *A* indicates *advanced* (second-year graduates and students beginning research in plasma physics).

Additional copies: Available from American Institute of Physics, 335 East 45 Street, New York, New York 10017. When ordering, request Resource Letter PP-2 and enclose a stamped return envelope.

I. SMALL-AMPLITUDE WAVES AND OSCILLATIONS IN PLASMAS

A PLASMA can support a large variety of waves and natural modes of oscillation and these can be grouped into two classes: essentially transverse modes which are electromagnetic in character and longitudinal modes which are somewhat like sound waves. To determine the properties of these modes one solves, in a self-consistent way, equations for the particle motions in conjunction with Maxwell's field equations. This leads to nonlinear equations which are then linearized subject to the assumption that the oscillation amplitudes are small.

The equations for the motions of the charged particles can be given in three ways. In increasing order of sophistication and accuracy, they are: Newton's laws of motion of a single particle; fluid equations of magnetohydrodynamics; the Boltzmann equations.

The literature cited below is in large part concerned with the model of an infinite, homogeneous plasma where collisions between particles are neglected. If an external magnetic field is applied, it is assumed to be uniform.

1.E **Classical Electrodynamics.** J. D. Jackson. (John Wiley & Sons, Inc., New York, 1962), Chap. X. Incomplete but very readable outline on waves and oscillations as determined from magnetohydrodynamic equations.

2.E **Plasmas and Controlled Fusion.** D. J. Rose and M. Clark, Jr. (The M.I.T. Press, Cambridge, Mass., and John Wiley & Sons, Inc., New York, 1961), Chap. IX. This covers similar ground to Ref. 1, and like that reference, the treatment is elementary.

3.E **Plasma Physics.** S. Chandrasekhar. (University of Chicago Press, Chicago, Ill., 1960), Chap. VI. Lucid presentation of longitudinal oscillations in the absence of an external magnetic field. The Boltzmann equation is introduced.

4.I **Waves in Anisotropic Plasmas.** W. P. Allis, S. J. Buchsbaum, and A. Bers. (The M.I.T. Press, Cambridge, Mass., 1963), Pt. I. Geometric representation of wave propagation in an anisotropic plasma in terms of phase velocity surfaces. This mode of presentation is analogous to that customarily used in crystal optics. In the model, the particles of the plasma undergo no collisions and possess no thermal motion.

5.I **Plasma Waves.** J. F. Denisse and J. L. Delcroix. (Interscience Publishers, Inc., New York, 1963), 143 pp. Covers the same ground as Ref. 4 but the emphasis is on a representation through dispersion diagrams as customarily used by radio engineers and students of the ionosphere. A deceptively "small" book.

6.A **The Theory of Plasma Waves.** T. H. Stix. (McGraw-Hill Book Co., Inc., New York, 1962.) Elegant exposition of a broad spectrum of wave–plasma interactions in a fully ionized medium, including damped and unstable oscillations.

7.A **Propagation of Electromagnetic Waves in Plasma.** V. L. Ginzburg. (Gordon and Breach Science

* This is the second of two resource letters on Plasma Physics. The first (PP-1) deals with electrical phenomena in gases and in fusion and was published in the July 1961 issue of the American Journal of Physics. Copies of both resource letters are available from the American Institute of Physics.

Publishers, New York, 1961.) Reference book, emphasizing problems in the ionosphere.

II. DAMPING OF PLASMA WAVES

There are two main damping processes whereby a wave decreases in amplitude as it travels through the plasma. The one results from collisions between the different species of particles. The other is a resonance mechanism ("Landau" and "cyclotron" damping) between the wave and those particles whose velocity is in synchronism with the phase velocity of the wave.

8.E **The Magneto-Ionic Theory and its Applications to the Ionosphere.** J. A. RATCLIFFE. (Cambridge University Press, London, 1959), Chaps. IV and V. The effect of collisions on wave propagation is explained from microscopic and macroscopic points of view.

9.E **Ionization Phenomena in Gases.** G. FRANCIS. (Butterworth, Inc., Washington, D. C., 1960), Chap. VII. Presents a qualitative picture of Landau damping.

10.A **The Theory of Plasma Waves.** T. H. STIX. (McGraw-Hill Book Co., Inc., New York, 1962), Chaps. VII and VIII. Thorough treatment of Landau and cyclotron damping is presented.

11.A **"Longitudinal Plasma Oscillations."** J. D. JACKSON. J. Nucl. Energy [Pt. C] **1**, 171 (1960). Particularly lucid mathematical treatment of Landau damping.

12.I **"Propagation and Damping of Ion Acoustic Waves in Highly Ionized Plasmas."** A. Y. WONG, N. D'ANGELO, AND R. W. MOTLEY. Phys. Rev. Letters **9**, 415 (1962). Elegant experiments demonstrating Landau and viscous damping of low-frequency ion-acoustic waves.

13.I **"Collisionless Damping of Electrostatic Plasma Waves."** J. H. MALMBERG AND C. B. WHARTON. Phys. Rev. Letters **13**, 184 (1964). First experimental demonstration of Landau damping of high-frequency longitudinal waves.

III. OSCILLATIONS IN BOUNDED AND NONUNIFORM PLASMAS

Boundaries and inhomogeneities of the medium give rise to reflections, standing waves, and coupling between different normal modes of oscillation that would exist in an infinite homogeneous medium. The literature below refers to a small selection from a great variety of possible phenomena.

14.I **Plasma Diagnostics with Microwaves.** M. A. HEALD AND C. B. WHARTON. (John Wiley & Sons, Inc., New York, 1965), Chap. IV. Discusses reflection and transmission of transverse electromagnetic waves at plasma surfaces and from plasma slabs.

15.A **Propagation of Electromagnetic Waves in Plasma.** V. L. GINZBURG. (Gordon and Breach Science Publishers, New York, 1961), Chaps. IV and V. Mathematical treatment of reflection and wave coupling in plasmas whose refractive index varies slowly with position so that adiabatic (WKB) approximations are applicable.

16.I **"Oscillations of a Finite Cold Plasma in a Strong Magnetic Field."** J. DAWSON AND C. OBERMAN. Phys. Fluids **2**, 103 (1959). Discusses the dispersion characteristics of waves in and outside a slab and cylinder of plasma due to excitation of longitudinal oscillations.

17.I **"Longitudinal Oscillations in a Nonuniform Plasma."** F. C. HOH. Phys. Rev. **133**, A1016 (1964). Gives a physical and mathematical explanation of the spectrum of standing longitudinal oscillations in a plasma slab.

18.A **"Resonance Oscillations in a Hot Nonuniform Plasma."** J. V. PARKER, J. C. NICKEL, AND R. W. GOULD. Phys. Fluids **7**, 1489 (1964). Covers the same ground as Ref. 17 together with a description of the experiments.

19.A **"Excitation of Longitudinal Plasma Oscillations Near Electron Cyclotron Harmonics."** S. J. BUCHSBAUM AND A. HASEGAWA. Phys. Rev. Letters **12**, 685 (1964). Explains the spectrum of longitudinal oscillations when a magnetic field is applied to a plasma column.

20.A **Waves in Anisotropic Plasmas.** W. P. ALLIS, S. J. BUCHSBAUM, AND A. BERS. (The M.I.T. Press, Cambridge, Mass., 1963), Pt. II. Very mathematical exposition of wave propagation in waveguides partially or wholly filled with plasma.

IV. FLUCTUATIONS

The charged particles of a plasma are subjected to mutual frictional forces and consequently local rf electric and magnetic fields are generated. Knowledge of the spectrum of the fluctuations is a starting point in the calculation of emission and scattering of electromagnetic waves. When the plasma is in thermal equilibrium, the spectrum can be derived from an extension of Nyquist's theorem.

21.E **Elementary Statistical Physics.** C. KITTEL. (John Wiley & Sons, Inc., New York, 1958), Secs. 27 to 31. A review of Fourier integral transforms, theory of random processes and Nyquist's theorem.

22.A **Statistical Physics.** L. D. LANDAU AND E. M. LIFSHITZ. (Addison-Wesley Publ. Co., Reading, Mass., 1958), Secs. 122 to 124. Quantum mechanical derivation of generalized Nyquist theorem.

23.A **Advanced Plasma Theory.** M. N. ROSENBLUTH, Ed. (Academic Press Inc., New York, 1964.) Article on kinetic theory by W. B. Thompson. Course of lectures on kinetic theory of plasmas including fluctuation theory in thermal and nonthermal media.

24.A "Friction and Diffusion Coefficients of the Fokker-Planck Equation in a Plasma." J. HUBBARD. Proc. Roy. Soc. (London) **A260**, 114 (1961). Derives on a few lines the fluctuation spectrum in a manner similar to that of Ref. 23.

25.A "Fluctuations of a Plasma (I)." N. ROSTOKER. Nucl. Fusion **1**, 101 (1961). Detailed mathematical exposition for experts only.

V. RADIATION OF ELECTROMAGNETIC WAVES

The two main processes are bremsstrahlung and cyclotron radiation. In a very tenuous plasma, where many-particle collective interactions can be neglected, elementary theory based on single-particle and two-particle encounters suffices to explain the phenomena. In dense plasmas, application of results of Sec. IV can be used to determine the emission spectra.

26.E Elementary Plasma Physics. C. L. LONGMIRE. (Interscience Publishers, Inc., New York, 1963), Chap. XII. Elementary treatment of radiation.

27.I "Radiation from Plasmas." J. M. DAWSON. Plasma Physics Laboratory Report No. MATT-428 (1965), Princeton University. A brief introductory review of bremsstrahlung and cyclotron radiation given in a series of five lectures at the Plasma Physics Summer Institute (1964) at Princeton University.

28.I Plasma Diagnostics with Microwaves. M. A. HEALD AND C. B. WHARTON. (John Wiley & Sons, Inc., New York, 1965.) Chapter VII of this book contains a somewhat more detailed discussion of the subject matter of Ref. 27, plus a brief note on Čerenkov radiation. Chapter VIII describes pertinent experiments conducted on laboratory-produced plasmas.

29.I "Emission, Absorption, and Conductivity of a Fully Ionized Gas at Radio Frequencies." L. OSTER. Rev. Mod. Phys. **33**, 525 (1961). Theory of bremsstrahlung due to electron–ion collisions. The plasma is tenuous and only binary collisions are considered.

30.A Electrodynamics of Continuous Media. L. D. LANDAU AND E. M. LIFSHITZ. (Addison-Wesley Publ. Co., Reading, Mass., 1960), Chap. XIII. Derives from Nyquist's theorem the blackbody spectrum in a dispersive medium.

31.A "The Radio-Frequency Emission Coefficient of a Hot Plasma." R. P. MERCIER. Proc. Phys. Soc. (London) **83**, 819 (1964). Application of Nyquist's theorem to calculation of the bremsstrahlung spectrum in a fully ionized gas, taking account of collective effects.

32.I The Sun. G. P. KUIPER, Ed. (University of Chicago Press, Chicago, Ill., 1953), Chap. VII. Describes observations of radio emission from the solar corona.

33.A "Radio Emission from Shock Waves and Type II Solar Outbursts." D. A. TIDMAN. Planet. Space Sci. **13**, 781 (1965). Attempt to explain solar bursts in terms of enhanced bremsstrahlung in a plasma with a non-Maxwellian velocity distribution of electrons.

34.I Cosmic Radio Waves. I. S. SHKLOVSKY. (Harvard University Press, Cambridge, Mass., 1960.) Fascinating account of bremsstrahlung and cyclotron radiation from cosmic objects and use of the observations in cosmological theory.

35.I The Origin of Cosmic Rays. V. L. GINZBURG AND S. I. SYROVATSKII. (The Macmillan Co., New York, 1964.) Includes a good exposition of the role of cyclotron radiation in the theory of cosmic rays.

36.I "Microwave Emission and Absorption at Cyclotron Harmonics of a Warm Plasma." G. BEKEFI, J. D. COCCOLI, E. B. HOOPER, AND S. J. BUCHSBAUM. Phys. Rev. Letters **9**, 6 (1962). An experiment on cyclotron harmonic emission caused by the excitation of longitudinal waves by suprathermal electrons.

37.I "Excitation of Electrostatic Waves near Electron Cyclotron Harmonic Frequencies." P. M. STONE AND P. L. AUER. Phys. Rev. **138**, A695 (1965). A theoretical treatment of the process described in Ref. 36.

VI. SCATTERING OF ELECTROMAGNETIC WAVES FROM ELECTRON DENSITY FLUCTUATIONS

In a highly ionized plasma, the electrons are the only important centers of scattering. But, since the electron and ion motions are coupled, the ions can, under certain conditions, completely dominate the spectrum of the incoherently scattered radiation. Determination of the scattered spectrum gives much important information about the plasma. Measurements using both high-power lasers and microwave sources have been reported.

38.E Introduction to Modern Physics. F. K. RICHTMYER AND E. H. KENNARD. (McGraw-Hill Book Co., Inc., New York, 1942), Chap. X. Classical (Thomson) scattering of light by a single stationary electron.

39.I Electrodynamics of Continuous Media. L. D. LANDAU AND E. M. LIFSHITZ. (Addison-Wesley Publ. Co., Reading, Mass., 1960), Chap. XIV. Excellent review of scattering theory including scattering from density fluctuations in un-ionized gases.

40.I "A Theory of Incoherent Scattering of Radio Waves by a Plasma." J. P. DOUGHERTY AND D. T. FARLEY. Proc. Roy. Soc. (London) **A259**, 79 (1960). Derives the spectrum of scattered radiation in a fully ionized, thermal plasma using Nyquist's theorem (see Sec. IV).

41.A Advanced Plasma Theory. M. N. ROSENBLUTH, Ed. (Academic Press Inc., New York, 1964.) Article on Kinetic Theory by W. B. Thompson. Covers similar ground to that of Ref. 40, but derives the spectrum for a plasma with an arbitrary distribution of electron and ion velocities.

42.I "Thomson Scattering of Optical Radiation from an

Electron Beam." G. Fiocco and E. Thompson. Phys. Rev. Letters **10**, 89 (1963). Experiment showing the scattering of laser light from individual electrons of of electron beam.

43.I **"Radiation Scattered from the Plasma Produced by a Focused Ruby Laser Beam."** S. A. Ramsden and W. E. R. Davies. Phys. Rev. Letters **13**, 227 (1964). Experiment on scattering of laser light from a dense laboratory-produced plasma, where the electrons are shielded by the ion cloud.

44.I **"Ionospheric Backscatter Observations."** J. V. Evans and M. Loewenthal. Planet. Space Sci. **12** 915 (1964). An experiment equivalent to that of Ref. 43 carried out with microwaves. The plasma medium is now the ionosphere. Very clean experiment that demonstrates without doubt the effect of ion shielding.

45.A **"Microwave Scattering due to Acoustic-Ion-Plasma-Wave Instability."** V. Arunasalam and S. C. Brown. Phys. Rev. **140**, A471 (1965). Experiment on the scattering of microwaves from unstable, low-frequency oscillations in a plasma column.

VII. GROWING WAVES (INSTABILITIES)

Waves in a nonthermal plasma can, under certain conditions, grow both with distance traversed and with time. Conditions for the occurrence of such unstable modes, their frequency and growth rates, are one of the major fields of study in plasma physics. The diversity of unstable modes appears to be almost limitless. Below we cite but a few special cases.

46.I **Advanced Plasma Theory.** M. N. Rosenbluth, Ed. (Academic Press Inc., New York, 1964.) Article on microinstabilities by M. N. Rosenbluth. A fairly elementary physical discussion of several instabilities with and without externally applied magnetic fields.

47.A **"Dissipation of Currents in Ionized Media."** O. Buneman. Phys. Rev. **115**, 503 (1959). Treats on the instability caused by relative motion between streams of charged particles.

48.A **Electron-Stream Interaction with Plasmas.** R. J. Briggs. (The M.I.T. Press, Cambridge, Mass., 1964.) Treats in detail on instabilities caused by the interaction between a plasma and an electron beam. Differentiates between waves that grow in time and those that grow with distance.

49.A **The Theory of Plasma Waves.** T. H. Stix. (McGraw-Hill Book Co., Inc., New York, 1962.) Almost the entire text is sprinkled with a large assortment of instabilities in fully ionized, hot plasmas.

VIII. LARGE-AMPLITUDE WAVES (TURBULENCE IN PLASMAS)

This is one of the most challenging fields for today's plasma theoreticians. Relatively little is understood about large-amplitude waves and turbulence. In addition, there is a lack of meaningful experiments.

50.I **"Anomalous Diffusion of a Plasma Across a Magnetic Field."** S. Yoshikawa and D. J. Rose. Phys. Fluids **5**, 335 (1962). Discusses observations of enhanced particle loss caused by turbulent fluctuations in plasma density.

51.A **Plasma Turbulence.** B. B. Kadomtsev. (Academic Press Inc., New York, 1965.) Chapters on the quasilinear approximation in the Vlasov equation, weak turbulence, strong turbulence, and various effects of turbulence on a plasma, such as heating and anomalous diffusion.

52.A **Advanced Plasma Theory.** M. N. Rosenbluth, Ed. (Academic Press Inc., New York, 1964.) Article on Nonlinear Theory of Electrostatic Waves by P. A. Sturrock. By comparison with other papers in the field, a readable discussion of the degradation of large-amplitude waves into random wave and particle motion.

53.A **"Nonlinear Plasma Oscillations."** W. E. Drummond and D. Pines. Ann. Phys. (NY) **28**, 478 (1964). Develops quasilinear theory for an initially unstable electron distribution in one dimension.

54.A **"Resonant Wave–Wave Scattering of Plasma Oscillations."** R. E. Aamodt and W. E. Drummond. Phys. Fluids **7**, 1816 (1964). Similar to 52 but for three dimensions in a strong magnetic field.

IX. PLASMA DIAGNOSTICS WITH WAVES

Studies of a plasma through its interaction with electromagnetic waves have been made by many workers over frequencies ranging from optical to radio. Below we give a small selection of references in order of increasing wavelength.

55.E **"Optical Refractivity of High Temperature Gases."** R. Alpher and D. White. Phys. Fluids **2**, 153, 162 (1959). Use is made of an optical interferometer and a fringe-counting technique to determine the electron density.

56.E **"Some Results of Using Optical Interferometry for Plasma Diagnostics."** A. Klein. Phys. Fluids **6**, 310 (1963). This technique is similar to that of Ref. 55.

57.E **"Measurement of Plasma Density using a Gas Laser as an Infrared Interferometer."** D. E. T. F. Ashby and D. F. Jephcott. Appl. Phys. Letters **3**, 13 (1963). A novel type of interferometer that uses a gas laser and a Fabry–Perot etalon.

58.E **"A Laser Interferometer for Repetitively Pulsed Plasmas."** E. B. Hooper and G. Bekefi. Appl. Phys. Letters **7**, 133 (1965). A more sensitive version of the instrument of Ref. 57.

59.E **"Far Infrared Interferometer for the Measurement of High Electron Densities."** S. C. Brown, G. Bekefi, and R. E. Whitney. J. Opt. Soc. Am. **53**, 448 (1963).

60.I **Plasma Diagnostics with Microwaves.** M. A. Heald and C. B. Wharton. (John Wiley & Sons, Inc., New York, 1965.) Gives a detailed description of microwave techniques.

61.I **Plasma Diagnostic Techniques.** R. H. Huddlestone and S. Leonard, Eds. (Academic Press Inc., New York, 1965.) Discusses infrared, microwave, and other techniques.

Chapter 1

GENERAL PROPERTIES OF WAVES IN ANISOTROPIC MEDIA

1.1 The Material Equations

The solution of any theory in plasma physics is generally obtained by assuming a form for the electric field $\underset{\sim}{E}$, using this to calculate the charge density ρ and current $\underset{\sim}{J}$, and then requiring that $\underset{\sim}{E}$, ρ, and $\underset{\sim}{J}$ be consistent with Maxwell's equations. We wish to study periodic waves and shall therefore assume the time and space variation of $\underset{\sim}{E}$ to be as $\exp j(\omega t - \underset{\sim}{k} \cdot \underset{\sim}{r})$ and shall further specify that ω is real and let the propagation vector $\underset{\sim}{k}$ come out as it may. There are several choices for the next step: In Chapters 2 to 4 we use the equation of motion for a single particle of mass m_i and charge e_i with the Lorentz $(\underset{\sim}{E} + \underset{\sim}{v}_i \times \underset{\sim}{B})$ and Langevin $(-m_i \nu_{ci} \underset{\sim}{v}_i)$ forces

$$m_i \frac{\partial \underset{\sim}{v}_i}{\partial t} = e_i(\underset{\sim}{E} + \underset{\sim}{v}_i \times \underset{\sim}{B}) - m_i \nu_{ci} \underset{\sim}{v}_i \tag{1.1}$$

In Chapter 5 we use the transport equations for the particle density N_i and the particle current $\underset{\sim}{\Gamma}_i$:

$$\left.\begin{aligned} &\frac{\partial N_i}{\partial t} + \underset{\sim}{\nabla} \cdot \underset{\sim}{\Gamma}_i = 0 \\ &\frac{\partial \underset{\sim}{\Gamma}_i}{\partial t} + \underset{\sim}{\nabla} \frac{N_i e_i T_i}{m_i} - \frac{e_i}{m_i}(N_i \underset{\sim}{E} + \underset{\sim}{\Gamma}_i \times \underset{\sim}{B}) = -\nu_{ci} \underset{\sim}{\Gamma}_i \end{aligned}\right\} \tag{1.2}$$

In Chapter 6 we use the Boltzmann equation for the particle distribution function $f_i(\underset{\sim}{r}, \underset{\sim}{v}, t)$

$$\frac{\partial f_i}{\partial t} + \underset{\sim}{\nabla}_r \cdot \underset{\sim}{v} f_i + \frac{e_i}{m_i} \underset{\sim}{\nabla}_v \cdot (\underset{\sim}{E} + \underset{\sim}{v} \times \underset{\sim}{B}) f_i = \nu_{ci}(f_{0i} - f_i) \tag{1.3}$$

In each case the equations are first linearized because we do not choose to study the nonlinear effects, and are then applied separately to electrons and ions, several kinds of ions if desired (Section 4.5), and the results added to get the charges

$$\rho = \sum_i e_i N_i \quad \text{or} \quad \sum_i e_i \int f_i(\underset{\sim}{r}, \underset{\sim}{v}, t)\, d^3v \tag{1.4}$$

and currents

$$\underset{\sim}{J} = \sum_i e_i \underset{\sim}{v}_i N_i \quad \text{or} \quad \sum_i e_i \underset{\sim}{\Gamma}_i \quad \text{or} \quad \sum_i e_i \int \underset{\sim}{v} f_i(\underset{\sim}{r}, \underset{\sim}{v}, t)\, d^3v \qquad (1.4a)$$

These must satisfy the continuity equation

$$\frac{\partial \rho}{\partial t} + \underset{\sim}{\nabla} \cdot \underset{\sim}{J} = 0 \qquad (1.5)$$

In this chapter we shall assume Ohm's law

$$\underset{\sim}{J} = \underset{\approx}{\sigma} \cdot \underset{\sim}{E} \qquad (1.6)$$

in which the conductivity $\underset{\approx}{\sigma}$ has tensor character because of the presence of a static magnetic field $\underset{\sim}{B}_0$ directed along the z axis. This conductivity can be made to include the effects of the spatial gradient terms of the transport or Boltzmann equations because, in the linear approximation, these are also proportional to $\underset{\sim}{E}$. Therefore, the relations obtained here have a considerable degree of generality. We shall not at this point make any assumptions about the dependence of $\underset{\approx}{\sigma}$ on the density N, temperature T, circular frequency ω, or other parameters, but we shall use the symmetry that follows from a special choice of coordinate axes and from the axial nature of the static magnetic field vector $\underset{\sim}{B}_0$.

According to the Onsager relations, the subscripts on the conductivity tensor are interchanged when the sign of an axial vector ($\underset{\sim}{B}_0$) is changed but are not affected by a change in sign of a polar vector such as the propagation vector $\underset{\sim}{k}$:

$$\sigma_{ij}(\underset{\sim}{B}_0, \underset{\sim}{k}) = \sigma_{ji}(-\underset{\sim}{B}_0, \underset{\sim}{k}) = \sigma_{ji}(-\underset{\sim}{B}_0, -\underset{\sim}{k}) \qquad (1.7)$$

Let the propagation vector $\underset{\sim}{k}$ be so oriented with respect to a Cartesian coordinate system that the z, y, x axes are along $\underset{\sim}{B}_0$, $\underset{\sim}{B}_0 \times \underset{\sim}{k}$, and $(\underset{\sim}{B}_0 \times \underset{\sim}{k}) \times \underset{\sim}{B}_0$, respectively. Changing the signs of $\underset{\sim}{B}_0$ and $\underset{\sim}{k}$ then changes the directions of the x and z axes but not of y, and hence changes the signs of σ_{xy} and σ_{yz} but not of σ_{xz} or of the diagonal elements. It follows that

$$\sigma_{xy} = -\sigma_{yx}, \quad \sigma_{yz} = -\sigma_{zy}, \quad \sigma_{zx} = \sigma_{xz} \qquad (1.8)$$

and this reduces the number of independent tensor components to six.

Starting with Section 2.4, we shall be particularly concerned with lossless plasmas. It then follows that $\underset{\approx}{\sigma}$ is anti-Hermitian, and hence that σ_{xy} and σ_{yz} are pure real, while σ_{zx} and the diagonal components are pure imaginary.

1.2 The Tensor Dielectric Coefficient

As $\underset{\approx}{\sigma}$ often turns out to be nearly pure imaginary, it is more convenient to use an equivalent dielectric coefficient defined by tensor dielectric coefficient

$$\underset{\approx}{K} = \underset{\approx}{I} + \frac{\underset{\approx}{\sigma}}{j\omega\epsilon_0} \tag{1.9}$$

where $\underset{\approx}{I}$ is the unity matrix and ϵ_0 the permittivity of free space.

The dielectric tensor has the same symmetry as the conductivity:

$$K_{xy} = -K_{yx}, \quad K_{yz} = -K_{zy}, \quad K_{zx} = K_{xz} \tag{1.10}$$

If there are no energy losses, the tensor is Hermitian, so that K_{xy} and K_{yz} are pure imaginary and K_{zx} as well as the diagonal terms is real, but no use will be made of this property at present.

It is convenient to use the left and right rotating coordinates

$$\left.\begin{aligned} \sqrt{2}\,\ell &= x - jy, & \sqrt{2}\,E_\ell &= E_x - jE_y \\ \sqrt{2}\,r &= x + jy, & \sqrt{2}\,E_r &= E_x + jE_y \end{aligned}\right\} \tag{1.11}$$

and the transformation is effected by the unitary matrix

$$U = \frac{1}{\sqrt{2}}\begin{bmatrix} 1 & -j & 0 \\ 1 & j & 0 \\ 0 & 0 & \sqrt{2} \end{bmatrix}, \quad U^{-1} = \frac{1}{\sqrt{2}}\begin{bmatrix} 1 & 1 & 0 \\ j & -j & 0 \\ 0 & 0 & \sqrt{2} \end{bmatrix} \tag{1.12}$$

The tensor $\underset{\approx}{K}$ transforms into the symmetric tensor

$$K' = UKU^{-1} = \begin{bmatrix} K_\ell & K_{\ell r} & K_{\ell p} \\ K_{\ell r} & K_r & K_{rp} \\ K_{\ell p} & K_{rp} & K_p \end{bmatrix} \tag{1.13}$$

whose components are

$$\begin{aligned} 2K_\ell &= K_{xx} + K_{yy} + 2jK_{xy} & 2K_{xx} &= K_\ell + K_r + 2K_{\ell r} \\ 2K_r &= K_{xx} + K_{yy} - 2jK_{xy} & 2K_{yy} &= K_\ell + K_r - 2K_{\ell r} \\ K_p &= K_{zz} & K_{zz} &= K_p \\ 2K_{\ell r} &= K_{xx} - K_{yy} & 2K_{xy} &= j(K_r - K_\ell) = -2K_{yx} \\ \sqrt{2}\,K_{\ell p} &= K_{xz} - jK_{yz} & \sqrt{2}\,K_{xz} &= K_{rp} + K_{\ell p} = \sqrt{2}\,K_{zx} \\ \sqrt{2}\,K_{rp} &= K_{xz} + jK_{yz} & \sqrt{2}\,K_{yz} &= K_{\ell p} - K_{rp} = \sqrt{2}\,K_{zy} \end{aligned} \tag{1.14}$$

The greatest advantage of this representation occurs when $K_{xx} = K_{yy}$ and $K_{xz} = K_{yz} = 0$, so that Equation 1.13 is a diagonal tensor indicating that the three waves represented by (E_ℓ, E_r, E_z) propagate independently of each other.

1.3 The Field Equations

Maxwell's equations are

$$\left.\begin{aligned} \nabla \cdot \mathbf{E} &= \frac{\rho}{\epsilon_0}, & \nabla \cdot \mathbf{B} &= 0 \\ \nabla \times \mathbf{E} &= -\mu_0 \frac{\partial \mathbf{H}}{\partial t}, & \nabla \times \mathbf{H} &= \epsilon_0 \frac{\partial \mathbf{E}}{\partial t} + \mathbf{J} \end{aligned}\right\} \quad (1.15)$$

in which the plasma appears through the space charge ρ and the conduction current $\mathbf{J}$.

In terms of the dielectric coefficient $\mathbf{K}$ and for fields that vary as $\exp j(\omega t - \mathbf{k} \cdot \mathbf{r})$, Maxwell's equations become

$$\mathbf{k} \cdot \mathbf{D} = \epsilon_0 \mathbf{k} \cdot \mathbf{K} \cdot \mathbf{E} = 0 \quad (1.16)$$

$$\mathbf{k} \cdot \mathbf{B} = 0 \quad (1.17)$$

$$\mathbf{k} \times \mathbf{E} = \omega \mathbf{B} \quad (1.18)$$

$$\mathbf{k} \times \mathbf{H} = -\omega \mathbf{D} = -\epsilon_0 \omega \mathbf{K} \cdot \mathbf{E} \quad (1.19)$$

In Equation 1.16, use was made of the continuity equation (1.5), and the total displacement $\mathbf{D}$ was defined as

$$\mathbf{D} = \epsilon_0 \mathbf{K} \cdot \mathbf{E} = \epsilon_0 \mathbf{E} + \frac{\mathbf{J}}{j\omega} \quad (1.20)$$

From Equations 1.16, 1.17, and 1.19, it follows that for a plane wave the vectors $\mathbf{k}$, $\mathbf{H}$, and $\mathbf{D}$ form an orthogonal set. The fields $\mathbf{H}$ and $\mathbf{D}$ are then always transverse to $\mathbf{k}$, but $\mathbf{E}$ and $\mathbf{J}$ are not necessarily so (Figure 1.1). In fact, the more interesting waves will be those in which $\mathbf{E}$ is partly (or wholly) longitudinal.

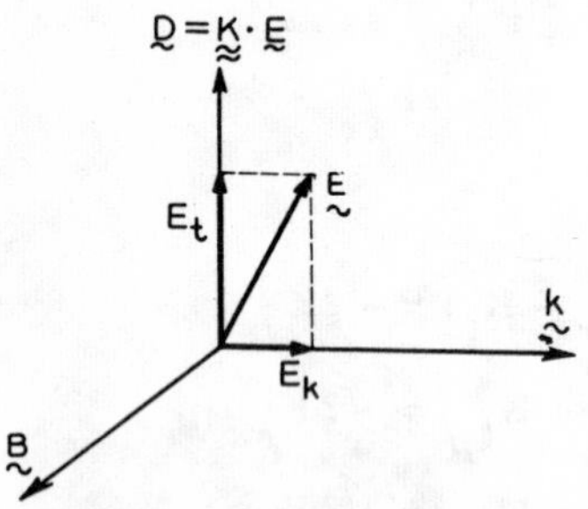

Figure 1.1. Directions of field vectors ($\mathbf{E}$, $\mathbf{B}$, $\mathbf{D}$) and of propagation vector $\mathbf{k}$ in a plane wave.

The relation between the propagation constant $\mathbf{k}$ and the dielectric coefficient $\mathbf{K}$ is obtained by iterating Equations 1.18 and 1.19. The result is

$$\mathbf{k} \times (\mathbf{k} \times \mathbf{E}) + k_0^2 \mathbf{K} \cdot \mathbf{E} = 0 \quad (1.21)$$

where $k_0 = \omega/c$ is the propagation constant in free space.

For some plasma models, it is easier to obtain the field $\mathbf{E}$ in terms of the current $\mathbf{J}$. In this case we write

$$j\omega\epsilon_0 \mathbf{E} = \mathbf{R} \cdot \mathbf{J} \quad (1.22)$$

where $\mathbf{R} = j\omega\epsilon_0 \boldsymbol{\sigma}^{-1}$ is the normalized plasma resistivity tensor. Then the wave equation is

$$\underset{\sim}{k} \times \underset{\sim}{k} \times (\underset{\approx}{R} \cdot \underset{\sim}{J}) + k_0^2 (\underset{\approx}{R} + \underset{\approx}{I}) \cdot \underset{\sim}{J} = 0 \tag{1.23}$$

where $\underset{\approx}{I}$ is the identity matrix.

1.4 The Dispersion Relation

Equation 1.21 represents a set of three linear homogeneous equations for the three field components (E_x, E_y, E_z). A nonzero solution exists only when the determinant of the coefficients vanishes.

$$\begin{vmatrix} k_0^2 K_{xx} - k_y^2 - k_z^2 & k_x k_y + k_0^2 K_{xy} & k_x k_z + k_0^2 K_{xz} \\ k_y k_x + k_0^2 K_{yx} & k_0^2 K_{yy} - k_z^2 - k_x^2 & k_y k_z + k_0^2 K_{yz} \\ k_z k_x + k_0^2 K_{zx} & k_z k_y + k_0^2 K_{zy} & k_0^2 K_{zz} - k_x^2 - k_y^2 \end{vmatrix} = 0 \tag{1.24}$$

Equation 1.24 can be solved for the propagation constant

$$k = \sqrt{k_x^2 + k_y^2 + k_z^2}$$

in terms of the direction cosines $(k_x : k_y : k_z)$ of $\underset{\sim}{k}$ and the components $\underset{\approx}{K}$. The properties of the vector $\underset{\sim}{k}$ determine the propagation and attenuation of the waves.

Let the y axis be taken along $\underset{\approx}{B}_0 \times \underset{\sim}{k}$ and let θ be the angle that $\underset{\sim}{k}$ makes with the direction of the static magnetic field, so that $k_x = k \sin\theta$, $k_y = 0$, $k_z = k \cos\theta$ (Figure 1.2). Then with the

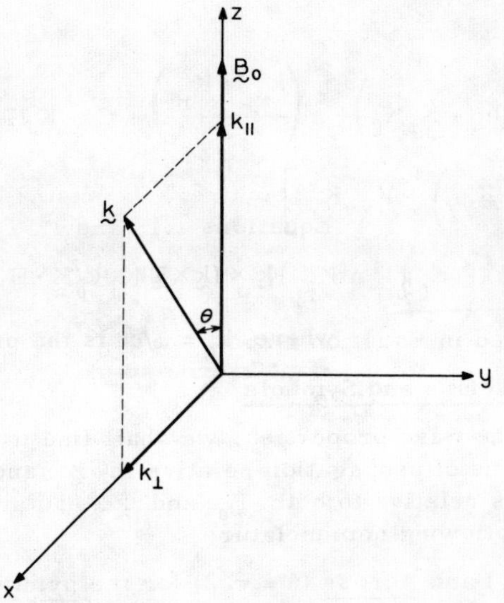

Figure 1.2. Orientation of coordinate axes with respect to static magnetic field $\underset{\approx}{B}_0$ and propagation vector $\underset{\sim}{k}$.

dielectric coefficient of the form given by Equation 1.10, the dispersion relation (1.24) can be put in the form

$$An^4 - Bn^2 + C = 0 \tag{1.25}$$

where $\underset{\sim}{n} = \underset{\sim}{k}/k_0$ is the vector index of refraction of the wave and where

$$A = K_{xx} \sin^2\theta + 2K_{xz}\cos\theta\sin\theta + K_{zz}\cos^2\theta \tag{1.26a}$$

$$B = K_{xx}K_{zz} - K_{xz}^2 + \left(K_{xx}K_{yy} + K_{xy}^2\right)\sin^2\theta + 2\left(K_{yy}K_{xz} - K_{xy}K_{yz}\right)\sin\theta\cos\theta + \left(K_{yy}K_{zz} + K_{yz}^2\right)\cos^2\theta \tag{1.26b}$$

$$C = |K| \tag{1.26c}$$

Equation 1.25 is quadratic in n^2, so that in general two distinct waves, propagating in either direction, can exist. However, when the dielectric coefficient $\underset{\approx}{K}$ itself is a function of the index of refraction, more than two waves may be possible. We shall find that in a plasma where thermal motions of the particles can be neglected, only two waves can propagate, but that in an N-component plasma with the thermal motion taken into account, $N+2$ distinct waves can exist.

It is often more convenient to solve the determinantal equation for $\tan\theta$ instead of for the index n. The equation we obtain is then

$$a\tan^2\theta + b\tan\theta + c = 0 \tag{1.27}$$

where

$$\left.\begin{aligned} a &= \left(n^2 - K_{\parallel}\right)\left(K_{xx}n^2 - K_rK_\ell\right) + n^2\left(\frac{k_{xz}^2 + K_{r\ell}^2}{2}\right) + C - K_{\parallel}K_rK_\ell \\ b &= 2n^2\left[K_{xz}\left(n^2 - K_{yy}\right) + K_{xy}K_{yz}\right] \\ c &= K_{\parallel}\left(n^2 - K_r\right)\left(n^2 - K_\ell\right) + n^2K_{\ell p}K_{rp} + C - K_{\parallel}K_rK_\ell \end{aligned}\right\} \tag{1.28}$$

where C is defined in Equation 1.26c.

1.5 Definition of Terms and Symbols

In the study of the wave properties, we shall find it necessary to talk about directions of propagation relative to $\underset{\sim}{B}_0$ and components of the field vectors relative to both $\underset{\sim}{B}_0$ and $\underset{\sim}{k}$. To avoid confusion, we shall use the following nomenclature:

> Along $(\theta = 0)$ and Across $(\theta = \pi/2)$ for the principal directions of propagation relative to the static magnetic field $\underset{\sim}{B}_0$.

Parallel (∥ or p) and Perpendicular (⊥) for the Cartesian components of any field vector relative to $\underset{\sim}{B}_0$. Left (ℓ) and Right (r) for rotating components of any field vector relative to $\underset{\sim}{B}_0$.

Longitudinal (k) and Transverse (t) for the components of any field vector relative to the direction of propagation. The transverse component is further decomposed into its polar (θ) and azimuthal (ϕ) components.

The static magnetic field will always be indicated by $\underset{\sim}{B}_0$, and the wave magnetic field by $\underset{\sim}{B}$ (or $\underset{\sim}{H}$).

Principal waves are waves that propagate either along or across $\underset{\sim}{B}_0$.

1.6 Cutoffs and Resonances

The term cutoff will be used for the condition in which the phase velocity of the wave $u = \omega/k$ is infinite ($u = \infty$, $n^2 = 0 = k^2$), and the term resonance for the condition in which the phase velocity is zero ($u = 0$, $n^2 = \infty = k^2$). When the plasma parameters and the frequency are varied, the index n^2 moves about the complex plane and may pass through, or close to, these two points. When n^2 is real, so that it passes through these points, the cutoffs and resonances are sharp, otherwise they are diffuse. We shall in what follows adopt a model in which they are sharp, that is, the absence of collisions.

From Maxwell's equation (1.18), it follows that

$$\frac{|E_t|}{|B|} = \frac{\omega}{k} = u \tag{1.29}$$

As $\underset{\sim}{B}$ is always transverse, the phase velocity measures the impedance of the medium. In order to transfer energy efficiently to or from a wave, it is necessary to match impedances. Electron beams can be used effectively near a resonance. It is difficult to match to a wave near cutoff.

At a cutoff, then $\underset{\sim}{B}$ and $\underset{\sim}{J} + \epsilon_0 \dot{\underset{\sim}{E}} = -j\underset{\sim}{k} \times \underset{\sim}{H} = 0$. The real and displacement currents, which always cancel in the longitudinal direction (because $\underset{\sim}{D}$ is transverse), now cancel in the transverse direction as well. At a resonance, $E_t = 0$, so that the electric vector is purely longitudinal, $\underset{\sim}{E} = \underset{\sim}{E}_k$, or is zero. The transverse current $\underset{\sim}{J}_t = -j\underset{\sim}{k} \times \underset{\sim}{H}$ is then infinite when $\underset{\sim}{H} \neq 0$ or is finite when $\underset{\sim}{H} = 0$. We shall find both situations.

In inhomogeneous plasmas a wave in general will be reflected from a cutoff surface but will be absorbed at a resonant surface. Consider the limit of geometrical optics. If the index of refraction n is a function of position, say, of x, then for the laws of geometrical optics to hold, the relative change in the refractive index per wavelength in the medium must be small; that is,

$$\frac{1}{n}\left|\frac{dn}{dx}\right| \lambda << 1 \tag{1.30}$$

Since $\lambda = \lambda_0/n$, where λ_0 is the free-space wavelength, Condition 1.30 becomes

$$\frac{1}{n^2}\left|\frac{dn}{dx}\right| \lambda_0 << 1 \tag{1.31}$$

When Condition 1.31 is satisfied, the ray is determined by the principle of least time $\delta \int \underset{\sim}{k} \cdot d\underset{\sim}{s} = 0$, and the field vectors are given by the WKB approximation

$$E \sim \frac{E}{\sqrt{n(x)}} \exp j\left(\omega t \pm k_0 \int n(x)dx\right) \tag{1.32}$$

The two waves given by the plus and minus signs in Equation 1.32 refer to waves that travel in opposite directions and are independent of each other. Should there be a sharp boundary where Condition 1.31 fails, the two waves are no longer independent: One transforms into the other, and reflection occurs. Consider a ray approaching a cutoff, $n \to 0$; then n is decreasing, and the ray is refracted away from the cutoff surface and may be reflected in this way (Figure 1.3). If it is not refracted away, it will necessarily violate Condition 1.31 and thus be at least partially reflected. On the other hand, for a wave approaching a resonance, $n \to \infty$. With

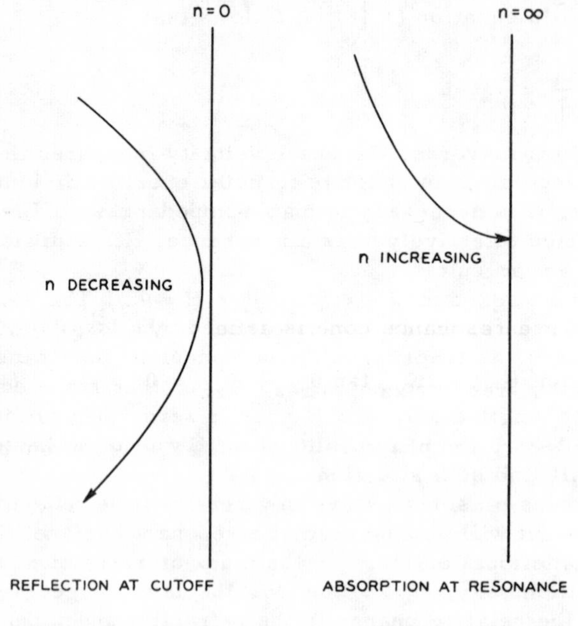

Figure 1.3. Rays in inhomogeneous plasma.

n increasing, it is refracted toward the resonant surface and reaches it normally (Figure 1.3). As it satisfies Condition 1.31 increasingly well, there is no reflection, the energy of the incoming wave being completely stored in the very large currents of the medium. In the presence of damping, however small, the stored energy is dissipated as heat. In the absence of any damping mechanism, there is no steady state and the currents increase indefinitely.

Cutoffs and resonances separate values of the plasma parameters in which n^2 is positive or negative and hence regions of propagation and of nonpropagation. The attenuation $\sqrt{-k^2}$ is small just beyond a cutoff but large just beyond a resonance. The characteristics of cutoffs and resonances are listed in Table 1.1.

Table 1.1. Characteristics of Cutoffs and Resonances

Cutoff	Resonance
$u = \infty$	$u = 0$
$k = n = 0$	$k = n = \infty$
$\underset{\sim}{H} = 0$	$E_t = 0$
$\underset{\sim}{J} + \epsilon_0 \dot{\underset{\sim}{E}} = 0$	$J/H = \infty$
Reflection	Absorption
All directions	Resonance cone

It can be seen from Equation 1.25 that if $C = 0$ and either A or $B \neq 0$, at least one root of the equation is zero. This represents, then, the cutoff condition. As C is independent of θ, the cutoff condition does not depend on the direction of propagation.

Similarly, $A = 0$ represents the resonance condition. As A does depend on θ, a resonance cone is defined by

$$K_{xx} \tan^2 \theta_{res} + 2K_{xz} \tan \theta_{res} + K_{zz} = 0 \qquad (1.33)$$

At angles near θ_{res}, the phase velocity of the wave is much below that of light in free space, and therefore the conditions of Cerenkov radiation are readily satisfied. An electron beam in any direction within the resonance cone, in particular, one along $\underset{\sim}{B}_0$, will produce Cerenkov radiation along the resonance cone[1] (Figure 1.4).

The direction of propagation along $\underset{\sim}{B}_0$ is, however, singular, and as we shall see shortly, the cutoff and resonance conditions given above do not necessarily hold in this direction.

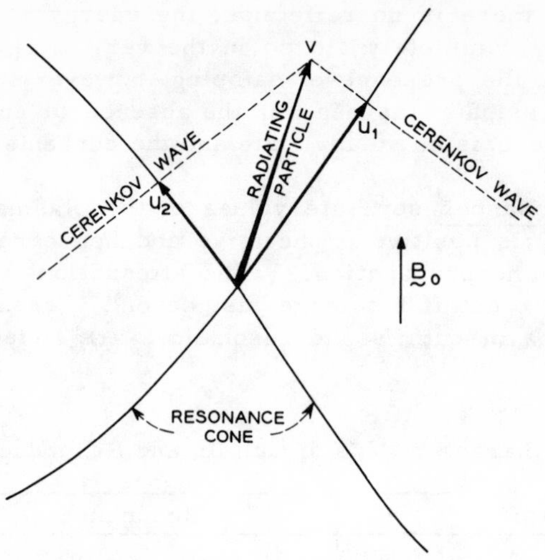

Figure 1.4. Cerenkov radiation at resonance cone.

1.7 Polarization of the Waves

When the determinant (1.24) vanishes, the relative magnitude of the components of the electric field vector $E_x : E_y : E_z$ are given by the ratio of the cofactors of the coefficients in Equation 1.21. Taking cofactors of the top row, we find in Cartesian coordinates

$$\left.\begin{aligned} E_x &\approx \left(n^2 - K_{yy}\right)\left(n^2 \sin^2\theta - K_{zz}\right) + K_{yz}^2 \\ E_y &\approx K_{yx}\left(n^2 \sin^2\theta - K_{zz}\right) + K_{yz}\left(n^2 \sin\theta\cos\theta + K_{xz}\right) \\ E_z &\approx \left(n^2 - K_{yy}\right)\left(n^2 \sin\theta\cos\theta + K_{xz}\right) + K_{xy}K_{yz} \end{aligned}\right\} \quad (1.34)$$

in rotating coordinates

$$\left.\begin{aligned} \sqrt{2}\,E_{r,\ell} = &\left(n^2 \sin^2\theta - K_{zz}\right)\left(n^2 - K_{yy} \pm jK_{yx}\right) \\ &\pm jK_{yz}\left(n^2 \sin\theta\cos\theta + K_{xz} \mp jK_{yz}\right) \end{aligned}\right\} \quad (1.35)$$

and the components of $\underset{\sim}{E}$ in the spherical coordinate system (k, θ, ϕ) are proportional to polarization of the waves

$$
\left.\begin{aligned}
E_\theta &\approx \left(K_{yy} - n^2\right)\left(K_{zx} \sin\theta + K_{zz} \cos\theta\right) \\
&\quad + K_{yz}\left(K_{yx} \sin\theta + K_{yz} \cos\theta\right) \\
E_\phi &\approx n^2 \sin\theta\left(K_{yx} \sin\theta + K_{yz} \cos\theta\right) \\
&\quad + K_{yz}K_{zx} + K_{xy}K_{zz} \\
E_k &\approx \left(K_{yy} - n^2\right)\left[\left(K_{zz} - n^2\right) \sin\theta - K_{zx} \cos\theta\right] \\
&\quad + K_{yz}\left(K_{yz} \sin\theta - K_{yx} \cos\theta\right)
\end{aligned}\right\} \tag{1.36}
$$

Then E_k is the longitudinal component of the wave. We note that E_k contains n^4, whereas E_θ and E_ϕ contain only n^2, confirming that near a resonance, and except when $\theta = 0$, the electric field becomes longitudinal.

2.1 The "Temperate" Plasma

There are two main difficulties in the solution of Equations 1.1 through 1.3. First, the product $\underset{\sim}{E} \cdot \partial f / \partial \underset{\sim}{v}$, occurring in the Boltzmann equation renders this equation nonlinear in $\underset{\sim}{E}$. The condition for linearization may best be seen by considering the induced velocity $\underset{\sim}{v}_E$ of the average particle in the absence of a magnetic field

$$\underset{\sim}{v}_E = \frac{e\underset{\sim}{E}}{m} \frac{1}{(\nu_c + j\omega)} \tag{2.1}$$

Since the collision frequency ν_c depends on the total velocity, $\underset{\sim}{v}_E$ plus $\underset{\sim}{v}_{thermal}$, this equation is nonlinear unless the thermal speed

$$v_T = \sqrt{\frac{eT}{m}} \tag{2.2}$$

is much larger than v_E ($v_E << v_T$). This is also the condition for convergence of small-signal approximations of the Boltzmann equation even in the absence of collisions.

Second, Equation 2.1 is itself not correct because the induced velocity v_E should be obtained by an integral of $\underset{\sim}{E}$ over the particle's trajectory, and the spatial variation of $\underset{\sim}{E}$ has not been taken into account in deriving Equation 2.1. This is acceptable only if the wavelength is sufficiently long or, more specifically, if $v_T << u$, where $u = \omega/k$ is the phase velocity of the wave. Thus the analysis, and also the phenomena, are peculiarly simple if the temperature is bracketed:

$$v_E << v_T << u \tag{2.3}$$

and such a plasma will be termed "temperate."

Most plasmas are, in fact, temperate except at resonances. Phase velocities are generally of the order of 3×10^8 m/sec. The electron thermal velocity of a 10-ev plasma is $v_T = 2 \times 10^6$ m/sec, which then requires that $E/|\nu_c + j\omega| << 10^{-5}$ volt-sec/m, which, if ν_c or ω, whichever is larger, is 10^7/sec, requires that $E << 1$ volt/cm; ν_c is about 10^7/sec in weakly ionized argon or mercury at a pressure of 1 micron.

2.2 Equations of Motion

For a temperate plasma, the induced motion is given by Newton's law with the Lorentz and Langevin forces..

$$m_i \frac{d\underset{\sim}{v}_E}{dt} = e_i(\underset{\sim}{E} + \underset{\sim}{v}_E \times \underset{\sim}{B}) - m_i \nu_c \underset{\sim}{v}_E \qquad (2.4)$$

By Inequality 2.3, ν_c is an average over the thermal motions, the precise average to be given in a later section, and therefore ν_c is temperature- and not field-dependent. We also linearize by including in $\underset{\sim}{B}$ only the static applied magnetic field $\underset{\sim}{B}_0$ and neglecting the alternating magnetic field of the wave. This amounts to neglecting v_E/u, which by Inequality 2.3 is a fortiori satisfied.

We define the cyclotron frequency vector for the ith constituent by

$$\underset{\sim}{\omega}_{b_i} = -\frac{e_i}{m_i}\underset{\sim}{B}_0 \qquad (2.5)$$

where $\underset{\sim}{B}_0$ is the static magnetic field. Inserting Equation 2.5 in Equation 2.4 and dropping the subscripts give

$$(\nu_c + j\omega - \underset{\sim}{\omega}_b \times)\underset{\sim}{v}_E = \frac{e\underset{\sim}{E}}{m} \qquad (2.6)$$

where we have assumed that both the field and the drift velocity vary harmonically with time as exp $(j\omega t)$, but have not used the factor exp $(-j\underset{\sim}{k}\cdot\underset{\sim}{r})$ because of Inequality 2.3.

The solution of the vector Equation 2.6 in vector form is

$$\underset{\sim}{v}_{E\perp} = \frac{(\nu_c + j\omega + \underset{\sim}{\omega}_b \times)\dfrac{e\underset{\sim}{E}_\perp}{m}}{[\nu_c + j(\omega - \omega_b)][\nu_c + j(\omega + \omega_b)]} \; ; \quad v_{E\parallel} = \frac{\dfrac{eE_\parallel}{m}}{\nu_c + j\omega} \qquad (2.7)$$

and in tensor form

$$\underset{\sim}{v}_E = \begin{vmatrix} \ell + r & j(\ell - r) & 0 \\ j(r - \ell) & \ell + r & 0 \\ 0 & 0 & 2p \end{vmatrix} \cdot \frac{e\underset{\sim}{E}}{2m} \qquad (2.8)$$

where

$$\ell, r = \frac{1}{j(\omega \pm \omega_b) + \nu_c} \; ; \quad p = \frac{1}{j\omega + \nu_c} \qquad (2.9)$$

are times that correspond to left circular, right circular, and parallel motions relative to $\underset{\sim}{B}_0$. In Equations 2.7, $\underset{\sim}{E}_\perp$ and $\underset{\sim}{E}_\parallel$ are the components of $\underset{\sim}{E}$ perpendicular to and parallel with the static magnetic field, which is in the z direction.

When ν_c is a function of velocity, the quantities ℓ, r, and p are proper averages over particle distribution functions. For electrons these are [2]

$$\left.\begin{aligned} \ell, r &= -\frac{4\pi}{3}\int_0^\infty \frac{v^3 \frac{\partial f_0}{\partial v}\, dv}{j(\omega \pm \omega_b) + \nu_c(v)} \\ p &= -\frac{4\pi}{3}\int_0^\infty \frac{v^3 \frac{\partial f_0}{\partial v}\, dv}{j\omega + \nu_c(v)} \end{aligned}\right\} \tag{2.10}$$

where $f_0(v)$ is the spherically symmetric part of electron distribution function. The quantity $\nu_c(v)$ that appears in these integrals represents an expansion in powers of (m_-/M_s) of the collision integral that appears in the Boltzmann equation, where m_- is the electron mass and M_s is the effective mass of the scattering center (atom, molecule, or ion). Thus the integrals can properly describe the effect of electron-atom or electron-ion collisions provided $f_0(v)$ is known. No corresponding expressions have yet been derived for ions where (m_+/M_s) is of the order of unity.[3] In this monograph we shall not consider in detail the effect of collisions on wave propagation. We shall thus assume that Equations 2.8 and 2.9 are sufficiently accurate to represent the effect of collisions of both electrons and ions.

The significance of the terms ℓ, r, and p in Equation 2.8 is best shown by transforming to a rotating system of coordinates through the unitary transformation (1.12). Then

$$\underset{\sim}{v}_E = \frac{e}{m}\begin{bmatrix} \ell & 0 & 0 \\ 0 & r & 0 \\ 0 & 0 & p \end{bmatrix} \cdot \underset{\approx}{E} \tag{2.11}$$

From $\underset{\sim}{v}_E$ we obtain the conductivity by adding the currents:

$$\sum N_i e_i \underset{\sim}{v}_E = \underset{\approx}{\sigma} \cdot \underset{\sim}{E} \tag{2.12}$$

where N_i is the density of ith charged-particle species. Hence, in Cartesian coordinates the dielectric coefficient $\underset{\approx}{K}$ has the form

$$\underset{\approx}{K} = \begin{bmatrix} K_\perp & -K_\times & 0 \\ K_\times & K_\perp & 0 \\ 0 & 0 & K_\parallel \end{bmatrix} \tag{2.13}$$

where the subscript $\times$ refers to the "cross-product" component of the tensor. In rotating coordinates, the tensor components

$$\underset{\approx}{K} = \begin{bmatrix} K_\ell & 0 & 0 \\ 0 & K_r & 0 \\ 0 & 0 & K_p \end{bmatrix} \tag{2.14}$$

where $K_p \equiv K_\parallel$, $K_\perp = (K_\ell + K_r)/2$, $K_\times = j(K_\ell - K_r)/2$.

2.3 The Tensor Components

Let us define for electrons (-) the parameters†

$$\left.\begin{aligned} \omega_{p_-}^2 &= \frac{Ne^2}{\epsilon_0 m_-}, & \alpha_- &= \frac{\omega_{p_-}}{\omega} \\ \omega_{b_-} &= \frac{eB_0}{m_-}, & \beta_- &= \frac{\omega_{b_-}}{\omega} \\ & & \gamma_- &= \frac{\nu_{c_-}}{\omega} \end{aligned}\right\} \tag{2.15}$$

and consider first waves of frequency high enough so that ions do not contribute appreciably to the current. We then have

$$\left.\begin{aligned} K_\parallel &= 1 - \frac{\alpha_-^2}{1 - j\gamma_-} \\ K_\ell &= 1 - \frac{\alpha_-^2}{1 + \beta_- - j\gamma_-} \\ K_r &= 1 - \frac{\alpha_-^2}{1 - \beta_- - j\gamma_-} \end{aligned}\right\} \tag{2.16}$$

There exists a simple geometrical construction[4] that represents these coefficients in the complex plane (Figure 2.1).

The figure is centered at the point $K = 1$, because all points of the figure move outward along radii from here as α_-^2 increases.

The point $K_\parallel$ is on a radius that passes through the point $-j\gamma_-$, and as the vectors

$$\left.\begin{aligned} K_\parallel - 1 &= -\frac{\alpha_-^2}{(1 - j\gamma_-)} \\ K_\parallel - 1 + \alpha_-^2 &= -\frac{j\gamma_-\alpha_-^2}{(1 - j\gamma_-)} \end{aligned}\right\} \tag{2.17}$$

are orthogonal, the circle for which 1 and $1 - \alpha_-^2$ are diametrical points passes through $K_\parallel$. Thus the coordinate lines corresponding

† Our symbols α_-^2, β_-, and γ_- have the same meanings as the U.R.S.I. symbols X, Y, and Z.

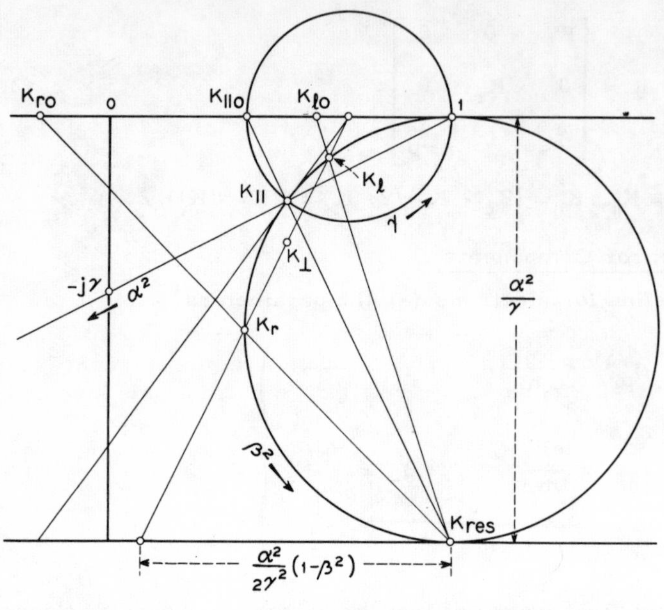

Figure 2.1. Geometrical representation of the components of dielectric tensor in the complex dielectric-coefficient plane.

to the parameters α_-^2 and γ_- are the lines $(1, -j\gamma_-)$ and the circles $(1, 1 - \alpha_-^2)$.

Consider now the quantities

$$K_{\ell,r} - 1 + \frac{j\alpha_-^2}{2\gamma_-} = \frac{j\alpha_-^2}{2\gamma_-} \frac{1 \pm \beta_- + j\gamma_-}{1 \pm \beta_- - j\gamma_-} \tag{2.18}$$

These quantities, as also $K_{\parallel} - 1 + (j\alpha_-^2/2\gamma_-)$, have the same absolute value $\alpha_-^2/2\gamma_-$. Therefore, the points K_ℓ, K_r, $K_\parallel$, and 1 are all on a circle centered at $1 - (j\alpha_-^2/2\gamma_-)$. The points K_ℓ and K_r move along this circle when β_-^2 varies at constant α_-^2/γ_-. How they move is determined by the vectors

$$K_{\ell,r} - 1 + \frac{\alpha_-^2}{2} = \frac{\alpha_-^2}{2} \frac{\beta_-^2 - (1 + j\gamma_-)^2}{(1 \pm \beta_-^2) + \gamma_-^2} \tag{2.19}$$

These vectors have the same direction [slope $-2j\gamma_-/(\beta_-^2 + \gamma_-^2 - 1)$] and hence the points $1 - (\alpha_-^2/2)$, K_ℓ, and K_r are on the same line. This line passes through the point $1 + [(\beta_-^2 - 1)\alpha_-^2/2\gamma_-]$, $-j\alpha_-^2/\gamma_-$ that moves linearly with β_-^2 to the right. Thus K_ℓ and K_r are the intersections of the β_-^2 circle and a radius vector of the γ_- circle. This radius vector rotates counterclockwise as β_-^2 increases. It is tangent to the β_-^2 circle for $\beta_-^2 = 0$ and $\beta_-^2 = \infty$ and passes through the point $K_{res} = 1 - (j\alpha_-^2/\gamma_-)$ at cyclotron resonance $(\beta_-^2 = 1)$.

The point $K_\perp$ is on the same radius vector halfway between K_ℓ and K_r. The point $K_\times$ is not easily represented on this diagram.

The diagram of Figure 2.1 cannot be drawn if $\gamma_- = 0$, because all the points K_ℓ, $K_\parallel$, and K_r fall on the real axis. However, it is readily shown that these points, represented by K_{ℓ_0}, $K_{\parallel_0}$, and K_{r_0} on the diagram, are obtained by projecting the points K_ℓ, $K_\parallel$, and K_r on the real axis from the point K_{res}. This is so because K_ℓ, $K_\parallel$, and K_r all move on γ_- circles as γ_- decreases.

We shall henceforth neglect collisions entirely, setting $\gamma_- = 0$. They can be retained in a perfectly straightforward manner, but to do so results in complex expressions that are otherwise real or pure imaginary, and this complicates the discussion unnecessarily

For a neutral plasma with electrons (-) and a single kind of ion (+),

$$\left.\begin{aligned} K_\ell &= 1 - \frac{a_-^2}{1+\beta_-} - \frac{a_+^2}{1-\beta_+} = 1 - \frac{a^2}{(1+\beta_-)(1-\beta_+)} \\ K_r &= 1 - \frac{a^2}{(1-\beta_-)(1+\beta_+)} \\ K_\parallel &= 1 - a_-^2 - a_+^2 = 1 - a^2 \end{aligned}\right\} \qquad (2.20)$$

$$\left.\begin{aligned} K_\perp &= \frac{(K_\ell + K_r)}{2} = 1 - \frac{a^2(1-\beta_+\beta_-)}{(1-\beta_-^2)(1-\beta_+^2)} \\ K_\times &= \frac{j(K_\ell - K_r)}{2} = j\,\frac{a^2(\beta_- - \beta_+)}{(1-\beta_-^2)(1-\beta_+^2)} \end{aligned}\right\} \qquad (2.21)$$

where

$$a^2 = \frac{\omega_p^2}{\omega^2} = \frac{Ne^2}{\epsilon_0\omega^2}\,\frac{m_+ + m_-}{m_+ m_-} \qquad (2.22)$$

Note that

$$K_\perp^2 + K_\times^2 = K_r K_\ell \qquad (2.23)$$

When a is written without a subscript, the reduced mass is to be used in the plasma frequency formula.

2.4 The Dispersion Relation

The dispersion relation

$$F(\underset{\sim}{n}) = An^4 - Bn^2 + C = 0 \qquad (2.24)$$

now has the coefficients

$$\left.\begin{aligned} A &= K_\perp \sin^2\theta + K_\parallel \cos^2\theta \\ B &= K_r K_\ell \sin^2\theta + K_\parallel K_\perp (1 + \cos^2\theta) \\ C &= K_r K_\ell K_\parallel \end{aligned}\right\} \qquad (2.25)$$

The discriminant of this equation is

$$D^2 = B^2 - 4AC = -4K_\parallel^2 K_\times^2 \cos^2\theta + (K_r K_\ell - K_\parallel K_\perp)^2 \sin^4\theta \qquad (2.26)$$

As $K_\times^2$ is negative, the discriminant D^2 is positive. Consequently, for this plasma model, n^2 is always real, and n is either real or imaginary. This sharp distinction between conditions of propagation and nonpropagation exists by virtue of the simple assumption made in deriving the tensor $\underset{\approx}{K}$, namely, the absence of collisions and the neglect of thermal motion.

It is somewhat easier to understand the properties of the waves if Equation 2.24 is solved for the direction of propagation θ in terms of index of refraction n, as was done first by Åström:[5]

$$\tan^2\theta = -\frac{K_\parallel(n^2 - K_r)(n^2 - K_\ell)}{(n^2 - K_\parallel)(K_\perp n^2 - K_r K_\ell)} \qquad (2.27)$$

The indices along the principal directions of propagation, along $\underset{\approx}{B}_0$ $(\theta = 0)$ and across $\underset{\approx}{B}_0$ $(\theta = 90°)$, are then particularly simple to discuss.

2.5 Geometrical Representations

The usual geometrical representations of the dielectric coefficient $\underset{\approx}{K}$ are the Fresnel and index ellipsoids. Both of these represent the equation

$$\underset{\sim}{E} \cdot \underset{\sim}{D} = 1 \qquad (2.28)$$

the first being a polar plot of $\underset{\sim}{E}$ and the second a polar plot of $\underset{\sim}{D}$. These surfaces are ellipsoids of revolution with axes proportional to $K_\perp^{-\frac{1}{2}}$, $K_\perp^{-\frac{1}{2}}$, $K_\parallel^{-\frac{1}{2}}$ or $K_\perp^{\frac{1}{2}}$, $K_\perp^{\frac{1}{2}}$, $K_\parallel^{\frac{1}{2}}$, respectively. Because $K_\perp$ occurs twice in these ratios, it determines a circular diameter of the ellipsoids, and one diameter of all central sections of the ellipsoids. It follows, in crystal optics, that one wave has an index $n = K_\perp^{\frac{1}{2}}$ independently of the direction of propagation. This wave obeys Snell's law and is called the "ordinary" wave. The other wave has an index depending on both $K_\perp$ and $K_\parallel$ and on the direction of propagation and is called the "extraordinary" wave.

Students of the ionosphere have been concerned with the frequency dependence of the index of refraction, and have noticed that one of the waves propagating across the magnetic field had an index $n = K_\parallel^{\frac{1}{2}}$ which did not depend on the strength of the magnetic field, and in particular did not exhibit cyclotron resonance. They named this wave "ordinary" and the other one "extraordinary. The large volume of literature on ionospheric propagation makes it impossible now to correct this conflict in terminology, but the situation is not too serious because the crystal definition applies to nongyratory media, whereas the ionosphere definition applies to nonpolarizable media. We are adopting the ionosphere notation, but we shall restrict it to the wave that is strictly independent of $\underset{\sim}{B}_0$ according to the original ionospheric definition.

Students of magnetohydrodynamics have adopted the terminology of crystal optics. This is in direct conflict with the ionosphere terminology, as the magnetoionic waves go continuously into the magnetohydrodynamic ones.

The Fresnel and index ellipsoids are not suitable figures to represent gyratory media because the antisymmetric parts of the dielectric tensor cancel out in Equation 2.28.

There are three surfaces that are of use in representing wave propagation: (1) the "slowness surface," (2) the "phase velocity surface," and (3) the "ray surface."

William Rowan Hamilton defined the slowness surface (sometimes called the reciprocal wave surface or the index surface) as a polar plot of the vector $\underset{\sim}{k}/\omega = \underset{\sim}{n}/c$, and its equation for our case is Equation 2.24. Its importance derives from the fact that the net energy flow, that is, the time-averaged Poynting vector, is at a right angle to it (Part II, Equation 7.75; but see also Equation 8.100).

The inverse of the slowness surface is the phase velocity surface, or wave normal surface, which is a polar plot of the phase velocity

$$\underset{\sim}{u} = \frac{\omega \underset{\sim}{k}}{k^2} \tag{2.29}$$

In this monograph, we adopt the "phase velocity surface" to represent wave propagation, but we shall occasionally abbreviate it "velocity surface." Its equation is readily obtained from Equation 2.24 and can be written in the normal form

$$\frac{\cos^2\theta}{u^2 - u_0^2} + \frac{1}{2}\,\frac{\sin^2\theta}{u^2 - u_r^2} + \frac{1}{2}\,\frac{\sin^2\theta}{u^2 - u_\ell^2} = 0 \tag{2.30}$$

where

$$u_0^2 = \frac{c^2}{K_\parallel}, \quad u_r^2 = \frac{c^2}{K_r}, \quad u_\ell^2 = \frac{c^2}{K_\ell} \tag{2.31}$$

Equation 2.30 can be compared with the similar phase velocity equation in crystal optics

$$\frac{\sin^2\theta\,\cos^2\phi}{u^2 - u_1^2} + \frac{\sin^2\theta\,\sin^2\phi}{u^2 - u_2^2} + \frac{\cos^2\theta}{u^2 - u_3^2} \tag{2.32}$$

in which u_1, u_2, and u_3 are the principal velocities.

Although the phase velocity surfaces in a gyrotropic plasma have three independent velocities, they have cylindrical symmetry, which the crystal waves do not. The variety of surfaces to be displayed in the next chapter does not arise from the form of the wave surface equation but from the dependence of the coefficients K_r and K_ℓ on α^2 and β^2 which allows these coefficients to take all values from $-\infty$ to ∞. In crystal optics the principal velocities differ by minute amounts.

The envelope at time $t = 1$ of wave planes that passed the origin at time $t = 0$ is the <u>ray surface</u>. The phase velocity surface is the pedal surface[6] of the ray surface. The slowness surface is the polar reciprocal of the ray surface. The ray surface is the one that must be used in Huyghen's construction. Its equation is given in parametric form by

$$\underset{\sim}{v} = \frac{c\underset{\sim}{\nabla}_n F}{\underset{\sim}{n} \cdot \underset{\sim}{\nabla}_n F} \tag{2.33}$$

where $F(n)$ is the dispersion equation (2.24) and $\underset{\sim}{\nabla}_n$ denotes the gradient operator with respect to the components of the index n. The group velocity $\underset{\sim}{u}_g$ has the same direction, but not the same magnitude, as the ray velocity. It is given by

$$\underset{\sim}{u}_g = -\frac{c\underset{\sim}{\nabla}_n F}{\omega \dfrac{\partial F}{\partial \omega}} \tag{2.34}$$

3.1 Principal Waves along $\underset{\sim}{B}_0$

From Equation 2.27, it is seen that for propagation along the magnetic field ($\theta = 0$) the two possible waves have the indices

$$\frac{c^2}{u_r^2} = n_r^2 = K_r \tag{3.1}$$

and

$$\frac{c^2}{u_\ell^2} = n_\ell^2 = K_\ell \tag{3.2}$$

Recourse to the discussion leading to Equation 1.13 indicates that these waves are right and left circularly polarized with respect to the static magnetic field. These waves do or do not propagate depending on the signs of K_r and K_ℓ, and these change at the cutoffs and resonances that, from Equations 2.20, are determined by the expressions in Table 3.1.

Table 3.1. Definition of Cyclotron Cutoffs and Resonances

	Cyclotron Cutoff	Cyclotron Resonance
Left-hand Wave	$\alpha^2 = (1 + \beta_-)(1 - \beta_+)$ (3.3a)	$\beta_+ = 1$ (3.4a)
Right-hand Wave	$\alpha^2 = (1 - \beta_-)(1 + \beta_+)$ (3.3b)	$\beta_- = 1$ (3.4b)

These will be called the cyclotron resonances and the cyclotron cutoffs. At low plasma densities, $\alpha^2 \ll 1$, the two cutoffs are quite close to the corresponding resonances, so that the frequency range over which these waves do not propagate is a narrow interval above the resonance frequency, but at high plasma densities the cutoff is far from the resonance.

The dispersion relation is shown by a conventional propagation constant plot (k^2c^2 versus ω^2) and ($kc = n\omega$ versus ω) in Figures 3.1 and 3.2 by curves marked r and ℓ. More information can be shown on a single diagram using the normalized variables α^2, $\beta_-\beta_+$, and n^2. Such diagrams will be referred to as (α^2, β^2) diagrams, or (α^2, β^2) planes. The cutoff and resonance conditions are shown in a plot of $\beta_-\beta_+$ against α^2 (Figure 3.3). Increasing the plasma

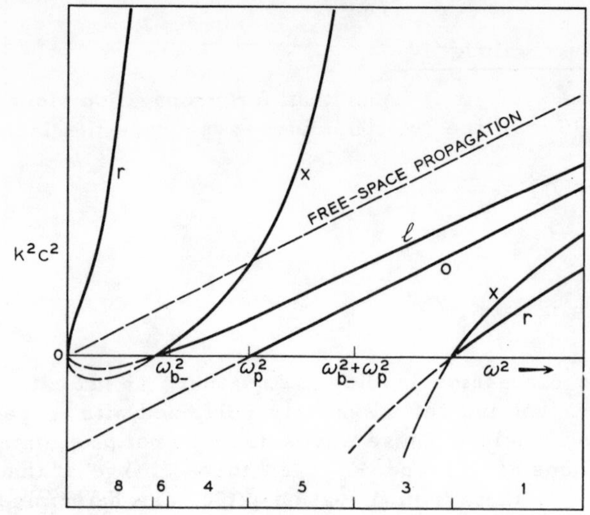

Figure 3.1. Propagation constant plot for the principal waves when ions are assumed immobile. The numbers at the bottom scale refer to regions of the (α^2, β^2) plane (Section 3.3).

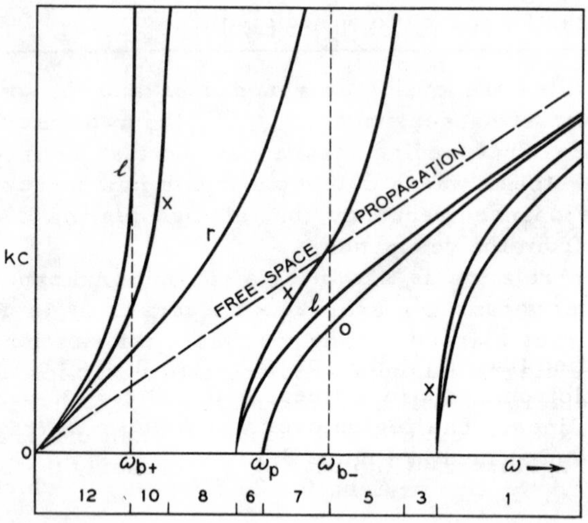

Figure 3.2. Propagation constant plot for the principal waves with ion motion included. The numbers at the bottom scale refer to regions of the (α^2, β^2) plane (Section 3.3).

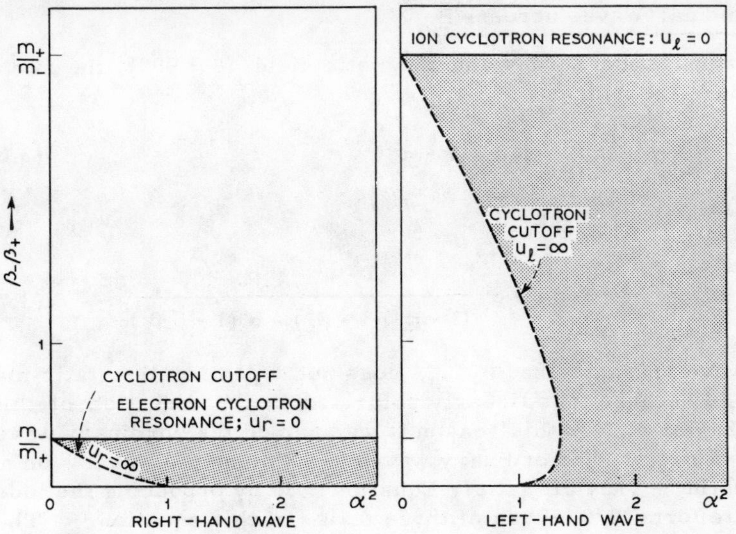

Figure 3.3. The (α^2, β^2) plot for propagation along $\underset{\sim}{B}_0$ for ion-to-electron mass ratio of 3 to 1. In the dotted regions the waves do not propagate $(u^2 < 0)$.

density N corresponds to displacement of a point on such a plot to the right, increasing the magnetic field to a displacement upward, and increasing the frequency to a radial displacement toward the origin. The two cyclotron resonances are horizontal lines whose ordinates are in the ratio $(m_+/m_-)^2$. For practical reasons, Figure 3.3 and succeeding figures are drawn for an assumed ratio $m_+/m_- = 3$. This would indeed be possible for holes and electrons in a semiconductor or a metal plasma, but for an ionized gas it must be realized that the figures are greatly off scale. The two cutoff lines belong to the same parabola whose summit is near $\alpha^2 = 1$, $\beta^2 = 0$ and whose axis is inclined at an angle $\sqrt{m_-/m_+}$ to the vertical, so that it passes through the two points $(\alpha^2 = 0, \beta_-^2 = 1)$ and $(\alpha^2 = 0, \beta_+^2 = 1)$.

It can be verified that $K_\ell < K_r$ or $u_r < u_\ell$ between the electron and ion cyclotron resonance lines, and conversely $u_\ell < u_r$ outside of these lines. The region over which these waves do not propagate has been shaded in Figure 3.3.

There is a third solution of Equation 2.27 for $\theta = 0$ which is

$$K_{\parallel} = 0 \quad \text{or} \quad \omega = \omega_p \tag{3.5}$$

This is a longitudinal oscillation at the plasma frequency. It cannot be properly called a "wave" because n and, therefore, λ are arbitrary. It is a "plasma oscillation" and does not in this model extend to directions other than those along $\underset{\sim}{B}_0$.

3.2 Principal Waves across $\underset{\sim}{B}_0$

For propagation across the magnetic field ($\theta = 90°$), the two waves have the indices

$$\frac{c^2}{u_o^2} = n_o^2 = K_{\parallel} = 1 - \alpha^2 \tag{3.6}$$

and

$$\frac{c^2}{u_\times^2} = n_\times^2 = \frac{K_r K_\ell}{K_\perp} = 1 - \alpha^2 \frac{1 - \alpha^2 - \beta_+\beta_-}{(1 - \beta_-^2)(1 - \beta_+^2) - \alpha^2(1 - \beta_-\beta_+)} \tag{3.7}$$

The wave characterized by n_o does not depend on the static magnetic field because it is linearly polarized in the direction of this field (Chapter 4). For this reason it was named the "ordinary wave."

The left, right, and ordinary waves are "principal waves" on an equal footing: They all satisfy Equation 2.30 by producing the indeterminate form 0/0 of one of three terms of this equation. The fourth principal wave is different, and has been named "extraordinary," in that it is obtained by equating the sum of the coefficients of $\sin^2\theta$ in Equation 2.30 to zero so that

$$2u_\times^2 = u_r^2 + u_\ell^2 \tag{3.8}$$

Thus the velocity of the extraordinary wave is always intermediate between the velocities of the right and left circularly polarized waves. It is "extraordinary" also, as will be seen in Chapter 4, in that it has the polarization appropriate to the right or left waves although it travels across $\underset{\sim}{B}_0$. The polarizations of all principal waves are shown in Figure 3.4.

The propagation constant plots of the ordinary and extraordinary waves are shown in Figures 3.1 and 3.2 and are denoted by o and $\times$.

The cutoff and resonance conditions for the ordinary and extraordinary waves are given in Table 3.2.

Table 3.2. Definition of Plasma Cutoffs and Resonances

	Plasma Cutoff	Plasma Resonance
Ordinary Wave	$\alpha^2 = 1$ (3.9a)	None
Extraordinary Wave	$(\alpha^2 - 1 + \beta_+\beta_-)^2 = (\beta_- - \beta_+)^2$ (3.9b)	$\alpha^2(1 - \beta_-\beta_+) = (1 - \beta_-^2)(1 - \beta_+^2)$ (3.10)

The ordinary wave cuts off at the plasma frequency (Figure 3.5). We emphasize that this is a cutoff and not a resonance frequency.

The extraordinary wave cuts off at both cyclotron cutoffs (Equations 3.3 and 3.4). Its resonance will be called "plasma resonance," and it plots on an (α^2, β^2) diagram as a hyperbola. One branch

principal waves across $\underset{\sim}{B}_0$

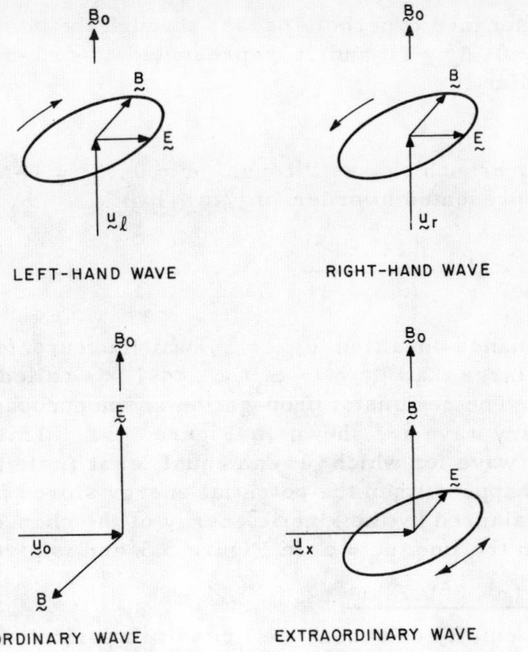

Figure 3.4. Polarization of the principal waves. The extraordinary wave can rotate either left- or right-handed with respect to $\underset{\sim}{B}_0$.

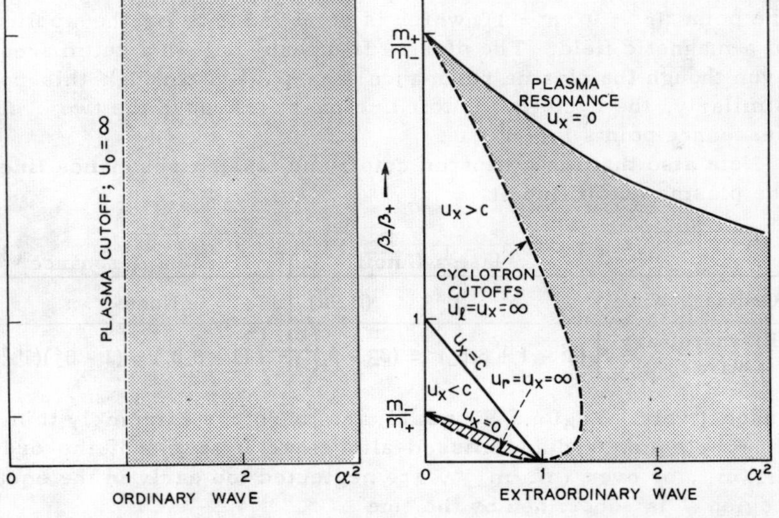

Figure 3.5. The (α^2, β^2) plot for propagation across $\underset{\sim}{B}_0$ for ion-to-electron mass ratio of 3 to 1. In the dotted regions the waves do not propagate $(u^2 < 0)$.

of the resonance hyperbola passes through the points ($\alpha^2 = 1$, $\beta_-^2 = 0$) and ($\alpha^2 = 0$, $\beta_-^2 = 1$) and is represented to order m_-/m_+ by the straight line

$$\alpha^2 = 1 - \beta_-^2 \tag{3.11}$$

The other branch passes through ($\alpha^2 = 0$, $\beta_+^2 = 1$) and ($\alpha^2 = \infty$, $\beta_-\beta_+ = 1$) and is represented to order m_-/m_+ by

$$\alpha^2 = \frac{\beta_-^2(1 - \beta_+^2)}{(\beta_-\beta_+ - 1)} \tag{3.12}$$

The resonance condition $\beta_-\beta_+ = 1$, which occurs for densities sufficiently large that $\beta_-^2/\alpha^2 = \omega_{b_-}^2/\omega_p^2 << 1$, is called the "hybrid resonance." The regions of propagation and nonpropagation of the extraordinary wave are shown in Figure 3.5. This is the only principal wave for which u can equal c at finite plasma densities, and this happens when the potential energy stored in the space-charge field is balanced by the kinetic energy of the charged particles. This occurs on the line $u_x = c$ in Figure 3.5, and is given by $\alpha^2 = 1 - \beta_-\beta_+$.

3.3 The (α^2, β^2) Plane

All the cutoff and resonance lines of the principal waves are shown in Figure 3.6. They divide the (α^2, β^2) plane into thirteen regions that are numbered alternately left and right of plasma cutoff, the numbers increasing with $\beta_-\beta_+$ as indicated. Part of the reason for this system of numbering is that areas whose numbers differ by 6 are found to have quite similar properties. Note the degeneracy at the point ($\beta^2 = 0$, $\alpha^2 = 1$) which is removed only by the application of a magnetic field. The plasma frequency ω_p is a cutoff frequency even though the plasma resonance line passes through this point. Similarly, the cyclotron cutoff line passes through the two cyclotron resonance points for $\alpha^2 = 0$.

Note also that the cyclotron cutoff and plasma resonance lines cut the plasma cutoff line at

$$\alpha^2 = 1, \quad \beta_+ = 1 - \frac{m_-}{m_+} \tag{3.13}$$

and

$$\alpha^2 = 1, \quad \beta_+^2 = 1 - \frac{m_-}{m_+} + \left(\frac{m_-}{m_+}\right)^2 \tag{3.14}$$

respectively. Regions 9 and 11 are therefore extremely thin for a real plasma, and are missed altogether if terms of the order m_-/m_+, or even $(m_-/m_+)^2$, are neglected too early in the equations. Region 7 is subdivided by the line

$$K_{\parallel}K_{\perp} = K_r K_{\ell} \quad \text{or} \quad \alpha^2 = \frac{m_+}{m_-} - 1 + \frac{m_-}{m_+} - \beta_+\beta_- \tag{3.15}$$

the (α^2, β^2) plane

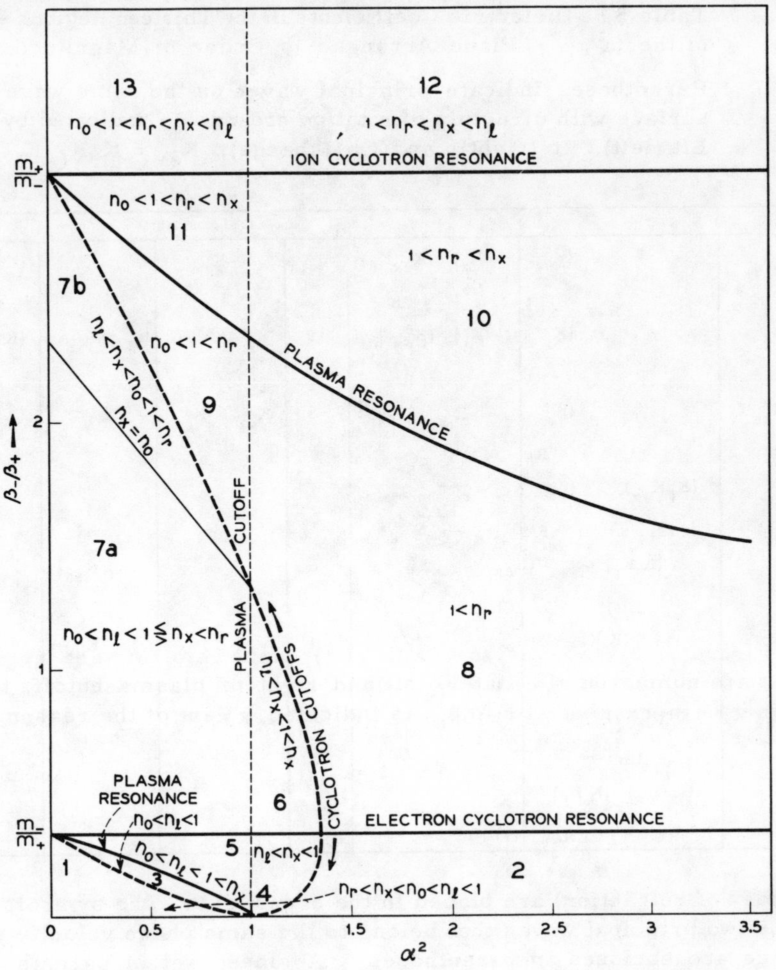

Figure 3.6. The division of the (α^2, β^2) plane into thirteen regions by the cutoff curves (dashed lines) and resonance curves (solid lines) of the principal waves. In each of the thirteen regions the waves possess different topological properties. The indices of the principal waves in each region are written in order of increasing magnitude. The absence of an index indicates that the corresponding wave does not propagate in the region.

along which $n_x = n_o$. At this line the magnitudes of n_x and n_o cross.

In Figure 3.6 and Table 3.3, the four principal indices are ordered according to their magnitude for each of the thirteen regions of the (α^2, β^2) plane, and the values zero (cutoff) and unity (free-space

Table 3.3. Dielectric Coefficients in the Thirteen Regions of the (α^2, β^2) Plane Arranged in Order of Magnitude.

Parentheses indicate principal waves on the same wave surface with direction of rotation around $\underset{\sim}{B}_0$ indicated by Lft (left), Rt (right), and Ch (change); $K_{ex} = K_r K_\ell / K_\perp$.

	$-\infty$ to 0	0 to 1	1 to $+\infty$		$-\infty$ to 0	0 to 1	1 to ∞
13		$(K_{\parallel}$ Rt	$K_r)$ $(K_{ex}K_\ell)$ Ch	12	$K_{\parallel}$		(K_rK_{ex}) $(K_\ell$ Rt Lft
11	K_ℓ	$(K_{\parallel}$ Rt	$K_r)$ $(K_{ex}$ Rt	10	K_ℓ $K_{\parallel}$		(K_rK_{ex}) Rt
9	$K_{ex}K_\ell$	$(K_{\parallel}$ Rt	$K_r)$	8	K_{ex} $K_{\parallel}K_\ell$		$(K_r$ Rt
7b		$(K_\ell K_{ex})$ $(K_{\parallel}$ Lft Rt	K_r				
7a		$(K_{\parallel}K_\ell)$ Lft	$(K_{ex}$ $K_r)$ Ch	6	$K_{\parallel}$	$(K_\ell$ $K_{ex})$ Lft	$(K_r$ Rt
5	K_r	$(K_{\parallel}K_\ell)$ Lft	$(K_{ex}$ Lft	4	K_r $K_{\parallel}$	$(K_\ell$ $K_{ex})$ Lft	
3	K_{ex} K_r	$(K_{\parallel}K_\ell)$ Lft		2	$K_rK_{\parallel}K_{ex}K_\ell$		
1		(K_rK_{ex}) $(K_{\parallel}K_\ell)$ Rt Lft					

index of refraction) are placed in the order also. The symbols for the two principal waves that belong to the same phase velocity surface are enclosed in parentheses. A closed set of parentheses indicates that a complete velocity surface exists in the region. When the set is open, it indicates the presence of a resonant cone (see the following section) and thus the absence of one of the principal waves. The symbols Lft, Rt, and Ch refer to the sense of rotation of the waves around $\underset{\sim}{B}_0$, and will be described in greater detail in subsequent chapters.

3.4 Propagation in Arbitrary Directions

The index of refraction for an arbitrary direction of propagation is given implicitly by the tangent formula (2.27) and in the following figures will be represented by polar plots of the phase velocity $\underset{\sim}{u} = c/\underset{\sim}{n}$. In these plots the magnetic field is directed upward, and the phase velocity surface is obtained by rotating the polar diagram of $\underset{\sim}{u}$ about the vertical axis passing through the origin of $\underset{\sim}{u}$. It should be noted again that these are not ray surfaces; that is, the planes of constant phase are perpendicular to the radius vector and are not tangent to the surface.

As one of the principal waves appears or disappears whenever a cutoff or a resonance line is crossed, the velocity surface is topologically different in each of the thirteen areas of the (α^2, β^2) plane. It is significant, therefore, to plot a sample velocity surface in each of the areas, and this has been done in Figures 3.7 and 3.8 for the lower and upper halves of the (α^2, β^2) plane, and in Figure 3.9 for the entire plane. As the thirteen areas are very different in size, it was necessary to draw each figure to a different scale, and this is shown in each case by the dotted circle that represents the velocity of light.

The velocity surface is in general double, corresponding to the two solutions for n^2. The two surfaces intersect only when the discriminant D (Equation 2.26) vanishes, which does not happen in general because D^2 is the sum of the two squares. However, the two surfaces do touch at the poles when $K_{\parallel} K_{\times} = 0$. This happens (a) when $\beta = 0$, $K_{\times} = 0$, but the medium is then isotropic, and the two surfaces are identical spheres; (b) when $\alpha = 1$, $K_{\parallel} = 0$, but this situation is quite singular, and will be discussed in the next paragraph; (c) when $\beta \to \infty$ and $K_{\times} \to 0$ as β^{-3}, and will be discussed in Section 3.7. When $K_r K_{\ell} = K_{\parallel} K_{\perp}$, which defines the straight line (3.15) along which $n_{\times} = n_o$, the two surfaces are in contact along the equator.

In general, one velocity surface contains the other, and we shall let u_1 denote the outer surface, u_2 the inner one. Eventually we shall find other velocity surfaces u_3 and u_4 inside u_2, and there may be further surfaces inside those when there are more than two kinds of particles. The principal waves u_{ℓ}, u_r occur at the poles, and u_o, $u_{\times}$ at the equator, of u_1 and u_2, and the proper correspondence is obtained by reference to Table 3.3. The principal waves u_{ℓ} and u_r are joined separately to u_o and $u_{\times}$ in such a way that the surfaces do not cross. If only three principal waves are real, the outer two are joined and the third joins with the origin, as shown on the diagrams. The distinction between u_1 and u_2 is not clear when there is only one surface as in regions 3, 4, 8, 9, and 10.

The resonance condition is obtained by setting $n = \infty$ in Equation 2.27. This yields

$$\tan^2 \theta_{res} = -\frac{K_{\parallel}}{K_{\perp}} = \frac{(\alpha^2 - 1)(1 - \beta_-^2)(1 - \beta_+^2)}{(1 - \beta_-^2)(1 - \beta_+^2) - \alpha^2 (1 - \beta_+\beta_-)} \tag{3.16}$$

or

$$\sin^2 \theta_{res} = \frac{\alpha^2 - 1}{\alpha^2} \, \frac{(1 - \beta_-^2)(1 - \beta_+^2)}{(1 - \beta_-^2)(1 - \beta_+^2) - 1 + \beta_+\beta_-}$$

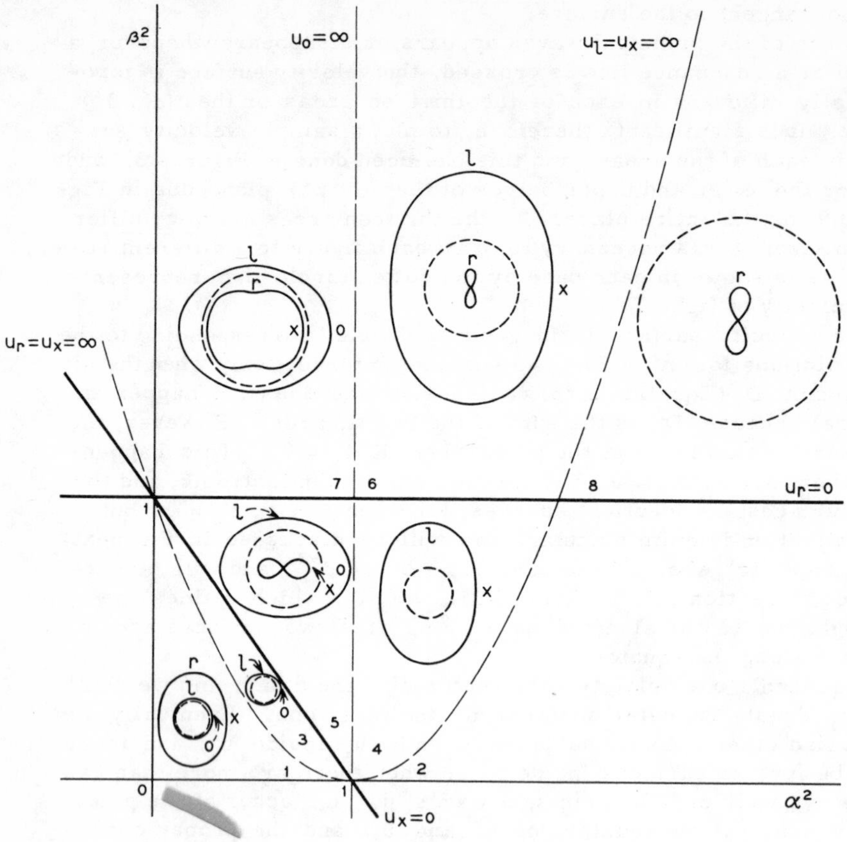

Figure 3.7. Phase velocity surfaces for electromagnetic waves at low magnetic fields or high frequencies, $m_+ \to \infty$. The symbols ℓ and r denote the left and right principal waves at the poles of the wave surface, and o and × the ordinary and extraordinary waves at the equator of the wave surface. The plots are not to scale, but the speed of light in relation to the velocities is shown by the dashed circle.

which is, of course, the same as setting $A = 0$ in Equation 2.25. Equations 3.16 show that a resonance cone exists whenever $K_{\parallel}$ and $K_{\perp}$ are of opposite sign. This occurs only in regions 5, 6, 8, 11, and 12.

The resonance cone is very thin ($\theta_{res} \rightarrow 0$) near the cyclotron resonances and very flat ($\theta_{res} \rightarrow \pi/2$) near plasma resonance, and thus provides a continuous transition between these resonances in regions 5, 8, and 11. It is also very thin near plasma cutoff. Loci of constant cone angle $\theta_{res} = 0$ (cyclotron resonance), $\pi/12$, $\pi/6$, $\pi/4$, $\pi/3$, and $\pi/2$ (plasma resonance) are shown in Figure 3.10. Note that the resonance loci for small cone angles fall very close not only to the cyclotron resonances but also to the plasma cutoff. This is why the plasma cutoff condition $\alpha^2 = 1$ frequently appears as a resonance condition. This happens in particular for guided waves (see Part II). Some corresponding values of α^2 and β^2 are given in Table 3.4. Slight approximations have been made for the asymptotes at $\alpha^2 = \infty$, and the symbol $\mu = m_-/m_+$ has been

Table 3.4. Critical Values for the Resonance-Cone Loci

Region	β_+^2	α^2	Region	β_-^2	α^2
12	∞	$\sec^2 \theta_{res}$	8	$1 - \frac{1}{\mu} + \frac{1}{\mu^2}$	1
12	$1 + \mu \tan^2 \theta_{res}$	∞	8	$\frac{\sec^2 \theta_{res}}{1 + \mu \tan^2 \theta_{res}}$	∞
11	1	0	5	1	0
11	$1 - \mu + \mu^2$	1	5	0	1

used. In regions 6, 8, and 12, the directions of allowed propagation are inside the resonant cone, giving a somewhat dumbbell-shaped velocity surface; in regions 5 and 11, they are outside the cone, giving somewhat torus-shaped wave surfaces.

Studies of ray velocity show that for the dumbbell-shaped modes the group velocity is confined even more narrowly to directions close to the magnetic field. Thus radio waves in region 8 may be guided by the earth's magnetic field lines from one hemisphere to the other and even be reflected and come back quite close to their source. This gives rise to the phenomenon of "whistlers."[7] These are radio waves of audible frequencies which are produced by lightning flashes and travel along the earth's magnetic field lines from one hemisphere to the other with very little angular dispersion, and may then be reflected back again. The frequency dispersion produced by this long trajectory causes the whistling tone of steadily falling pitch when the wave train is received.

Equations 3.16 may be solved for the plasma density at which

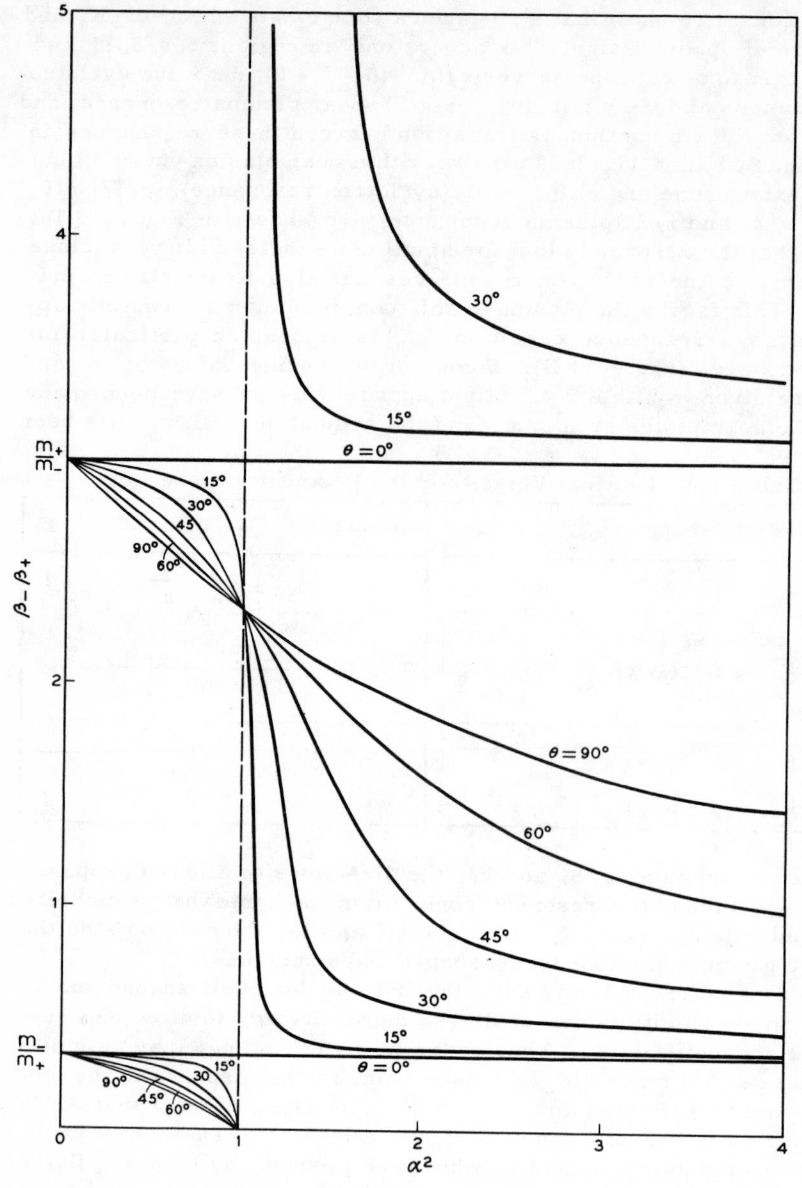

Figure 3.10. Loci of constant resonant angle θ_{res}. The 90° limit is the plasma resonance hyperbola. The 0° limit includes the cyclotron resonance and tends to plasma cutoff.

resonance occurs. This can be expanded to

$$\frac{\omega_p^2}{\omega^2} = \frac{(\omega^2 - \omega_{b-}^2)(\omega^2 - \omega_{b+}^2)}{(\omega^2 - \omega_{b-}^2)(\omega^2 - \omega_{b+}^2)\cos^2\theta_{res} + (\omega^2 - \omega_{b-}\omega_{b+})\sin^2\theta_{res}} \tag{3.17}$$

This equation is linear in ω_p^2, quadratic in B_0^2, and, provided θ is neither zero nor $\pi/2$, cubic in ω^2. This implies that for a given angle θ, an experiment in which B_0 and ω are held constant and the plasma density varied will yield one resonance, an experiment in which ω^2 and ω_p^2 are held constant but the magnetic field B_0 varied will yield two resonances, and an experiment in which B_0 and ω_p are held constant but the frequency ω varied will yield three resonances, provided propagation is neither along nor across $\underset{\sim}{B}_0$.

For a plasma consisting of g distinct species (different charge-to-mass ratios), the equation for the resonant cone is linear in ω_p^2, is of order g in B_0^2, and provided $\theta \neq 0$ or $\pi/2$, is of order $(g + 1)$ in ω^2, all ω^2 roots being real and positive definite. For $\theta = 0$ or $\pi/2$, one of the ω^2 roots is zero, so that there are only g resonant frequencies.

3.5 Waves with Stationary Ions

At sufficiently low magnetic fields or high frequencies (regions 1 to 5 and lower parts of regions 6 to 8), the ion motions can be neglected ($\beta_+ << 1$). Considerable simplification then results in the expression for n^2, which now is

$$n^2 = 1 - \frac{2\alpha^2(1 - \alpha^2)}{2(1 - \alpha^2) - \beta_-^2\sin^2\theta \pm \sqrt{\beta_-^4\sin^4\theta + 4\beta_-^2(1 - \alpha^2)^2\cos^2\theta}} \tag{3.18}$$

The corresponding velocity surfaces have been shown in Figure 3.7. Equation 3.18 is in a form first written down by Appleton and Hartree and is used extensively in ionospheric research. The plus sign gives the "ordinary" wave as defined by the students of the ionosphere. It possesses no resonance but has a cutoff at $\alpha^2 = 1$ for $\theta \neq 0$. The minus sign gives the "extraordinary" wave, which has a resonance at

$$\alpha^2 = \frac{1 - \beta_-^2}{1 - \beta_-^2\cos^2\theta} \tag{3.19}$$

for $\theta \neq 0$. Its cutoff is given by $\alpha^2 = 1 + \beta_-$ and $\alpha^2 = 1 - \beta_-$ for $\theta \neq 0$. At $\theta = 0$, Equation 3.18 becomes

$$n^2 = 1 - \frac{\alpha^2(1 - \alpha^2)}{(1 - \alpha^2) \pm \beta_-|1 - \alpha^2|} \tag{3.20}$$

where the absolute value of $1 - \alpha^2$ must be used after taking a square root. Thus

$$n^2 = \begin{cases} 1 - \dfrac{\alpha^2}{1 \pm \beta} & \text{for } \alpha^2 < 1 \\ 1 - \dfrac{\alpha^2}{1 \mp \beta} & \text{for } \alpha^2 > 1 \end{cases} \tag{3.21}$$

The + sign in Equation 3.20 gives n_ℓ^2 for $\alpha^2 < 1$ and n_r for $\alpha^2 > 1$. Thus by taking the absolute value of $1 - \alpha^2$, Equation 3.18 correctly represents the discontinuity at the poles of the velocity surface at $\alpha^2 = 1$, as described in Section 3.7. As these waves have been thoroughly discussed in the literature,[8] and also by Ratcliffe,[9] they will not be emphasized here.

3.6 Quasi-Circular and Quasi-Plane Waves

As was noted in Section 2.4, the discriminant

$$D^2 = (K_r K_\ell - K_\| K_\perp)^2 \sin^4\theta - 4K_\|^2 K_\times^2 \cos^2\theta \tag{3.22}$$

is a sum of two squares. When either of these is negligibly small, we obtain formulas without radicals. These approximations also have a physical meaning as it will be seen that the corresponding waves are circularly or plane-polarized, and hence we shall name them the quasi-circular and quasi-plane approximations[10]† and denote them QC or QP. A more detailed definition of "circular" and "plane polarization" will emerge in Chapter 4.

The QC approximation is obtained by setting

$$D = 2jK_\times K_\| \cos\theta \tag{3.23}$$

and yields

$$n_{R,L}^2 = K_\| \frac{K_\perp \pm jK_\times \cos\theta}{K_\| \cos^2\theta + K_\perp \sin^2\theta} \tag{3.24}$$

which represents two surfaces tangent at the equator $(\cos\theta = 0)$ and has the correct values for n_r^2, n_ℓ^2, and n_O^2, but not for n_X^2.

The QP approximation is obtained by setting

$$D = (K_r K_\ell - K_\| K_\perp) \sin^2\theta \tag{3.25}$$

and yields

$$n_O^2 = \frac{K_\| K_\perp}{K_\perp \sin^2\theta + K_\| \cos^2\theta} \tag{3.26}$$

$$n_X^2 = \frac{K_r K_\ell \sin^2\theta + K_\| K_\perp \cos^2\theta}{K_\perp \sin^2\theta + K_\| \cos^2\theta} \tag{3.27}$$

† Booker calls these approximations quasi-longitudinal and quasi-transverse, which would translate into our terminology as quasi-along and quasi-across.

This approximation yields two surfaces tangent at the poles and gives the correct values for n_o^2 and $n_\times^2$ and the average of n_r^2 and n_ℓ^2 at the poles.

The QC expression is exact for waves propagating along $\underset{\sim}{B}_0$, which are circularly polarized, and waves propagating nearly along $\underset{\sim}{B}_0$ are quasi-circular and given by Equation 3.24. Similarly, waves propagating across $\underset{\sim}{B}_0$ are plane-polarized; that is, the electric vector remains in a plane containing $\underset{\sim}{k}$ (Section 4.2). Those waves propagating nearly across $\underset{\sim}{B}_0$ are quasi-plane and given by Equation 3.26 or 3.27. The velocity surface is therefore divided into polar caps that are quasi-circular and an equatorial zone that is quasi-plane, and these are separated by a cone of angle θ_q defined by

$$q = \frac{2\cos\theta_q}{\sin^2\theta_q} = \frac{K_r K_\ell - K_{\parallel} K_\perp}{jK_{\parallel} K_\times} = \frac{\beta_- \beta_+}{\beta_- - \beta_+} + \frac{\beta_- - \beta_+}{1 - \alpha^2} - \frac{\beta_-^2 \beta_+^2}{(1-\alpha^2)(\beta_- - \beta_+)} \tag{3.28}$$

The notation "right-" and "left-polarized" may appropriately be extended over the polar caps where the QC approximation is valid, and similarly "ordinary" and "extraordinary" may be extended over an equatorial zone, but these notations should never be extended beyond the cone θ_q.

There are considerable areas of the (α^2, β^2) plane in which the angle θ_q is either very small or is close to $\pi/2$, so that almost the entire wave surface is quasi-plane or quasi-circular. At plasma cutoff, $K_{\parallel} = 0$, or $n_o = 0$, the entire surfaces, excluding the poles, are quasi-plane. Along the line $K_{\parallel} K_\perp = K_r K_\ell$, or $n_o = n_\times$, the entire surfaces, excluding the equator, are quasi-circular. At the equator, as has been seen (Equation 3.15), the two velocity surfaces are in contact, and the polarization is arbitrary.

On either side of the line $K_{\parallel} K_\perp = K_r K_\ell$ (Equation 3.15), the two wave surfaces are distinct, but on one side of the line (indicated in Figure 3.6) the ordinary wave is on the outer surface and has the left circular polarization; on the other side of Equation 3.15, the ordinary wave is on the inner surface and has right circular polarization. As the line (3.15) is crossed, the two wave surfaces touch at the equator and exchange the ordinary and extraordinary waves.

The QP and QC approximations will be valid for some distance in the neighborhood of the lines $n_o = 0$ and $n_o = n_\times$, and we can obtain an estimate of the extent over which they are valid by considering the lines $q = \pm 1$.

This yields the two lines

$$q = \pm 1 \begin{cases} \beta_+ = \dfrac{1 - \beta_+}{\beta_-} \\ \alpha^2 = 1 - \beta_+ \beta_- \mp (\beta_- - \beta_+) \end{cases} \tag{3.29}$$

The first is a horizontal line on the (α^2, β^2) plane slightly below ion cyclotron resonance. The second is precisely the cyclotron cutoff (3.9b). Thus we see that the validity of the approximations in the thirteen regions is as follows:

13 QP	12 QP
11 QP	10 QP and QC
9 Neither	8 QC
7 QP and QC	6 QP
5 QP	4 QP
3 Neither	2 QC
1 QC	

and this is indicated in Figure 3.11. Note that the "whistler" modes that propagate only within a small cone angle along the magnetic field are quasi-circular.

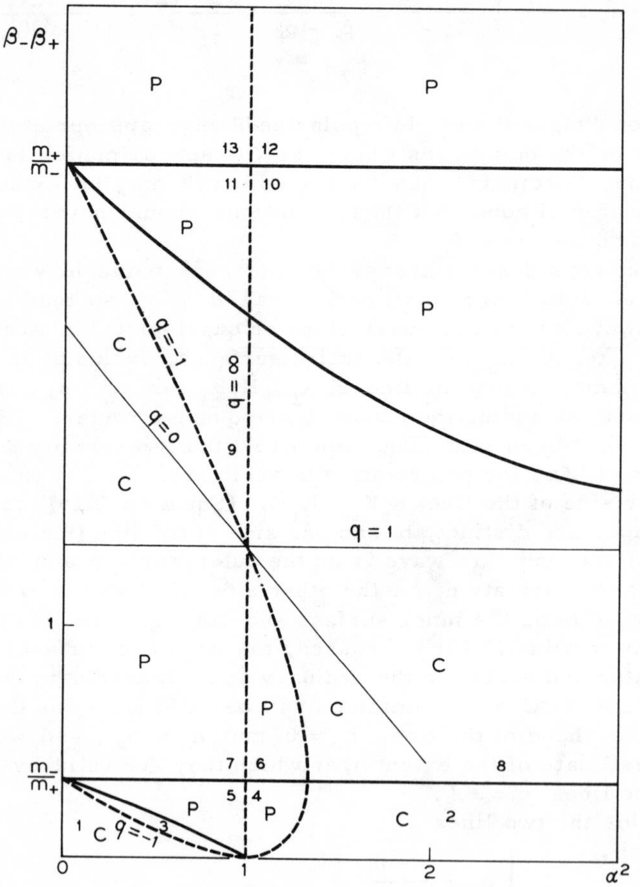

Figure 3.11. Division of the (α^2, β^2) plane into quasi-circular and quasi-plane regions.

3.7 The Quasi-Plane Approximation

The quasi-plane approximation is very good near plasma cutoff, and we see from Equations 3.26 and 3.27 that the velocity surfaces at $K_{\parallel} \approx 0$ are an "extraordinary" sphere

$$u = u_X \tag{3.30}$$

and a very large "ordinary" torus-shaped figure

$$u = u_o \sin\theta \tag{3.31}$$

where $u_o \to \infty$ as plasma cutoff is approached from $\alpha < 1$. However, the "torus" does not come in to the origin, as indicated by Equation 3.31, but to u_r or u_ℓ, whichever is larger. The extraordinary sphere is missing its poles, which are replaced by "dimples" extending into the smaller of u_r and u_ℓ, or to the origin if one of these is imaginary. Similarly, on the $\alpha > 1$ side of cutoff, the sphere has a "pimple" extending to the larger of u_r or u_ℓ, and there may or may not be an "ordinary" "figure-8" surface closing the resonant cone. This transition is shown in Figure 3.12.

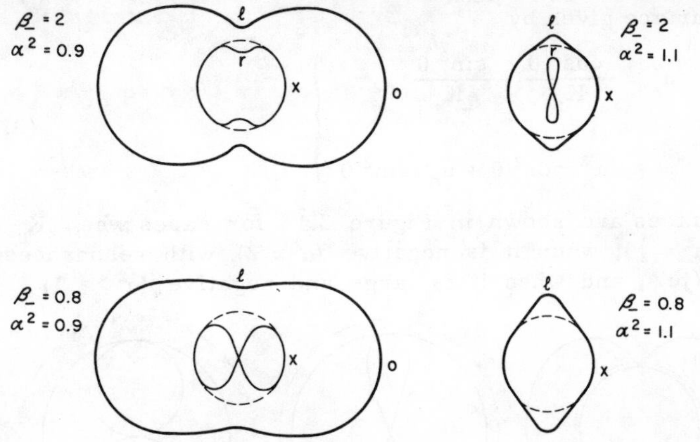

Figure 3.12. Wave surfaces near the plasma cutoff when $m_+ >> m_-$.

Thus the right- and left-handed waves jump discontinuously between the ordinary and extraordinary surfaces as plasma cutoff is crossed. The ordinary and extraordinary waves make similar jumps as the line $K_r K_\ell = K_\parallel K_\perp$ is crossed, and this is why it is often difficult to follow the "ordinary" and "extraordinary" waves by continuity arguments on propagation vector plots (k versus ω).

The QP approximation is particularly good at very large magnetic fields ($\beta_+ >> 1$) (upper parts of regions 12 and 13), because here $n_r \approx n_\ell$, since for $\beta_+ >> 1$

$$\left.\begin{aligned} K_r &\approx K_\ell \approx K_\perp \approx 1 + \frac{\omega_{p-}^2}{\omega_{b-}^2} + \frac{\omega_{p+}^2}{\omega_{b+}^2} = 1 + \frac{\omega_p^2}{\omega_{b-}\omega_{b+}} \\ K_\times &\approx j\left(\frac{\omega}{\omega_{b+}}\right)\left(\frac{\omega_p^2}{\omega_{b-}\omega_{b+}}\right) \to 0 \end{aligned}\right\} \quad (3.32)$$

Thus, here the QP approximation gives all four principal waves correctly (see the discussion after Equation 3.27). This arises because at the poles the left- and right-hand circularly polarized waves have the same phase velocity, and a linearly polarized plane wave can be constructed from them.

At large magnetic fields the QP approximation always yields a spherical extraordinary surface

$$u^2 = u_\times^2 = \frac{c^2}{K_\perp} \quad (3.33)$$

and as this wave obeys Snell's law, it is called the "ordinary" wave in texts that start from the magnetohydrodynamic approximations. The other wave, which we prefer to call the "ordinary," has a phase velocity surface given by

$$\left.\begin{aligned} u^2 &= \frac{\cos^2\theta}{K_\perp} + \frac{\sin^2\theta}{K_\parallel} \\ &= u_\times^2 \cos^2\theta + u_o^2 \sin^2\theta \end{aligned}\right\} \quad (3.34)$$

These surfaces are shown in Figure 3.13 for cases when $K_\parallel$ is positive ($\alpha^2 = \frac{1}{2}$), when it is negative ($\alpha^2 = 2$) with resonances at $\tan\theta = u_\times/ju_o$, and when it is large and negative ($\alpha^2 >> 1$).

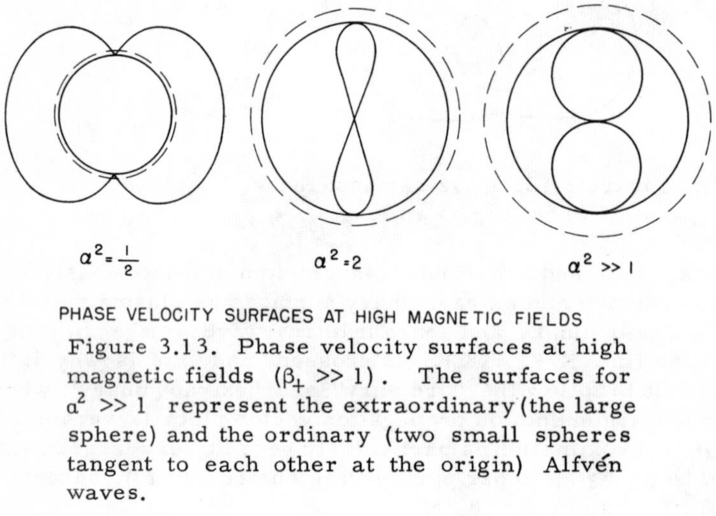

PHASE VELOCITY SURFACES AT HIGH MAGNETIC FIELDS

Figure 3.13. Phase velocity surfaces at high magnetic fields ($\beta_+ >> 1$). The surfaces for $\alpha^2 >> 1$ represent the extraordinary (the large sphere) and the ordinary (two small spheres tangent to each other at the origin) Alfvén waves.

This last condition, in which the displacement current is negligible, coupled with the condition $\beta_+ >> 1$, defines the so-called magnetohydrodynamic region (the upper right-hand corner of region 12). Here, the phase velocity surface of the ordinary wave is a double-sphere, that is, the surface consists of two spheres tangent to each other at the origin and tangent internally to the extraordinary sphere at the poles (Figure 3.13). It is the spherical extraordinary wave that is the fast wave. Its phase velocity is very nearly the Alfvén speed u_a, because in this limit

$$K_r \rightarrow K_\ell \rightarrow K_\perp \rightarrow 1 + \frac{c^2}{u_a^2} \tag{3.35}$$

where

$$u_a^2 = \frac{c^2 \beta_+ \beta_-}{\alpha^2} = \frac{B_0 H_0}{N(m_+ + m_-)} \tag{3.36}$$

is the square of the Alfvén speed. Then the speed of the fast wave is given by

$$\frac{1}{u^2} = \frac{1}{u_a^2} + \frac{1}{c^2} \tag{3.37}$$

and is generally close to the Alfvén speed.

The QP approximation is also valid in regions 6 and 7 provided the location specified is far enough away from cyclotron cutoff and cyclotron resonance. This is easier to accomplish than would appear from Figure 3.11 because the cyclotron cutoff curve extends much farther to the right for large ion-to-electron mass ratios. Formulas 3.33 and 3.34 hold in this region, but Condition 3.35 must be replaced by

$$\left.\begin{aligned} K_r &\rightarrow 1 + \frac{\alpha^2}{\beta_-} + \frac{\alpha^2}{\beta_-^2} \\ K_\ell &\rightarrow 1 - \frac{\alpha^2}{\beta_-} + \frac{\alpha^2}{\beta_-^2} \\ K_\perp &\rightarrow 1 + \frac{\alpha^2}{\beta_-^2} \end{aligned}\right\} \tag{3.38}$$

Thus, for $\alpha^2/\beta_- << 1$, the sequence of Figure 3.13 is repeated, but with the extraordinary wave propagating as though it were in free space. The reason for this behavior is that, within the appropriate limits, the ions effectively have infinite mass ($\beta_+ << 1$) and the electrons have zero mass ($\beta_- >> 1$). The restoring force arises from Coulomb interactions, but the entire inertia is caused by the magnetic field, so that no particle masses enter the effective dielectric coefficients.

Reprinted from Nuclear Fusion 1 (1960) pp.3-41, published by International Atomic Energy Atomic, Kaertner Ring, Vienna 1, Austria, by Permission

PLASMA OSCILLATIONS (I)*

I. B. BERNSTEIN** and S. K. TREHAN***

PROJECT MATTERHORN, PRINCETON UNIVERSITY, PRINCETON, NEW JERSEY, USA

This article is the first part of a review of the theory of wave phenomena in plasmas. The basic kinetic theory is developed taking into account coulomb collisions. From this magnetohydrodynamic equations are derived. It is demonstrated that it is legitimate to deal with a closed subset of these equations either in the limit of collision-dominated phenomena, or in the limit where the effective phase velocities of the phenomena of interest are much greater than thermal speeds. In case of collision-dominated plasmas the theory of transport coefficients is discussed.

These equations are then applied to an extensive treatment of small amplitude wave phenomena in plasmas. A discussion of the dissipative effects on hydromagnetic waves is given. Hydromagnetic waves are also considered from the Chew, Goldberger and Low theory. Longitudinal and transverse oscillations in current-carrying plasmas are also discussed.

Oscillations of a cylindrical plasma are considered and the phenomenon of ion cyclotron resonance is discussed. The possibility of radiation by plasma oscillations by a uniform sphere is exhibited. Some general results on the stability of longitudinal electron oscillations in non-uniform plasmas are given.

A brief treatment of large amplitude electron oscillations is given and the breaking of these oscillations as a dissipative mechanism for the organized plasma motion is discussed.

Part II of this paper, to appear in a future issue of this journal, will be devoted to the discussion of plasma oscillations directly from the kinetic theory.

CONTENTS

I INTRODUCTION 4

II THE BASIC EQUATIONS 4

1. Boltzmann Equation 5
   1.1 Fokker-Planck form of the Boltzmann Equation . 5
   1.2 Fokker-Planck Equation for Coulomb Force . . . 6
   1.3 The Moment Equations 6
2. The Case of Strong Collisions 8
   2.1 Weak Magnetic Field 9
   2.2 The A. C. Conductivity 10
3. The Case of Weak Collisions 10
   3.1 Equivalence of Collisionless Boltzmann Equation and Particle Orbit Theory 11
   3.2 The Low Temperature Approximation 11
   3.3 Chew, Goldberger, and Low Approximation . . . 11

III WAVE PHENOMENA IN PLASMAS 12

1. General Remarks 12
2. Unbounded Plasmas in the Absence of External Fields 13
   2.1 Longitudinal Electron Plasma Oscillations 13
   2.2 Transverse Electron Plasma Oscillations 14
   2.3 Effect of Thermal Motions on Electron Plasma Oscillations 14
   2.4 Ion Oscillations 15
3. Unbounded Cold Plasmas in the Presence of an External Magnetic Field 16
   3.1 Oscillations in a Static Plasma 17
   3.11 No Magnetic Field Case 17
   3.12 Propagation along the Magnetic Field 17
   a) High frequency oscillations 17
   b) Oscillations near the electron cyclotron frequency 18
   c) Oscillations much below the ion cyclotron frequency 18
   d) Oscillations near the ion cyclotron frequency . 18
   3.13 Propagation Transverse to the Magnetic Field . . 19
   3.14 Weak Magnetic Field 19
   3.15 Strong Magnetic Field 21
4. Instability in a Plasma Carrying Current 21
5. Plasma Carrying Current in a Magnetic Field 23
   5.1 Stream Instability (transverse oscillations) 24
   5.11 Oscillations much below the ion cyclotron frequency 25
   5.12 Oscillations near the ion cyclotron frequency . 26
6. Summary of Sections 2—5 26
7. Hydromagnetic Waves from Chew, Goldberger, and Low Theory 27
8. Hydromagnetic Waves: General Theory 28

IV OSCILLATIONS OF BOUNDED AND NON-UNIFORM PLASMAS 30

1. Oscillations of a Cylindrical Plasma 30
2. Radiation by Plasma Oscillations 33
3. Oscillations in Non-Uniform Plasmas 35

V NON-LINEAR OSCILLATIONS 36

ACKNOWLEDGEMENTS 38

BIBLIOGRAPHICAL NOTES 38

---

* Supported by the U.S. Atomic Energy Commission under contract AT(30-1)-1238 with Princeton University.

** Project Matterhorn, Princeton University.

*** Panjab University, Chandigarh, Panjab State, India.

I. Introduction

In this article we shall attempt to present a systematic survey of the theoretical knowledge of wave phenomena in plasmas. We shall use the term "plasma" to describe a fully ionized gas composed of positive and negative ions of effectively zero net charge density. For the sake of convenience we limit our attention to a plasma composed of only two species (positive ions and electrons); the extension of the results to gases consisting of more than two species is straightforward and will not be considered here. Some of the results are also applicable to conducting liquids and gases not fully ionized.

Astrophysical examples of such systems are the ionosphere, the solar corona, stellar interiors and the atmosphere of hot stars, the H_{II} regions of interstellar space, and cosmic radio sources. Plasmas are also of fundamental interest in the proposed schemes for controlled thermonuclear fusion, plasma propulsion of space ships, microwave generators, and gas discharge devices.

One distinctive feature of plasmas is the special nature of collisions, in contrast to the two-body collisions familiar in the conventional theory of neutral gases. Because of the long range nature of the Coulomb forces which govern the encounters of charged particles, cooperative phenomena are of major importance in describing the dynamics of a plasma. Also these long range collisions lead to a diffusion in velocity space and are most appropriately described by the Fokker-Planck equation. The elastic or inelastic two-body encounters of ions or electrons with neutrals or perhaps with the core of an incompletely ionized atom are usually negligible in plasmas and will be considered, effectively, only when dealing with dissipative effects in collision-dominated plasmas.

There are two levels of description of plasmas which have received major consideration during the past decade. The first of these is based on the direct solution of the Boltzmann transport equation—usually referred to as the kinetic theory description. This method has the intrinsic merit of providing a more complete description of the dynamics of a plasma. However, this procedure is mathematically more difficult to handle. The second method is based on using a closed set of moment equations to characterize the behaviour of a plasma. This description, usually referred to as the hydrodynamic or hydromagnetic description, though of limited applicability (in a sense to be discussed in detail later) has the merit of relative mathematical simplicity and is quite helpful in the physical understanding of the various phenomena involved. This method is applicable either when (1) collisions dominate so that one has local thermodynamic equilibrium and can apply the Chapman-Enskog expansion technique, or (2) the phase velocity of the wave is much larger than the characteristic thermal speed in a collision-free plasma. The latter will be referred to as the "Low Temperature Approximation."

For plasmas of interest under astrophysical and laboratory conditions quantum mechanical effects are unimportant in considering most of the dynamics of plasmas.

This work, therefore, divides itself naturally into two parts. In part I the kinetic theory description is formulated and its relation to the hydrodynamic description established. The resulting hydromagnetic equations are then applied to a variety of wave phenomena. Part II of this article, to appear in a later issue of this journal, will be devoted to the discussion of wave phenomena based directly on the kinetic theory.

The theory described here is concerned mainly with the small motions about a steady state of the plasma. The general case of large motions is considered only briefly in Section V.

Section III deals with oscillations in unbounded homogeneous plasmas, admittedly a severe idealization. However, these treatments do serve to give some insight into the basic physical processes and the mathematical methods. The neglect of boundaries would imply that the description is valid only for wavelengths much smaller than the characteristic length of the system and for time intervals short enough that the disturbance has not reached the boundaries and been reflected and transmitted.

Unfortunately, because of the inherent difficulty of establishing in the laboratory plasmas uncomplicated by boundary effects, impurities, etc., there has not been, as yet, much experimental verification of the theoretical investigations.

II. The basic equations

By and large one is interested only in the knowledge of some macroscopic properties of the plasma like the mean particle density, mean velocity, etc., rather than in the detail afforded by the description of the individual motion of the particles. It is, therefore, appropriate to characterize a given class of particles by a distribution function $f(\mathbf{x},\mathbf{v},t)$ such that $f\, d^3\mathbf{x}\, d^3\mathbf{v}$ represents at time t the probable number of particles with velocities between $\mathbf{v}$ and $\mathbf{v} + d\mathbf{v}$, and with positions between $\mathbf{x}$ and $\mathbf{x} + d\mathbf{x}$. It is possible to relate f to the more recondite density in the phase space of all the particles, but a discussion of this matter is beyond the scope of this article; suffice it to say that the introduction of f is compatible with the following notions about particle interactions in plasmas.

The particles, being charged and possessing no internal degrees of freedom at the range of energies of interest here, interact primarily through the electromagnetic fields. In particular, when two particles are close together it is their Coulomb interaction which predominates. Consider then such two-body Coulomb encounters. They can be characterized, in their center of mass system, by the impact parameter and the relative velocity. The collisions can then be conveniently divided into three classes.

The first of these corresponds to impact parameters less than the mean impact parameter for 90° deflection,

$$b = \frac{Z_1 Z_2 e^2}{\langle v^2 \rangle}\left[\frac{1}{m_1} + \frac{1}{m_2}\right], \tag{1}$$

where Z_1 and Z_2 are the charge numbers of particles involved, m_1 and m_2 are their masses, $\langle v^2 \rangle$ represents their mean square relative velocity, and e is the electronic charge. It is usually legitimate to describe such encounters by the familiar two-body collision integrals of the kinetic theory of gases when writing the kinetic equation for the distribution function. In most cases of interest these collisions are negligible.

The second class comprises the many-body encounters which can be regarded as composed of a succession of uncorrelated small angle Coulomb deflections. These correspond to elementary Coulomb scattering events characterized by impact parameters greater than the distance of closest approach b, but less than the electron Debye length

$$\lambda_D = \left[\frac{(1/3)\, m \langle v^2 \rangle}{4\pi N e^2}\right]^{\frac{1}{2}} \quad (2)$$

where m is the electron mass, $\langle v^2 \rangle$ is the electron mean square velocity, and N is the electron number density. These encounters are most appropriately described by the Fokker-Planck form for the collision integral in the Boltzmann equation.

When there are many particles in a sphere of radius λ_D (i.e., $\lambda_D^3 N \gg 1$), density fluctuations over distances $> \lambda_D$ are suppressed by macroscopic electric forces. Thus the third class of uncorrelated two-body encounters, those with impact parameters greater than λ_D, do not occur per se. These are replaced in the kinetic eqation by the correlated effect of many particles through the macroscopic electromagnetic fields described by the Maxwell equations; this leads to co-operative phenomena.

1. Boltzmann Equation

The distribution function for each species of particles is governed by the Boltzmann equation

$$\mathfrak{D} f = \left[\frac{\partial}{\partial t} + \mathbf{v}\cdot\nabla + \mathbf{F}\cdot\nabla_v\right] f = \left(\frac{\partial f}{\partial t}\right)_{\text{coll.}} \quad (3)$$

where ∇ and ∇_v represent the gradient operators in coordinate (x) and velocity (v) space respectively, $\mathbf{F}$ denotes the force per unit mass, and $(\partial f/\partial t)_{\text{coll.}}$ represents the time rate of change of f resulting from collisions. It may be remarked here that there is a separate Boltzmann equation for each species of particle. We now discuss the Fokker-Planck form for the collision term.

1.1 Fokker-Planck Form of the Boltzmann Equation

It has been demonstrated by Jeans that when particles interact through long range forces, the cumulative effect of weak deflections resulting from the relatively distant encounters is more important than the effect of occasional large deflections. The cumulative effect of weak deflections is most appropriately taken into account by writing the collision term in the Fokker-Planck form. This reduction is possible only if there exist time intervals Δt long enough for the particles to suffer a large number of collisions but small enough for the net mean square change in velocity, $\langle|\Delta \mathbf{v}|^2\rangle$, to be small compared with the mean square velocity, and to be of order Δt.

Let $P(\mathbf{v}; \Delta\mathbf{v})$ denote the probability that in the time interval Δt a particle with velocity co-ordinate $\mathbf{v}$ undergoes a displacement $\Delta\mathbf{v}$. The distribution function is then given by

$$f(\mathbf{x}, \mathbf{v}, t) = \int f(\mathbf{x}, \mathbf{v}-\Delta\mathbf{v}, t-\Delta t)\, P(\mathbf{v}-\Delta\mathbf{v}; \Delta\mathbf{v})\, d^3\Delta\mathbf{v}. \quad (4)$$

We may remark here that in expecting this integral equation to be true we are actually supposing that the course which a particle will take depends only on the instantaneous value of its physical parameters and is entirely independent of its past history. In general probability theory a stochastic process which has this characteristic, namely that what happens at a given instant of time t depends only on the state of the system at time t, is said to be a Markoff process.

Since Δt and $\Delta\mathbf{v}$ are both assumed small, using Taylor's expansion we can write (4) in the form

$$\begin{aligned} f(\mathbf{x}, \mathbf{v}, t) = & \int\!\Big\{ f(\mathbf{x}, \mathbf{v}, t)\, P(\mathbf{v}; \Delta\mathbf{v}) - \Delta t \frac{\partial f}{\partial t} P(\mathbf{v}; \Delta\mathbf{v}) \\ & - \Delta\mathbf{v}\cdot\left[\frac{\partial f}{\partial \mathbf{v}} P(\mathbf{v}; \Delta\mathbf{v}) + f \frac{\partial}{\partial \mathbf{v}} P(\mathbf{v}; \Delta\mathbf{v})\right] + \frac{1}{2}\Delta\mathbf{v}\Delta\mathbf{v} : \\ & \left[\frac{\partial^2 f}{\partial \mathbf{v}\partial \mathbf{v}} P(\mathbf{v}; \Delta\mathbf{v}) + 2\frac{\partial f}{\partial \mathbf{v}}\frac{\partial P}{\partial \mathbf{v}} + f\frac{\partial^2 P}{\partial \mathbf{v}\partial \mathbf{v}}\right] + \ldots \Big\} d^3\Delta\mathbf{v}. \end{aligned} \quad (5)$$

Using the fact that

$$\int P(\mathbf{v}; \Delta\mathbf{v})\, d^3\Delta\mathbf{v} = 1, \quad (6)$$

Eq. (5) gives for the time rate of change of f resulting from the cumulative effect of small deflections:

$$\left(\frac{\partial f}{\partial t}\right)_{\text{coll}} = -\frac{\partial}{\partial \mathbf{v}}\cdot\left[\langle\Delta\mathbf{v}\rangle - \frac{1}{2}\frac{\partial}{\partial \mathbf{v}}\cdot\langle\Delta\mathbf{v}\,\Delta\mathbf{v}\rangle\right], \quad (7)$$

where we have retained terms only to lowest significant order and

$$\Delta t\, \langle\Delta\mathbf{v}\rangle = \int f(\mathbf{x}, \mathbf{v}, t)\, P(\mathbf{v}; \Delta\mathbf{v})\, \Delta\mathbf{v}\, d^3\Delta\mathbf{v}, \quad (8)$$

$$\Delta t\, \langle\Delta\mathbf{v}\,\Delta\mathbf{v}\rangle = \int f(\mathbf{x}, \mathbf{v}, t)\, P(\mathbf{v}; \Delta\mathbf{v})\, \Delta\mathbf{v}\,\Delta\mathbf{v}\, d^3\Delta\mathbf{v}. \quad (9)$$

Eq. (7) represents the collision term in the Fokker-Planck form.

Consider the two-body encounters of particles of type i with those of type j and let $\sigma_{ij}(\theta, v)$ denote the differential cross section for scattering of their relative velocity vector $\mathbf{v} = \mathbf{v}_i - \mathbf{v}_j$ through an angle θ. Then the associated momentum transfer cross section is given by

$$Q_{ij}(v) = 2\pi \int \sigma_{ij}(\theta, v)\,(1-\cos\theta)\sin\theta\, d\theta. \quad (10)$$

In terms of Q, retaining only the dominant terms in the mean square scattering angle, one can write for the contribution of such two-body encounters to stochastic averages, when polarization effects are negligible,

$$\langle\Delta\mathbf{v}\rangle_{ij} = f_i(\mathbf{x}, \mathbf{v}_i, t)\frac{-m_j}{(m_i+m_j)}\int d^3\mathbf{v}_j f_j(\mathbf{x}, \mathbf{v}_j, t)\, v^2 Q_{ij}(v)\,\nabla_v v, \quad (11)$$

and

$$\langle\Delta\mathbf{v}\,\Delta\mathbf{v}\rangle_{ij} = f_i(\mathbf{x}, \mathbf{v}_i, t)\frac{m_i^2}{(m_i+m_j)^2}\int d^3\mathbf{v}_j f_j(\mathbf{x}, \mathbf{v}_j, t)\, v^3 Q_{ij}(v)\,\nabla_v\nabla_v v. \quad (12)$$

1.2 Fokker-Planck Equation for Coulomb Force

For the case of Coulomb collisions, the differential scattering cross section is given by

$$\sigma_{ij}(v) = \left[\frac{Z_i Z_j e^2 (m_i + m_j)}{2\, m_i\, m_j\, v^2}\right]^2 \frac{1}{\sin^4(\theta/2)}. \tag{13}$$

The integral occurring in Q will diverge at the lower limit of integration ($\theta = 0$). However, the small angle deflections correspond to scatterings with very large impact parameters, and the divergence arises from the long range nature of the Coulomb force. This divergence is eliminated when we take into account the shielding that arises from the polarization of charge surrounding the scatterer. The polarization screens the scattering particle and provides a natural cutoff on the maximum impact parameter of the order of the Debye length λ_D. We thus take for the minimum scattering angle

$$\psi = \frac{(m_i + m_j)\, e^2}{4 m_i\, m_j \langle v^2 \rangle \lambda_D} \tag{14}$$

Using Eqs. (13) and (14) into Eq. (10) we obtain

$$Q_{ij} = 4\pi \left[\frac{Z_i Z_j e^2 (m_i + m_j)}{m_i\, m_j\, v^2}\right]^2 \ln \frac{(m_i + m_j) e^2}{2\, m_i\, m_j \langle v^2 \rangle \lambda_D}. \tag{15}$$

Using the foregoing results in the Fokker-Planck equation we obtain after an integration by parts what is called the Landau form for the collision term:

$$\left(\frac{\partial f_i}{\partial t}\right)_{\text{coll.}} = \nabla_{v_i} \cdot \left\{ \frac{2\pi Z_i^2 Z_j^2 e^4}{m_i^2\, m_j} \ln\left[\frac{(m_i + m_j)\, e^2}{2 m_i\, m_j \langle v^2 \rangle_{ij} \lambda_D}\right] \times \int d^3 v_j \frac{v^2 \mathbf{I} - \mathbf{v}\mathbf{v}}{v^3} \cdot (m_j f_j \nabla_{v_i} f_i - m_i f_i \nabla_{v_j} f_j) \right\}. \tag{16}$$

It may be noted that, apart from the slowly varying logarithmic term, in order of magnitude the collision terms are inversely proportional to $\langle v^2 \rangle_{ij}$, the mean square relative kinetic energy. Thus in the limit where this factor is appropriately large, collisions are negligible.

1.3 The Moment Equations

The particle density and the local mean velocity are defined as

$$N = \int f(\mathbf{x}, \mathbf{v}, t)\, d^3\mathbf{v} \tag{17}$$

and

$$\mathbf{u} = \frac{1}{N} \int f(\mathbf{x}, \mathbf{v}, t)\, \mathbf{v}\, d^3 \mathbf{v}. \tag{18}$$

In terms of these moments we can define some of the other relevant macroscopic quantities*:

$$\varrho = \sum m N = \text{mass density}, \tag{19}$$

$$\mathbf{U}_0 = \frac{1}{\varrho} \sum m N \mathbf{u} = \text{velocity of the center of m}$$

$$\varepsilon = \sum e N = \text{charge density}, \tag{21}$$

$$\mathbf{J} = \sum e N \mathbf{u} = \text{current density}, \tag{22}$$

where the summation is to be carried over all the species of the system. The random velocity with respect to the center of mass is defined to be

$$\mathbf{w} = \mathbf{v} - \mathbf{U}_0. \tag{23}$$

It is convenient to define the other relevant quantities with respect to the center of mass velocity. Thus

$$\mathbf{U} = \frac{1}{N} \int \mathbf{w} f(\mathbf{x}, \mathbf{v}, t)\, d^3 \mathbf{v} \quad = \text{mean velocity of each of the species with respect to the center of mass}, \tag{24}$$

$$\mathsf{P} = m \int \mathbf{w}\,\mathbf{w} f(\mathbf{x}, \mathbf{v}, t)\, d^3 \mathbf{v} \quad = \text{pressure tensor}, \tag{25}$$

and

$$\mathsf{Q} = m \int \mathbf{w}\,\mathbf{w}\,\mathbf{w} f(\mathbf{x}, \mathbf{v}, t)\, d^3 \mathbf{v} = \text{heat flow tensor}, \tag{26}$$

where Q is a tensor of rank 3 completely symmetric in all its indices. We further define

$$\mathbf{P} = \sum \mathsf{P} \text{ and } \mathbf{Q} = \sum \mathsf{Q}. \tag{27}$$

It is clear that

$$\sum m N \mathbf{U} = 0. \tag{28}$$

Note that

$$\frac{1}{2} \text{Trace } \mathsf{P} = \int \frac{1}{2} m w^2 f(\mathbf{x}, \mathbf{v}, t)\, d^3 \mathbf{v} \tag{29}$$

represents the mean kinetic energy relative to the center of mass and is referred to as the internal energy, or the thermal energy of the gas. This suggests that we can define the generalized temperature by the relation

$$\frac{1}{2} \text{Trace } \mathsf{P} = \frac{3}{2} N \Theta, \tag{30}$$

where $\Theta = kT$, k is the Boltzmann constant, and T is the temperature. We shall always use Θ to denote the temperature in energy units.

This definition of temperature is natural when collisions dominate, in which case the various particle distribution functions are very closely locally Maxwellian, relative to the center of mass velocity, corresponding to the same temperature. Occasionally one encounters an alternative definition of temperature, where it is defined separately for each species of the plasma, as the mean kinetic energy of that species relative to its own mean mass velocity. The other moments can be similarly de- This latter definition is particularly convenient collisions are negligible and will be used in part II his review. The two notions, of course, coincide if we consider the motion of a single species of the plasma, a picture which is reasonable in investigating high frequency waves where only the electron motion is significant. In general, however, the two definitions are quite different and care must be exercised to make sure which is being employed in any given context.

* We shall adopt the convention that whenever m appears after a summation sign, it is the mass of any of the species of the plasma; otherwise m denotes the electron mass and M, the proton mass. The electron charge is taken to be $-e$ while that of the proton, $+e$. Similarly, ω_c will denote the electron or ion cyclotron frequency whereas ω_e and ω_i will denote the electron and ion cyclotron frequency respectively.

The vector

$$\mathbf{q} = \frac{1}{2}\,\mathbf{I} : \mathbf{Q} = \int \frac{1}{2} m\, w^2\, \mathbf{w} f(\mathbf{x}, \mathbf{v}, t)\, d^3\mathbf{v} \qquad (31)$$

represents the flow of internal energy relative to the center of mass and will be called the heat flow vector.

Since $\mathbf{x}$ and $\mathbf{v}$ are independent vectors, it is convenient to write the Boltzmann equation (3) as

$$\mathfrak{D} f = \frac{\partial f}{\partial t} + \nabla \cdot (\mathbf{v} f) + \nabla_v \cdot (\mathbf{F} f) = \left(\frac{\partial f}{\partial t}\right)_{\text{coll}} \qquad (32)$$

Quite generally, we can write

$$\mathbf{F} = \frac{e}{m}\left[\mathbf{E}(\mathbf{x}, t) + \frac{1}{c}\,\mathbf{v} \times \mathbf{B}(\mathbf{x}, t)\right] - \nabla \varphi, \qquad (33)$$

where $\mathbf{E}$ and $\mathbf{B}$ denote the electric and magnetic fields respectively, and φ is the gravitational potential. The electromagnetic fields, of course, satisfy Maxwell's equations:

$$\nabla \times \mathbf{B} = \frac{4\pi}{c}\mathbf{J} + \frac{1}{c}\frac{\partial \mathbf{E}}{\partial t}, \qquad \nabla \times \mathbf{E} = -\frac{1}{c}\frac{\partial \mathbf{B}}{\partial t}, \qquad (34)$$

$$\nabla \cdot \mathbf{E} = 4\pi\varepsilon, \quad \text{and} \quad \nabla \cdot \mathbf{B} = 0; \qquad (35)$$

Gaussian units will be used throughout in this work. The gravitational potential satisfies the Poisson equation

$$\nabla^2 \varphi = -4\pi G \varrho, \qquad (36)$$

where G denotes the gravitational constant.

In order to derive the equations governing the macroscopic quantities, it is convenient to write the Boltzmann equation in terms of the random velocity $\mathbf{w}$. This can be readily effected by the transformations

$$f(\mathbf{x}, \mathbf{v}, t) \to f(\mathbf{x}, \mathbf{w}, t), \qquad (37)$$

$$\frac{\partial}{\partial t} \to \frac{\partial}{\partial t} - \frac{\partial \mathbf{U}_0}{\partial t} \cdot \nabla_w, \qquad (38)$$

$$\nabla \to \nabla - (\nabla\, \mathbf{U}_0) \cdot \nabla_w, \qquad (39)$$

$$\nabla_v \to \nabla_w. \qquad (40)$$

The Boltzmann equation now takes the form

$$\mathfrak{D} f = \frac{\partial f}{\partial t} + \nabla \cdot \Big[(\mathbf{w} + \mathbf{U}_0) f \Big] + \nabla_w \cdot (\mathbf{b} f) = \left(\frac{\partial f}{\partial t}\right)_{\text{coll.}} \qquad (41)$$

where

$$\mathbf{b} = \frac{e}{m}\left[\mathbf{E}(\mathbf{x}, t) + \frac{1}{c}\mathbf{U}_0 \times \mathbf{B}(\mathbf{x}, t)\right] - \nabla \varphi - \frac{d\mathbf{U}_0}{dt} - (\mathbf{w} \cdot \nabla)\, \mathbf{U}_0 + \frac{e}{mc}\mathbf{w} \times \mathbf{B}(\mathbf{x}, t), \qquad (42)$$

and

$$\frac{d}{dt} = \frac{\partial}{\partial t} + \mathbf{U}_0 \cdot \nabla \qquad (43)$$

denotes the time derivative as we follow the motion of an element of the fluid.

Multiplying Eq. (41) by 1, $m\mathbf{w}$, and $m\mathbf{ww}$, and assuming that f vanishes sufficiently strongly in velocity space so that all the surface integrals vanish, we obtain for the moment equations

$$\frac{\partial N}{\partial t} + \nabla \cdot \Big[N\mathbf{U} + N\mathbf{U}_0\Big] = 0, \qquad (44)$$

$$mN\frac{d\mathbf{U}_0}{dt} = -\nabla \cdot \Big[\mathsf{P} + mN\mathbf{U}_0\mathbf{U}\Big] - \frac{\partial}{\partial t} mN\mathbf{U} + Ne\Big[\mathbf{E} + \frac{1}{c}\mathbf{U}_0 \times \mathbf{B}\Big] - mN\nabla\varphi - mN(\mathbf{U} \cdot \nabla)\,\mathbf{U}_0 + \frac{Ne}{c}\mathbf{U} \times \mathbf{B}, \qquad (45)$$

and

$$\frac{\partial}{\partial t}\mathsf{P} + \nabla \cdot (\mathbf{Q} + \mathbf{U}_0\mathsf{P}) + \mathsf{P} \cdot \nabla\mathbf{U}_0 + (\mathsf{P} \cdot \nabla\mathbf{U}_0)^T + \frac{e}{mc}(\mathbf{B} \times \mathsf{P} - \mathsf{P} \times \mathbf{B}) - mN\Big[\frac{e}{m}(\mathbf{E} + \frac{1}{c}\mathbf{U}_0 \times \mathbf{B}) - \nabla\varphi\Big]\mathbf{U} - mN\mathbf{U}\Big[\frac{e}{m}(\mathbf{E} + \frac{1}{c}\mathbf{U}_0 \times \mathbf{B}) - \nabla\varphi\Big] + mN\Big[\frac{d\mathbf{U}_0}{dt}\mathbf{U} + \mathbf{U}\frac{d\mathbf{U}_0}{dt}\Big] = \left(\frac{\partial}{\partial t}\mathsf{P}\right)_{\text{coll.}} \qquad (46)$$

where $(\mathsf{A})^T$ denotes the transpose of the matrix A. We now sum Eqs. (44)—(46) over all the species of the system and, making use of Eqs. (19)—(22), (27), and (28), we obtain

$$\frac{\partial \varrho}{\partial t} + \nabla \cdot (\varrho\, \mathbf{U}) = 0, \qquad (47)$$

$$\varrho\frac{d\mathbf{U}}{dt} = -\nabla \cdot \mathsf{P} + \varepsilon\mathbf{E} + \frac{1}{c}\mathbf{J} \times \mathbf{B} - \varrho\nabla\varphi, \qquad (48)$$

and

$$\frac{\partial}{\partial t}\mathsf{P} + \nabla \cdot (\mathbf{Q} + \mathbf{U}\mathsf{P}) + \mathsf{P} \cdot \nabla\mathbf{U} + (\mathsf{P} \cdot \nabla\mathbf{U})^T + \sum\frac{e}{mc}(\mathbf{B} \times \mathsf{P} - \mathsf{P} \times \mathbf{B}) - (\mathbf{J} - \varepsilon\mathbf{U})(\mathbf{E} + \frac{1}{c}\mathbf{U} \times \mathbf{B}) - (\mathbf{E} + \frac{1}{c}\mathbf{U} \times \mathbf{B})(\mathbf{J} - \varepsilon\mathbf{U}) = \left(\frac{\partial}{\partial t}\mathsf{P}\right)_{\text{coll.}} \qquad (49)$$

where in writing Eq. (49) we have made use of the fact that

$$\sum e N\mathbf{U} = \sum e N(\mathbf{u} - \mathbf{U}_0) = \mathbf{J} - \varepsilon\,\mathbf{U}_0, \qquad (50)$$

and we have dropped the subscript on $\mathbf{U}_0$ in Eqs. (47)—(49) as it is no longer necessary. If we take the trace of Eq. (49) and make use of the relation (30), we obtain

$$\frac{\partial}{\partial t}\left(\frac{3}{2}n\Theta\right) + \nabla \cdot \left(\mathbf{q} + \frac{3}{2}n\Theta\,\mathbf{U}\right) + \mathsf{P} : \nabla\mathbf{U} - (\mathbf{J} - \varepsilon\mathbf{U}) \cdot \left(\mathbf{E} + \frac{1}{c}\mathbf{U} \times \mathbf{B}\right) = 0, \qquad (51)$$

where the right hand side vanishes since collisions conserve the internal energy of the system.

We recognize Eqs. (47) and (48) as the well-known hydrodynamical equations of continuity and motion. Eqs. (47)—(49) are rather useless in their present form; they do not constitute a closed set of equations as they contain more unknowns than the number of equations. One could obtain an equation governing the heat flow tensor $\mathbf{Q}$ by taking the fourth moment of the Boltzmann equation; however, this equation would involve the next higher order moment of the distribution function and the system of equations is not closed again.

The Case of Strong Collisions

We now consider the case where collisions dominate. Then, to a high degree of approximation, the particle distribution functions tend to be locally Maxwellian and we may set

$$f(\mathbf{x}, \mathbf{v}, t) = f_0(\mathbf{x}, \mathbf{v}, t)\,[1 + \Phi(\mathbf{x}, \mathbf{v}, t)], \qquad (52)$$

where

$$f_0(\mathbf{x}, \mathbf{v}, t) = N(\mathbf{x}, t)\left[\frac{m}{2\pi\Theta(\mathbf{x}, t)}\right]^{3/2} \exp\left\{-m\frac{[\mathbf{v} - \mathbf{U}_0(\mathbf{x}, t)]^2}{2\Theta(\mathbf{x}, t)}\right\}, \qquad (53)$$

and Φ is considered small compared to unity. The density N, temperature Θ, and mass velocity $\mathbf{U}_0$ are assumed to be slowly-varying functions of space and time such that their spatial variations over one mean free path, and temporal variations over one mean free time, are very small. This limiting situation forms the basis of the Chapman-Enskog theory of gases and leads to a truncation of the hierarchy of moment equations.

The rigorous Chapman-Enskog theory for a plasma composed of two or more species, interacting with electromagnetic and gravitational fields, is quite complex. However, the smallness of the electron to ion mass ratio and the inability of a plasma to support large electric fields—referred to as the condition of quasi-neutrality—results in a substantial simplification of the Chapman-Enskog expansion technique.

The condition of quasi-neutrality implies that the ratio of the net charge density to the charge density of each of the species is very small compared to unity. We shall systematically neglect both these ratios compared with unity in our discussion of the transport co-efficients.

Consider for simplicity a plasma composed of N electrons and an equal number of protons of masses m and M and charges $-e$ and $+e$ respectively. Following the Chapman-Enskog procedure we can show that, within the approximation outlined earlier, the small quantities Φ are determined by the integro-differential equations (cf. Eqs. (3), (16), (52), (53)):

$$\left\{\left(\frac{Mw^2}{2\Theta} - \frac{5}{2}\right)\mathbf{w}\cdot\nabla\ln\Theta + \frac{M}{\Theta}\left(\mathbf{w}\mathbf{w} - \frac{1}{3}w^2\mathbf{I}\right):\nabla\mathbf{U}_0 - \left[\frac{e}{\Theta}\left(\mathbf{E} + \frac{1}{c}\mathbf{U}_0\times\mathbf{B}\right) + \nabla\ln(N\Theta)\right]\cdot\mathbf{w}\right\}f_0^+ =$$
$$-\frac{1}{N\Theta c}(\mathbf{J}\times\mathbf{B})\cdot\mathbf{w}f_0^+ + \frac{e}{Mc}\mathbf{B}\cdot\mathbf{w}\times(\nabla_w\Phi^+)f_0^+ - \nabla_{w'}\Gamma^+ \qquad (54)$$

and

$$\left\{\left(\frac{mw^2}{2\Theta} - \frac{5}{2}\right)\mathbf{w}\cdot\nabla\ln\Theta + \frac{m}{\Theta}\left(\mathbf{w}\mathbf{w} - \frac{1}{3}w^2\mathbf{I}\right):\nabla\mathbf{U}_0 + \left[\frac{e}{\Theta}\left(\mathbf{E} + \frac{1}{c}\mathbf{U}_0\times\mathbf{B}\right) + \nabla\ln(N\Theta)\right]\cdot\mathbf{w}\right\}f_0^- =$$
$$-\frac{e}{mc}\mathbf{B}\cdot\mathbf{w}\times(\nabla_w\Phi^-)f_0^-\ \nabla_w\cdot\Gamma^-. \qquad (55)$$

The currents in velocity space Γ, obtained by an appropriate expansion of the Fokker-Planck Eq. (16), are given by

$$-\Gamma^+ = \frac{2\pi e^4\ln\Lambda}{M^2}\left\{\int d^3\mathbf{w}' f_0^+(\mathbf{w})f_0^+(\mathbf{w}')\frac{g^2\mathbf{I} - \mathbf{g}\mathbf{g}}{g^3}\cdot\left[\nabla_w\Phi^+(\mathbf{w}) - \nabla_{w'}\Phi^+(\mathbf{w}')\right] - \frac{M}{m}\int d^3\mathbf{w}' f_0^+(\mathbf{w})f_0^-(\mathbf{w}')\frac{w'^2\mathbf{I} - \mathbf{w}'\mathbf{w}'}{w'^3}\cdot\nabla_{w'}\Phi^-(\mathbf{w}')\right\} \qquad (56)$$

and

$$-\Gamma^- = \frac{2\pi e^4\ln\Lambda}{m^2}\left\{\int d^3\mathbf{w}' f_0^-(\mathbf{w})f_0^-(\mathbf{w}')\frac{g^2\mathbf{I} - \mathbf{g}\mathbf{g}}{g^3}\cdot\left[\nabla_w\Phi^-(\mathbf{w}) - \nabla_{w'}\Phi^-(\mathbf{w}')\right] + \frac{N}{\Lambda}f_0^-(\mathbf{w})\frac{w^2\mathbf{I} - \mathbf{w}\mathbf{w}}{w^3}\cdot\nabla_w\Phi^-(\mathbf{w})\right\}; \qquad (57)$$

where

$$\mathbf{g} = \mathbf{w} - \mathbf{w}', \quad \Lambda^{-1} = \frac{e^2}{3\Theta}\left(\frac{4\pi Ne^2}{\Theta}\right)^{1/2} \qquad (58)$$

Equations (54)—(57) yield, correct to first order in $\Phi^\pm$, the following closed system of moment equations:

$$\frac{\partial\varrho}{\partial t} + \nabla\cdot(\varrho\mathbf{U}_0) = 0, \qquad (59)$$

$$\varrho\left(\frac{\partial}{\partial t} + \mathbf{U}_0\cdot\nabla\right)\mathbf{U}_0 + \nabla p + \varrho\nabla\varphi - \frac{1}{c}\mathbf{J}\times\mathbf{B} - \varepsilon\mathbf{E} = -\nabla\cdot(\mathbf{P} - p\mathbf{I}), \qquad (60)$$

and

$$\left(\frac{\partial}{\partial t} + \mathbf{U}_0\cdot\nabla\right)p + \frac{5}{3}p\nabla\cdot\mathbf{U}_0 = -\frac{2}{3}(\mathbf{P} - p\mathbf{I}):\nabla\mathbf{U}_0 - \frac{2}{3}\nabla\cdot\mathbf{q} + \frac{2}{3}(\mathbf{J} - \varepsilon\mathbf{U}_0)\cdot\left(\mathbf{E} + \frac{1}{c}\mathbf{U}_0\times\mathbf{B}\right), \qquad (61)$$

where $p = (N_+ + N_-)\Theta = 2N\Theta$ is the isotropic part of the stress tensor. In the foregoing equations the quantities on the right hand side are determined in terms of Φ by the equations:

$$\mathbf{J} = \sum_{+,-} e\int d^3\mathbf{w}\,\mathbf{w}f_0^\pm\Phi^\pm, \qquad (62)$$

$$\mathbf{P} - p\mathbf{I} = \sum_{+,-} m\int d^3\mathbf{w}\,\mathbf{w}\mathbf{w}f_0^\pm\Phi^\pm \qquad (63)$$

and

$$\mathbf{q} = \sum_\pm \frac{m}{2}\int d^3\mathbf{w}\,\mathbf{w}w^2 f_0^\pm\Phi^\pm. \qquad (64)$$

The most comprehensive calculations of transport coefficients for a fully ionized gas are due to Marshall using effectively the model outlined here. We shall simply state his results. Introducing the auxiliary electric field

$$\mathbf{D} = \mathbf{E} + \frac{1}{c}\mathbf{U}_0\times\mathbf{B} + \frac{1}{2Ne}\nabla p, \qquad (65)$$

and $\mathbf{n}$, the unit vector along the magnetic field, we obtain

$$\mathbf{J} - \varepsilon\mathbf{U}_0 = \sigma_1\mathbf{n}\mathbf{n}\cdot\mathbf{D} + \sigma_2\mathbf{n}\times(\mathbf{D}\times\mathbf{n}) + \sigma_3\mathbf{n}\times\mathbf{D} + \varkappa_1\mathbf{n}\mathbf{n}\cdot\nabla\Theta + \varkappa_2\mathbf{n}\times[(\nabla\Theta)\times\mathbf{n}] + \varkappa_3\mathbf{n}\times\nabla\Theta, \qquad (66)$$

where the various co-efficients are given by

$$\left.\begin{aligned} \sigma_1 &= 1.93\sigma_0 \\ \sigma_2 &= a\sigma_0(\omega_e^2\tau^2 + 1.80) \\ \sigma_3 &= -a\sigma_0\omega_e\tau(\omega_e^2\tau^2 + 4.38) \end{aligned}\right\}, \qquad (67)$$

$$\left.\begin{aligned} \varkappa_1 &= 1.55\,\varkappa_0 \\ \varkappa_2 &= -1.50\,a\varkappa_0\,(\omega_e^2\tau^2 - 0.97) \\ \varkappa_3 &= -4.30\,a\varkappa_0\,\omega_e\,\tau \end{aligned}\right\}, \tag{68}$$

and

$$\left.\begin{aligned} \sigma_0 &= \frac{N e^2 \tau}{m}, \qquad \varkappa_0 = \frac{N e \tau}{m} \\ a &= \frac{1}{\omega_e^4\tau^4 + 6.28\,\omega_e^2\tau^2 + 0.93} \end{aligned}\right\}. \tag{69}$$

Here ω_e denotes the electron cyclotron frequency and τ, the effective collision time, is given by

$$\tau = \frac{3}{(2\pi)^{3/2}}\left(\frac{m}{\Theta}\right)^{1/2}\frac{\Theta^2}{2Ne^4 \ln \Lambda} \tag{70}$$

where, it may be recalled, that $2N$ is the total number density.

The heat flow vector is given by

$$\mathbf{q} = -\lambda_1 \mathbf{n}\,\mathbf{n}\cdot\nabla\Theta - \lambda_2 \mathbf{n}\times[(\nabla\Theta)\times\mathbf{n}] - \lambda_3 \mathbf{n}\times\nabla\Theta$$
$$-\nu_1 \mathbf{n}\,\mathbf{n}\cdot\mathbf{D} - \nu_2 \mathbf{n}\times(\mathbf{D}\times\mathbf{n}) - \nu_3 \mathbf{n}\times\mathbf{D}, \tag{71}$$

where

$$\left.\begin{aligned} \lambda_1 &= 3.59\,\lambda_0 \\ \lambda_2 &= \lambda_0\,[a\,(.458\,\omega_e^2\tau^2 + 3.01) + 4.46\,b] \\ \lambda_3 &= 1.25\,\lambda_0\,[b\,\omega_e\,\tau - a\,\omega_e\,\tau\,(\omega_e^2\tau^2 + 6.2)] \end{aligned}\right\}, \tag{72}$$

$$\left.\begin{aligned} \nu_1 &= 3.19\,\nu_0 \\ \nu_2 &= a\nu_0\,(0.5\,\omega_e^2\tau^2 + 2.98) \\ \nu_3 &= -a\nu_0\omega_e\tau\,(1.25\,\omega_e^2\tau^2 + 7.63) \end{aligned}\right\}, \tag{73}$$

and

$$\left.\begin{aligned} \lambda_0 &= \frac{2N\Theta\tau}{m}, \qquad \nu_0 = \frac{2Ne\Theta\tau}{m} \\ b &= \frac{1}{\omega_e^2\tau^2 + 12.72} \end{aligned}\right\}, \tag{74}$$

It is clear from Eqs. (66) and (71) that, in the presence of a temperature gradient, not only will there appear a flow of heat $\mathbf{q}$, but also, a flow of electric current. Similarly, an electric field produces a flow of heat. According to the thermodynamics of irreversible processes, these four co-efficients are not independent as three of them are linked by the Onsager relations

$$\nu_i = \Theta\left(\varkappa_i + \frac{5}{2}\frac{\sigma_i}{e}\right), \tag{75}$$

where i takes the value 1, 2, or 3.

In a representation in which the magnetic field is along the z-axis, Eqs. (66) and (71) take the form

$$\mathbf{J} - \varepsilon\,\mathbf{U}_0 = \boldsymbol{\sigma}\cdot\mathbf{D} + \boldsymbol{\varkappa}\cdot\nabla\Theta \tag{76}$$

and

$$\mathbf{q} = -\boldsymbol{\lambda}\cdot\nabla\Theta - \boldsymbol{\nu}\cdot\mathbf{D}, \tag{77}$$

where

$$\boldsymbol{\sigma} = \begin{pmatrix} \sigma_2 & -\sigma_3 & 0 \\ \sigma_3 & \sigma_2 & 0 \\ 0 & 0 & \sigma_1 \end{pmatrix}, \tag{78}$$

and the dyadics $\boldsymbol{\varkappa}$, $\boldsymbol{\lambda}$, and $\boldsymbol{\nu}$ also have similar structure.

A particularly interesting situation results when, in the equilibrium state, $\varepsilon = 0$, and

$$J_1 = 0, \quad \nabla p = 0, \quad \nabla\Theta = 0, \quad \text{and } D_3 = 0. \tag{79}$$

Eq. (78) then yields

$$D_1 = \frac{\sigma_3}{\sigma_2} D_2 \tag{80}$$

and

$$J_2 = \sigma_\perp D_2, \tag{81}$$

where

$$\sigma_\perp = \frac{\sigma_2^2 + \sigma_3^2}{\sigma_2}, \tag{82}$$

$$\simeq \sigma_1 \qquad \text{when } \omega_e\tau < 1. \tag{83}$$

$$\simeq \sigma_1/1.93 \qquad \text{when } \omega_e\tau > 1. \tag{84}$$

In presenting the expressions for the components of the stress tensor, it is convenient to introduce the co-efficient of viscosity, in the absence of a magnetic field,

$$\mu = \frac{1}{3}N\Theta\tau_2, \qquad \text{where } \tau_2 = \frac{5}{3\,(2)^{1/2}}\left(\frac{M}{m}\right)^{1/2}\tau, \tag{85}$$

and the symmetric traceless tensor

$$\mathbf{A} = \frac{1}{2}\left[\nabla\mathbf{U}_0 + (\nabla\mathbf{U}_0)^T\right] - \frac{1}{3}\nabla\cdot\mathbf{U}_0\mathbf{I}. \tag{86}$$

Then, in a co-ordinate system in which $\mathbf{B}$ is along the z-axis, we have

$$\left.\begin{aligned} P_{zz} &= p - 2\mu A_{zz}, \\ P_{yy} &= p - 2\mu\frac{1}{1+4\omega_i^2\tau_2^2} \\ &\quad [A_{yy} + 2\omega_i^2\tau_2^2(A_{xx}+A_{yy}) + 2\omega_i\tau_2 A_{yx}], \\ P_{xx} &= p - 2\mu\frac{1}{1+4\omega_i^2\tau_2^2} \\ &\quad [A_{xx} + 2\omega_i^2\tau_2^2(A_{xx}+A_{yy}) - 2\omega_i\tau_2 A_{yx}], \\ P_{xz} &= P_{zx} = -\frac{2\mu}{1+\omega_i^2\tau_2^2}(A_{xz} + \omega_i\tau_2 A_{yz}) \\ P_{yz} &= P_{zy} = -\frac{2\mu}{1+\omega_i^2\tau_2^2}(A_{yz} - \omega_i\tau_2 A_{xz}), \\ P_{xy} &= P_{yx} = \\ &\quad -\frac{2\mu}{1+\omega_i^2\tau_2^2}\left[A_{xy} - \omega_i\tau_2(A_{xx} - A_{yy})\right]. \end{aligned}\right\} \tag{87}$$

where ω_i denotes the ion-cyclotron frequency.

2.1 *Weak Magnetic Fields*

In the limiting case of a weak magnetic field $\omega_{e,i}\,\tau \ll 1$, and it is to be observed from the foregoing relations that in this limit, to the lowest significant order,

$$\sigma_1 \simeq \sigma_2, \quad \sigma_3 \simeq 0, \quad \varkappa_1 \simeq \varkappa_2, \quad \varkappa_3 \simeq 0, \tag{88}$$
$$\lambda_1 \simeq \lambda_2, \quad \lambda_3 \simeq 0, \quad \nu_1 \simeq \nu_2, \quad \nu_3 \simeq 0.$$

Expressions (76), (77), and (87) now take the simple form

$$\mathbf{J} - \varepsilon\,\mathbf{U}_0 = \sigma_1\mathbf{D} + \varkappa_1\nabla\Theta, \tag{89}$$

$$\mathbf{q} = -\lambda_1\nabla\Theta - \nu_1\mathbf{D}, \tag{90}$$

and

$$\mathbf{P} = p\,\mathbf{I} + \frac{2}{3}\mu\nabla\cdot\mathbf{U}_0\mathbf{I} - \mu\left[\nabla\,\mathbf{U}_0 + (\nabla\,\mathbf{U}_0)^T\right]\cdot \qquad (91)$$

On substituting Eqs. (89)—(91) into the equation of state (61), we obtain

$$\begin{aligned}\varrho^\gamma \frac{d}{dt}(p\,\varrho^{-\gamma}) &= \frac{2}{3}\nabla\cdot(\lambda_1\nabla\Theta + \nu_1\mathbf{D})\\ &+\frac{4\mu}{3}\mathbf{A}:\mathbf{A} + \frac{2}{3\sigma_1}\left|\mathbf{J} - \varepsilon\,\mathbf{U}_0\right|^2\\ &-\left(\frac{1}{3Ne}\nabla p + \frac{2}{3}\varkappa_1\nabla\Theta\right)\cdot\left(\mathbf{E} + \frac{1}{c}\mathbf{U}_0\times\mathbf{B}\right),\end{aligned} \qquad (92)$$

where $\gamma = 5/3$. From the Maxwell equation $c\nabla\times\mathbf{E} = -\partial\mathbf{B}/\partial t$ we obtain

$$\frac{\partial\mathbf{B}}{\partial t} = \nabla\times(\mathbf{U}_0\times\mathbf{B}) - \frac{c}{\sigma_1}\nabla\times(\mathbf{J} - \varepsilon\,\mathbf{U}_0). \qquad (93)$$

Thus our complete set of hydromagnetic equations are:

$$\frac{\partial\varrho}{\partial t} + \nabla\cdot(\varrho\,\mathbf{U}_0) = 0, \qquad (94)$$

$$\begin{aligned}\varrho\left(\frac{\partial}{\partial t} + \mathbf{U}_0\cdot\nabla\right)\mathbf{U}_0 &= -\nabla p + \varepsilon\mathbf{E} + \frac{1}{c}\mathbf{J}\times\mathbf{B} - \varrho\nabla\varphi\\ &+\mu\nabla^2\mathbf{U}_0 + \frac{1}{3}\mu\nabla\nabla\cdot\mathbf{U}_0,\end{aligned} \qquad (95)$$

$$\frac{\partial\mathbf{B}}{\partial t} = \nabla\times(\mathbf{U}_0\times\mathbf{B}) - \frac{c}{\sigma_1}\nabla\times(\mathbf{J} - \varepsilon\,\mathbf{U}_0), \qquad (96)$$

$$\begin{aligned}\varrho^\gamma\left(\frac{\partial}{\partial t} + \mathbf{U}_0\cdot\nabla\right)(p\,\varrho^{-\gamma}) &= \frac{2}{3}\nabla\cdot(\lambda_1\nabla\Theta + \nu_1\mathbf{D})\\ &+\frac{4}{3}\mu\mathbf{A}:\mathbf{A} + \frac{2}{3\sigma_1}\left|\mathbf{J} - \varepsilon\,\mathbf{U}_0\right|^2\\ &-\left(\frac{1}{3Ne}\nabla p + \frac{2}{3}\varkappa_1\nabla\Theta\right)\cdot\left(\mathbf{E} + \frac{1}{c}\mathbf{U}_0\times\mathbf{B}\right),\end{aligned} \qquad (97)$$

where the charge and current densities are determined by the Maxwell equations. For an ideal, perfectly conducting fluid, $\sigma_1, \to \infty$,

$$\mathbf{E} + \frac{1}{c}\mathbf{U}_0\times\mathbf{B} = 0, \mu = 0, \mathbf{q} = 0,$$

and if the characteristic frequencies of interest are much less than the ion cyclotron frequency and the foregoing relations reduce to the well-known hydromagnetic equations:

$$\frac{\partial\varrho}{\partial t} + \nabla\cdot(\varrho\,\mathbf{U}) = 0, \qquad (98)$$

$$\varrho\left(\frac{\partial}{\partial t} + \mathbf{U}\cdot\nabla\right)\mathbf{U} = -\nabla p + \frac{1}{c}(\mathbf{J} - \varepsilon\,\mathbf{U})\times\mathbf{B} - \varrho\,\nabla\varphi, \qquad (99)$$

$$\frac{\partial\mathbf{B}}{\partial t} = \nabla\times(\mathbf{U}\times\mathbf{B}), \qquad (100)$$

and

$$\frac{d}{dt}\left(p\,\varrho^{-\gamma}\right) = 0, \qquad (101)$$

where in writing these equations we have dropped the subscript on $\mathbf{U}_0$, as it is no longer necessary.

2.2 *The A. C. Conductivity*

There is one further important transport co-efficient which has not yet been worked out for a plasma. Since one is often interested in frequencies of the electromagnetic fields comparable to the effective collision frequency, the usual Chapman-Enskog theory needs some modification. This can be effected readily by introducing terms in $\partial\Phi^\pm/\partial t$ on the left hand side of Eqs. (54) and (55). Now it is the electrons which primarily determine the conductivity. For the purpose of an order-of-magnitude estimate, we can neglect electron-electron collisions. Then, in the absence of temperature and density gradients, magnetic fields, or mass flows, Eq. (55) reduces to

$$f_0^-(\mathbf{w})\left(\frac{\partial\Phi^-}{\partial t} + \frac{e}{\Theta}\mathbf{E}\cdot\mathbf{w}\right) = \left(\frac{\Theta}{m}\right)^{3/2}\frac{1}{\tau_1}\frac{\partial}{\partial\mathbf{w}}\cdot\left[\frac{w^2\mathbf{I} - \mathbf{w}\,\mathbf{w}}{w^3}\cdot\frac{\partial\Phi^-}{\partial\mathbf{w}}f_0^-(w)\right], \qquad (102)$$

where

$$\tau_1 = \left(\frac{m}{\Theta}\right)^{1/2}\frac{\Theta^2}{2\pi Ne^4\ln\Lambda}\cdot \qquad (103)$$

If $\mathbf{E}$ varies in time like $\exp(+i\,\omega t)$, then so must Φ^-, and the solution of Eq. (102) is

$$\Phi^- = -e\frac{\mathbf{E}\cdot\mathbf{w}}{2\Theta}\tau_1\frac{[(m\,w)^2/2\Theta]^{3/2}}{1 + \frac{1}{2}i\,\omega\,\tau_1(m\,w^2/\Theta)^{3/2}}\cdot \qquad (104)$$

The associated current is then given by

$$\mathbf{J} = -e\int d^3\mathbf{w}\,\mathbf{w}\,f_0^-(\mathbf{w})\,\Phi^-, \qquad (105)$$

which, on using $(\Theta/m)^{1/2}$ as the unit of velocity, can be written in the form

$$\mathbf{J} = \sigma\,\mathbf{E}, \qquad (106)$$

where

$$\sigma = \frac{Ne^2\tau_1}{m}\frac{1}{(2\pi)^{1/2}}\frac{1}{3}\int_0^\infty\frac{d\,w\,w^7\,e^{-w^2/2}}{1 + \frac{1}{2}i\,\omega\,\tau_1\,w^3}\cdot \qquad (107)$$

If $\omega\tau_1 \ll 1$, Eq. (107) yields to the lowest significant order

$$\sigma = \frac{Ne^2\tau_1}{m}\frac{1}{(2\pi)^{1/2}}\frac{1}{3}\left(48 - \sqrt{2\pi}\,\frac{945}{4}\,i\,\omega\,\tau_1\right); \qquad (108)$$

whereas if $\omega\tau_1 \gg 1$, we obtain

$$\sigma \simeq -\frac{i\,Ne^2\tau_1}{m}\frac{1}{\omega\,\tau_1}\left(1 + i\frac{4}{3(2\pi)^{1/2}}\frac{1}{\omega\,\tau_1}\right). \qquad (109)$$

3. The Case of Weak Collisions

If the plasma is so dilute, or the temperature so high, that the direct interparticle collisions of the first and second class described earlier are negligible, then the particles interact mainly via the macroscopic electromagnetic fields. We may thus drop altogether the collision term in the Boltzmann equation (3) in treating the dynamics of the plasma. Firstly, we wish to emphasize that this description of a plasma via the collisionless Boltzmann equation is entirely equivalent to the solution of the equations of motion for the particle orbits. This can be shown as follows.

3.1 Equivalence of Collisionless Boltzmann Equation and Particle Orbit Theory

Consider the collisionless Boltzmann equation or what is referred to as the kinetic equation in the Russian literature:

$$\frac{\partial f}{\partial t}+(\mathbf{v}\cdot\nabla)f+\mathbf{F}\cdot\nabla_v f=0. \tag{110}$$

The Lagrangian subsidiary equations are:

$$\mathbf{F}=\frac{d\mathbf{v}}{dt}, \tag{111}$$

and

$$\mathbf{v}=\frac{d\mathbf{x}}{dt}. \tag{112}$$

Let the solutions to these equations be

$$\mathbf{v}=\mathbf{v}(\alpha_1,\alpha_2\cdots\alpha_6,t) \tag{113}$$

and

$$\mathbf{x}=\mathbf{x}(\alpha_1,\alpha_2,\cdots\alpha_6,t), \tag{114}$$

where the α's are the integration constants. We further suppose that Eqs. (113) and (114) can be solved for the α's. Now the general solution of Eq. (110) is an arbitrary function of the constants of motion, i.e.,

$$f(\mathbf{x},\mathbf{v},t)=\mathrm{f}(\alpha_1,\alpha_2,\cdots\alpha_6); \tag{115}$$

for substituting Eq. (115) into (110) we obtain

$$\sum_{i=1}^{6}\frac{\partial f}{\partial\alpha_i}\left(\frac{\partial\alpha_i}{\partial t}+\mathbf{v}\cdot\nabla\alpha_i+\mathbf{F}\cdot\nabla_v\alpha_i\right)=\sum_{i=1}^{6}\frac{\partial f}{\partial\alpha_i}\frac{d\alpha_i}{dt}=0 \tag{116}$$

since the α's are constants along a particle trajectory. Thus we have shown that the most general solution of Eq. (110) is an arbitrary function of the integrals of the Lagrangian subsidiary equations (111) and (112). But these are just the equations of motion for the particle orbits. The equivalence of the particle orbit theory and the collisionless Boltzmann equation was first demonstrated by Jeans, and in the astronomical literature is referred to as Jeans' theorem. When the α's are not true constants but adiabatic invariants, the resulting f satisfies the Boltzmann equation to within the accuracy of these invariants. The considerations of the orbit theory provide a better insight into the physical factors involved in a particular problem. However, the Boltzmann equation provides a rigorous treatment of complex problems which may not be easily accessible to the orbit theory.

3.2 The Low Temperature Approximation

Neglecting, then, the right hand side of Eq. (49), the equation for the stress tensor now becomes

$$\frac{\partial}{\partial t}\mathbf{P}+\nabla\cdot(\mathbf{Q}+\mathbf{U}\,\mathbf{P})+\mathbf{P}\cdot\nabla\mathbf{U}+(\mathbf{P}\cdot\nabla\mathbf{U})^{T}+\frac{e}{mc}(\mathbf{B}\times\mathbf{P}-\mathbf{P}\times\mathbf{B})-(\mathbf{J}-\varepsilon\mathbf{U})\left(\mathbf{E}+\frac{1}{c}\mathbf{U}\times\mathbf{B}\right)-\left(\mathbf{E}+\frac{1}{c}\mathbf{U}\times\mathbf{B}\right)(\mathbf{J}-\varepsilon\mathbf{U})=0. \tag{117}$$

In order of magnitude $|\partial\mathbf{P}/\partial t|\sim\omega v_{th}^3$ and $|\nabla\cdot\mathbf{Q}|\sim k v_{th}^4$ where $v_{th}=(\Theta/m)^{1/2}$, and ω and k denote the characteristic frequency and reciprocal length respectively. Therefore, it is clear that if

$$\frac{\omega}{k}\gg v_{th}, \tag{118}$$

the heat flow tensor can be neglected in Eq. (117). For the linearized equations of motion ω/k is the phase velocity of the wave, while for a non-linear system it might be termed the effective phase velocity. Thus if the phase velocity of the wave is much larger than the thermal speed of the ions or electrons, Eq. (117) reduces to

$$\frac{\partial}{\partial t}\mathbf{P}+\nabla\cdot(\mathbf{U}\,\mathbf{P})+\mathbf{P}\cdot\nabla\mathbf{U}+(\mathbf{P}\cdot\nabla\mathbf{U})^{T}+\frac{e}{mc}(\mathbf{B}\times\mathbf{P}-\mathbf{P}\times\mathbf{B})-(\mathbf{J}-\varepsilon\mathbf{U})\left(\mathbf{E}+\frac{1}{c}\mathbf{U}\times\mathbf{B}\right)-\left(\mathbf{E}+\frac{1}{c}\mathbf{U}\times\mathbf{B}\right)(\mathbf{J}-\varepsilon\mathbf{U})=0. \tag{119}$$

Thus, by virtue of the approximation (118) we are able to obtain a closed set of moment equations. This scheme will be referred to as the *Low Temperature Approximation* and will yield results correct to first significant order in the parameter of smallness kv_{th}/ω.

Clearly, one can decouple the nth moment equation from its dependence on the $(n+1)$th moment in an analogous fashion, and obtain the corresponding higher order thermal corrections. In all such calculations care must be taken to discard any spurious roots which may occur, that is, roots which are incompatible with the basic assumption (118).

3.3 Chew, Goldberger and Low Approximation

If we now assume that the magnetic field is so strong that the electron or ion cyclotron frequency is very large compared to the characteristic frequencies of interest, we can make a systematic expansion of the Boltzmann equation (110) in inverse powers of B. This has been carried out by Chew, Goldberger, and Low. An equivalent procedure is to carry out this expansion in the equation of motion (119) for the stress tensor. If we assume that the Joule dissipation is negligible, i.e.,

$$\left|\left(\mathbf{E}+\frac{1}{c}\mathbf{U}\times\mathbf{B}\right)(\mathbf{J}-\varepsilon\mathbf{U})\right|\ll\left|\mathbf{B}\times\mathbf{P}\right|, \tag{120}$$

then the leading term in Eq. (119) gives

$$\mathbf{B}\times\mathbf{P}=\mathbf{P}\times\mathbf{B}. \tag{121}$$

It immediately follows from this equation that

$$\mathbf{P} = P_\perp \mathbf{I} + (P_\parallel - P_\perp)\,\mathbf{n}\,\mathbf{n}, \tag{122}$$

where $\mathbf{n}$ denotes a unit vector along $\mathbf{B}$. Eq. (122) implies that the pressure tensor is diagonal in a local rectangular co-ordinate system, one of whose axes points along $\mathbf{n}$. In the plane perpendicular to $\mathbf{n}$ the pressure is a scalar of magnitude $P_\perp$, and the pressure along $\mathbf{B}$ is $P_\parallel$ which, in general, is not equal to $P_\perp$. Equation (119) now reduces to

$$\frac{d}{dt}[P_\perp \mathbf{I} + (P_\parallel - P_\perp)\,\mathbf{n}\,\mathbf{n}] + [P_\perp \mathbf{I} + (P_\parallel - P_\perp)\mathbf{n}\mathbf{n}]\,\nabla\cdot\mathbf{U} + [P_\perp \mathbf{I} + (P_\parallel - P_\perp)\,\mathbf{n}\mathbf{n}]\cdot\nabla\mathbf{U} + \{[P_\perp \mathbf{I} + (P_\parallel - P_\perp)\,\mathbf{n}\,\mathbf{n}]\cdot\nabla\mathbf{U}\}^T = 0, \tag{123}$$

where we have now set

$$\mathbf{E} + \frac{1}{c}\,\mathbf{U}\times\mathbf{B} = 0, \tag{124}$$

Eq. (124) implies that the medium has very high electrical conductivity so that it is unable to support, in its rest frame, any significant electric fields. Taking the trace of Eq. (123), we obtain

$$\frac{d}{dt}\left(P_\perp + \frac{1}{2}P_\parallel\right) + \left(P_\perp + \frac{1}{2}P_\parallel\right)\nabla\cdot\mathbf{U} + P_\perp\nabla\cdot\mathbf{U} + (P_\parallel - P_\perp)\,\mathbf{n}\,\mathbf{n}:\nabla\mathbf{U} = 0. \tag{125}$$

The $\mathbf{nn}$ component of Eq. (123) is

$$\frac{d}{dt}P_\parallel + P_\parallel\nabla\cdot\mathbf{U} + 2P_\parallel\mathbf{n}\,\mathbf{n}:\nabla\mathbf{U} = 0. \tag{126}$$

From Eqs. (125) and (126) we readily obtain

$$\frac{d}{dt}P_\perp + 2P_\perp\nabla\cdot\mathbf{U} - P_\perp\mathbf{n}\,\mathbf{n}:\nabla\mathbf{U} = 0, \tag{127}$$

Using the relation (124) in the Maxwell equation $c\nabla\times\mathbf{E} = -\partial\mathbf{B}/\partial t$, we obtain

$$\frac{\partial\mathbf{B}}{\partial t} = \nabla\times(\mathbf{U}\times\mathbf{B}). \tag{128}$$

It is convenient to write Eq. (128) as

$$\frac{d\mathbf{B}}{dt} = \left(\frac{\partial}{\partial t} + \mathbf{U}\cdot\nabla\right)\mathbf{B} = (\mathbf{B}\cdot\nabla)\,\mathbf{U} - \mathbf{B}\,(\nabla\cdot\mathbf{U}). \tag{129}$$

From Eq. (129) and the equation of continuity

$$\frac{d\varrho}{dt} + \varrho\nabla\cdot\mathbf{U} = 0, \tag{130}$$

it can be shown readily that

$$\mathbf{n}\,\mathbf{n}:\nabla\mathbf{U} = \frac{\varrho}{B}\frac{d}{dt}\left(\frac{B}{\varrho}\right) \tag{131}$$

where B denotes the magnitude of $\mathbf{B}$. On using this result in Eqs. (126) and (127), we obtain the two adiabatic relations

$$\frac{d}{dt}\left(\frac{P_\parallel B^2}{\varrho^3}\right) = 0 \tag{132}$$

and

$$\frac{d}{dt}\left(\frac{P_\perp}{\varrho B}\right) = 0. \tag{133}$$

Starting from the Boltzmann equation (110), Chew, Goldberger, and Low have derived the same adiabatic relations on the assumption that the heat transport along the lines of force is negligible.

Equation (133) implies that, if one moves along with an element of the fluid, the average transverse kinetic energy per particle is proportional to B. This is compatible with the well known constancy of the magnetic moment of a charged particle in the adiabatic approximation. It can be shown that Eq. (132) implies the constancy of the longitudinal invariant of Chew, Goldberger, and Low. Thus for a low density plasma in the presence of a strong magnetic field, in the framework of the low temperature approximation or on the assumption of negligible heat transport along the lines of force and when the conductivity is very high, we obtain the following complete system of equations:

$$\frac{\partial\varrho}{\partial t} + \nabla\cdot(\varrho\,\mathbf{U}) = 0, \tag{135}$$

$$\varrho\frac{d\mathbf{U}}{dt} = \varrho\left(\frac{\partial}{\partial t} + \mathbf{U}\cdot\nabla\right)\mathbf{U} = -\nabla\cdot\mathbf{P} + \frac{1}{c}(\mathbf{J} - \varepsilon\,\mathbf{U})\times\mathbf{B} - \varrho\nabla\varphi, \tag{136}$$

$$\frac{\partial\mathbf{B}}{\partial t} = \nabla\times(\mathbf{U}\times\mathbf{B}), \tag{137}$$

$$\mathbf{P} = P_\perp\mathbf{I} + (P_\parallel - P_\perp)\,\mathbf{n}\,\mathbf{n}, \tag{138}$$

$$\frac{d}{dt}\left(\frac{P_\parallel B^2}{\varrho^3}\right) = 0, \tag{139}$$

and

$$\frac{d}{dt}\left(\frac{P_\perp}{\varrho B}\right) = 0, \tag{140}$$

where the charge and current densities are determined by the Maxwell equations.

III. Wave Phenomena in Plasmas

1. General Remarks

We shall now discuss the behaviour of plasmas for states initially close to a steady state. This implies the existence of a time-independent, self-consistent solution of the appropriate equations of motion, jointly with the Maxwell equations, subject to proper boundary conditions. The notion of closeness implies the existence of some dimensionless parameter of smallness, in terms of which one can expand the time dependent quantities of the equations governing the system. In most situations the appropriate parameter is the ratio of the macroscopic velocity to the phase velocity. The lowest order system of the expanded equations is just that governing the steady state. To next order one obtains a set of linear equations, whose coefficients do not in general depend on time, which describe the small motions about the steady state.

If there exists no small initial perturbation whose amplitude grows monotonically or sinusoidally in time, then the system is said to be *stable*; otherwise, *unstable*. In the absence of any dissipative mechanisms the small motions of a stable system may tend to persist indefinitely; whereas in the presence of a dissipative mechanism they may tend to die out, the system returning to the steady state.

If the system is unstable, after a certain interval of time the amplitude of the motion will become so large that the linearized equations will cease to be valid. The subsequent behaviour of the system will be governed by non-linear equations, whose analysis, in general, is difficult to carry out.

There are two plausible situations into which these instabilities might possibly carry the system. The first of these might be termed a turbulent state, characterized by randomly fluctuating electromagnetic fields and motions, which could manifest itself by an enhancement of diffusion and resistivity over and above that resulting from collisions. The second situation is associated with instabilities whose exponentiation time is short, can affect significantly the heavy particles and may lead to coherent macroscopic motion of the plasma, resulting in a radically different final state. The former of these has been conjectured as a cause of the loss of containment in the stellarator type of controlled fusion devices. An example of the latter has been observed in pinch effect experiments where the discharge has destroyed itself upon achievement of a critical current.

Since the coefficients of the linearized equations do not depend explicitly on time, one can seek a complete set of characteristic solutions whose time dependence is of the form

$$\exp(-i\omega t). \tag{1}$$

This leads to a characteristic value problem for ω which, in general, may be complex. If there exists an ω for which

$$\operatorname{Im}\omega > 0, \tag{2}$$

then the system is unstable. If the coefficients also happen to be independent of one or more of the space variables, one can seek solutions of the form $\exp(ikx)$. The solution of the characteristic value problem, subject to the appropriate boundary conditions, then leads to a relation between ω and k which may be written implicitly in the form

$$F(\omega, k) = 0. \tag{3}$$

A relation of the form (3) is usually referred to as the *dispersion relation*. The solution of Eq. (3) for ω in terms of k would immediately disclose whether the system is stable or unstable.

Sometimes it is convenient to characterize the family of steady states by a certain parameter, say β. As one changes β continuously, the system may pass from stability to instability for some determinate value of β, say $\beta = \beta_c$; i.e., ω passes from the real axis into the complex ω plane (with $\operatorname{Im}\omega > 0$) at $\beta = \beta_c$. The state, characterized by β_c, which marks the boundary between the stable and the unstable regions is referred to as the *marginal state*.

In the case of static equilibria for non-dissipative systems governed by the hydromagnetic equations, it has been shown by Bernstein, Frieman, Kruskal, and Kulsrud that the linearized equations of motion are self-adjoint; consequently the characteristic values ω^2 are real. Therefore,

$$\omega^2 > 0 \tag{4a}$$

corresponds to stability and

$$\omega^2 < 0, \tag{4b}$$

to instability. However, for more general types of equilibria, the characteristic values ω may be complex. In case the imaginary part of ω is positive, the system will be unstable; following Eddington, this type of instability is referred to as *overstability*.

In addition to questions of stability which are usually posed for isolated systems, there is the important class of driven problems. In these situations a system in a steady state is excited by an external agency, perhaps at a fixed frequency. When the amplitude of excitation is small, the problem can again be treated by the same set of linear equations as those employed for the analysis of stability, but with appropriate modification of the boundary conditions. In the cases where a Fourier analysis in space is in order, one is again led to a dispersion relation, but now it is to be viewed as determining the wave number k (in general complex) as a function of the prescribed frequency ω, assumed real. The fact that k can be complex permits waves to grow or die out in space, giving rise to the phenomena of amplification and evanescence. Problems of reflection, transmission, scattering, and amplification of waves by plasmas fall into this category. It must be emphasized that when any particular problem is properly posed with due regard to boundary conditions, there will be no confusion about the interpretation of the resultant dispersion relation.

2. Unbounded Plasmas in the Absence of External Fields

2.1 *Longitudinal Electron Plasma Oscillation*

We first consider the simplest case of electron oscillations in a uniform plasma, neglecting the thermal motion of the electrons. The ions will be assumed to be at rest and to form the uniform neutralizing background for the electron charge in equilibrium. Let N denote the electron density (which is equal to the ion density) in equilibrium. In the perturbed state let the density be denoted by $N + n$, where n is considered small so that all terms quadratic or higher in n can be neglected. The equations of motion now are (cf. Eqs. (II-44) and (II-45)):

$$\frac{\partial n}{\partial t} + N\nabla\cdot\mathbf{v} = 0, \tag{5}$$

and

$$m\frac{\partial \mathbf{v}}{\partial t} = -e\mathbf{E}, \tag{6}$$

where $-e$ and m denote the charge and mass of the electron respectively. For longitudinal oscillations the electric field is determined simply by the Poisson equation

$$\nabla\cdot\mathbf{E} = 4\pi\varepsilon = -4\pi e n. \tag{7}$$

Eliminating **v** and **E** from Eqs. (5)—(7) we obtain for the equation of motion

$$\frac{\partial^2 n}{\partial t^2} = -\frac{4\pi N e^2 n}{m} = -\omega_p^2 n, \tag{8}$$

where

$$\omega_p = \left(\frac{4\pi N e^2}{m}\right)^{1/2} = 2\pi \times 8980\, N^{1/2}\,\text{sec}^{-1}. \tag{9}$$

It follows from Eq. (8) that the density fluctuations oscillate sinusoidally with the characteristic frequency ω_p. The frequency ω_p is referred to as the *plasma frequency*. Formula (9) was first obtained by Tonks and Langmuir in 1929.

The absence of space co-ordinates in Eq. (8) shows that these waves are non-dispersive—their group velocity vanishes — and there is no tendency for a wave packet of this type to propagate through the plasma. As a result we can specify the phases of the electron displacement in such a way as to obtain a traveling wave —a wave, however, which moves continuously through a fixed region without ever progressing beyond.

2.2 *Transverse Electron Plasma Oscillations*

We shall now consider the transverse (or electromagnetic) plasma oscillations, neglecting the thermal motions of the electrons. The equations governing the problem are the linearized equations of motion (cf. Eqs. (II-44) and (II-45)) and the Maxwell equations

$$\frac{\partial n}{\partial t} + N\nabla\cdot\mathbf{v} = 0, \tag{10}$$

$$m\frac{\partial \mathbf{v}}{\partial t} = -e\mathbf{E}, \tag{11}$$

$$\nabla\times\mathbf{B} = -\frac{4\pi N e}{c}\mathbf{v} + \frac{1}{c}\frac{\partial \mathbf{E}}{\partial t}, \tag{12}$$

and

$$\nabla\times\mathbf{E} = -\frac{1}{c}\frac{\partial \mathbf{B}}{\partial t}. \tag{13}$$

From Eqs. (11)—(13) we readily obtain

$$\frac{\partial^2 \mathbf{E}}{\partial t^2} = -\omega_p^2\mathbf{E} - c^2\nabla\times\nabla\times\mathbf{E}. \tag{14}$$

Taking **E** to be of the form $\exp i(-\omega t + \mathbf{k}\cdot\mathbf{r})$, Eq. (14) leads to

$$(\omega^2 - \omega_p^2 - c^2k^2)\,\mathbf{k}\times\mathbf{E} = 0, \tag{15}$$

and

$$(\omega^2 - \omega_p^2)\,(\mathbf{k}\cdot\mathbf{E}) = 0. \tag{16}$$

For transverse oscillations $\mathbf{k}\times\mathbf{E}$ does not vanish and Eq. (15) gives the dispersion relation

$$\omega^2 = \omega_p^2 + c^2k^2;$$

while for longitudinal oscillations $\mathbf{k}\cdot\mathbf{E}$ does not . and Eq. (16) gives the dispersion relation already discussed. In contrast to the longitudinal oscillations, the transverse oscillations propagate in the plasma with the group velocity.

$$\mathbf{v}_g = \frac{\partial\omega}{\partial\mathbf{k}} = \frac{c\,\mathbf{k}}{k\,[1 + (\omega_p^2/c^2k^2)]^{1/2}} \tag{18}$$

2.3 *Effect of Thermal Motions on Electron Plasma Oscillations*

We shall now treat electron plasma oscillations, taking into account the thermal motions of the electrons using the low temperature approximation developed in Section II. In the equilibrium state, we shall assume the plasma pressure to be a scalar; however, we do allow for anisotropy of the material stress tensor during the perturbations. The perturbed state is characterized by

$$\mathbf{v},\quad N+n,\quad p\mathbf{I}+\mathsf{p}_1, \tag{19}$$

where $p = N\Theta$ denotes the electron pressure in equilibrium, and p_1, the perturbation in the stress tensor. The linearized equations of motion now are (cf. Eqs. (II-47) to (II-)51):

$$\frac{\partial n}{\partial t} + N\nabla\cdot\mathbf{v} = 0, \tag{20}$$

$$mN\frac{\partial \mathbf{v}}{\partial t} = -\nabla\cdot\mathsf{p}_1 - Ne\mathbf{E}, \tag{21}$$

and

$$\frac{\partial}{\partial t}\mathsf{p}_1 = -p\,(\nabla\cdot\mathbf{v})\,\mathbf{I} - p\,[\nabla\mathbf{v} + (\nabla\mathbf{v})^T]. \tag{22}$$

Equations (20)—(22) must be solved in conjunction with the linearized Maxwell equations

$$\nabla\times\mathbf{B} = -\frac{4\pi Ne}{c}\mathbf{v} + \frac{1}{c}\frac{\partial\mathbf{E}}{\partial t} \tag{23}$$

and

$$\nabla\times\mathbf{E} = -\frac{1}{c}\frac{\partial\mathbf{B}}{\partial t}. \tag{24}$$

Introducing $\boldsymbol{\xi}$, the Lagrangian displacement of an element of the electron fluid from its equilibrium position, to a first approximation, we can write

$$\mathbf{v} = \frac{\partial\boldsymbol{\xi}}{\partial t}. \tag{25}$$

Eqs. (20) and (22) can then be readily integrated to give

$$n = -N\nabla\cdot\boldsymbol{\xi} \tag{26}$$

and

$$\mathsf{p}_1 = -p\,(\nabla\cdot\boldsymbol{\xi})\,\mathbf{I} - p\,[\nabla\boldsymbol{\xi} + (\nabla\boldsymbol{\xi})^T], \tag{27}$$

where the constants of integration have, by definition, been set equal to zero. Assuming the space time behaviour of all quantities to be of the form $\exp i(-\omega t + \mathbf{k}\cdot\mathbf{r})$, the foregoing equations yield

$$\omega^2\boldsymbol{\xi} = 2\frac{\Theta}{m}\mathbf{k}\,\mathbf{k}\cdot\boldsymbol{\xi} + \frac{\Theta}{m}k^2\boldsymbol{\xi} + \frac{e}{m}\mathbf{E}, \tag{28}$$

and

$$c^2\mathbf{k}\times\mathbf{k}\times\mathbf{E} = +4\pi Ne\,\omega^2\boldsymbol{\xi} - \omega^2\mathbf{E}, \tag{29}$$

Eqs. (28) and (29) we obtain for longitudinal tions the dispersion relation

$$\omega^2 = \omega_p^2 + 3\frac{\Theta}{m}k^2, \tag{30}$$

while for transverse oscillations we obtain

$$(\omega^2 - c^2k^2)\left(\omega^2 - \frac{\Theta}{m}k^2\right) - \omega^2\omega_p^2 = 0. \tag{31}$$

Eq. (31) leads to a quadratic in ω^2 whose roots are given by

$$\omega^2 = \frac{1}{2}\left(\omega_p^2 + c^2 k^2 + \frac{k^2 \Theta}{m}\right) \pm \frac{1}{2}\left(\omega_p^2 + c^2 k^2 + \frac{k^2 \Theta}{m}\right) \left\{1 - \frac{4 c^2 k^2 k^2 \Theta / m}{[\omega_p^2 + c^2 k^2 + (k^2 \Theta / m)]^2}\right\}^{1/2}. \quad (32)$$

In our approximation $\omega^2 \gg k^2 \Theta/m$. Retaining terms to the lowest order in $k^2 \Theta/m$, we obtain for the two transverse modes of oscillation (distinguished by the subscripts 1 and 2):

$$\omega_1^2 = \omega_p^2 + c^2 k^2 + \frac{k^2 \Theta}{m} \frac{\omega_p^2}{\omega_p^2 + c^2 k^2} \quad (33)$$

and

$$\omega_2^2 = \frac{k^2 \Theta}{m} \frac{1}{1 + (\omega_p^2 / c^2 k^2)} \quad (34)$$

The root ω_1^2 corresponds to the transverse oscillation; however, the root ω_2^2 is incompatible with our basic approximation that $\omega^2 > k^2 \Theta/m$ and therefore must be discarded.

It may be remarked here that if, instead of using the equation for the stress tensor, we had used the classical adiabatic relation

$$\frac{d}{dt}(p \varrho^{-\gamma}) = 0, \quad (35)$$

we would have obtained for longitudinal oscillations the dispersion relation

$$\omega^2 = \omega_p^2 + \gamma \frac{\Theta}{m} k^2 \quad (36)$$

instead of the relation (30). However, in the absence of collisions, it is necessary to allow for anisotropy in the pressure during the oscillations.

The effect of thermal motions on electron plasma oscillations was first considered by Thomson and later, by Bailey. They obtained the dispersion formula

$$\omega^2 = \omega_p^2 + \frac{\Theta}{m} k^2 \quad (37)$$

for longitudinal oscillations. It can be seen readily that the appearance of the factor $\Theta k^2/m$ instead of $3\Theta k^2/m$ or $\gamma \Theta k^2/m$ results from neglecting the change in temperature of the gas resulting from the density fluctuations. This amounts to considering the oscillations to be isothermal and not adiabatic. This is incorrect for the high frequency electron plasma oscillations; for a consistent approximation it is necessary to use the complete set of equations (20)—(22) to treat the problem.

In part II of this survey this problem will be discussed from the standpoint of kinetic theory, and it will be seen that expressions (30) and (33) determine correctly to first order in Θ the real part of ω. The higher order thermal corrections can be recovered by going to higher order moment equations. However, an essential consequence of the treatment from the kinetic equation in the absence of collisions, which is not recovered on using the truncated set of moment equations devoid of collision terms, is the phenomena of Landau damping. That is, the kinetic equation yields for isotropic equilibria a negative imaginary part effectively proportional to the number of particles moving with the phase velocity of the wave. This number, of course, tends to be exponentially small since, by assumption, the thermal spread is much less than the phase velocity in question.

It must be emphasized here that the longitudinal and transverse oscillations are strictly uncoupled only in the case of a non-relativistic plasma and in the absence of any external magnetic fields, temperature or density gradients. The presence of an external magnetic field or inhomogeneities in plasma density and/or temperature result in the coupling of longitudinal and transverse modes, and the behaviour of the plasma, in general, is quite complex. This will be discussed in detail later.

2.4 Ion Oscillations

So far we have considered only electron plasma oscillations on the assumption that these oscillations are too rapid for the heavy ions to follow, which implies that the ions, therefore, may be considered at rest. Another class of oscillations, which is possible in a collision-free plasma, is the so-called ion oscillations. These are so slow that electrons see them as quasi static and consequently are distributed according to the Boltzmann distribution. During the oscillations it is appropriate to treat the ions and electrons as having different temperatures. However, we shall restrict ourselves to the case of longitudinal oscillations only.

The linearized equations of motion now are (cf. Eqs. (II-44)—(II-46)):

$$\frac{\partial n_i}{\partial t} + N \nabla \cdot \mathbf{v} = 0, \quad (38)$$

$$M N \frac{\partial \mathbf{v}}{\partial t} = -\nabla \cdot \mathsf{p}_i + N e \mathbf{E}, \quad (39)$$

$$\frac{\partial}{\partial t} \mathsf{p}_i = -p_i \nabla \cdot \mathbf{v} \mathbf{I} - p_i [\nabla \mathbf{v} + (\nabla \mathbf{v})^T], \quad (40)$$

$$\nabla \cdot \mathbf{E} = 4 \pi e (n_i - n_e), \quad (41)$$

and

$$n_e = N\left(\exp \frac{e\varphi}{\Theta_e} - 1\right) \quad (42)$$

where n_i and n_e denote the perturbation in the ion and electron equilibrium densities (assumed equal) respectively, Θ_e is the electron temperature; $p_i = N\Theta_i$ where Θ_i is the ion temperature, p_i is the perturbation in the ion material stress tensor, and M is the ion mass. φ denotes the electrostatic potential defined as $\mathbf{E} = -\nabla\varphi$. Following the normal mode procedure outlined in § 2.3 of this section, we obtain for the dispersion relation

$$\omega^2 = \frac{1}{1 + (k\lambda_D)^{-2}} \omega_{pi}^2 + 3 k^2 \frac{\Theta_i}{M}, \quad (43)$$

where ω_{pi}, the ion plasma frequency, is given by

$$\omega_{pi} = \left(\frac{4\pi N e^2}{M}\right)^{1/2} \quad (44)$$

and we recall that λ_D, the Debye shielding distance, is given by

$$\lambda_D = \left(\frac{\Theta_e}{4\pi N e^2}\right)^{1/2} \quad (45)$$

Physically λ_D acts like a screening radius for electrical forces in ionized media. Thus the potential in the neighborhood of a sphere charged with q units of electricity is effectively given by

$$\varphi = \frac{q}{r} \exp(-r/\lambda_D) \tag{46}$$

in an ionized medium near thermal equilibrium, compared to q/r in a vacuum.

If $k\lambda_D \ll 1$, i.e., the wavelength of the disturbance is large compared to the Debye length, formula (43) reduces to

$$\omega^2 = \omega_{pi}^2 k^2 \lambda_D^2 + 3 k^2 \frac{\Theta_i}{M} = \frac{1}{M} (\Theta_e + 3 \Theta_i) k^2. \tag{47}$$

It is clear that if the ion temperature is very small compared to the electron temperature, the effect of the ion thermal motions can be neglected. We shall show in part II, using the kinetic description, that if Θ_i is not small compared with Θ_e, the ion oscillations are strongly damped. It may also be observed from Eq. (44) that the ion plasma frequency is much smaller than the electron plasma frequency.

The low frequency ion oscillations differ from the sound waves in the mechanism responsible for the organized motion. Ion oscillations are produced by long range Coulomb forces whereas sound waves are produced by short range collisions.

3. Unbounded Cold Plasmas in the Presence of an External Magnetic Field

We shall now consider oscillations in a uniform plasma in the presence of a constant external magnetic field B_0. We shall assume the plasma to be at zero temperature; this amounts to neglecting the thermal motions of the ions and electrons. The effect of thermal motions will be taken into account quite rigorously via the Boltzmann equation in part II. We shall further assume that each constituent of the plasma has in the equilibrium state a constant velocity $\mathbf{u}$. The motion of the constituents of the plasma will, in general, give rise to a current distribution $\mathbf{J}$. We shall, however, assume that the magnetic field which results from $\mathbf{J}$ is negligibly small compared with the external magnetic field.

The linearized equations of motion for each of the species of the plasma are*:

$$\frac{\partial \mathbf{v}}{\partial t} + (\mathbf{u} \cdot \nabla)\, \mathbf{v} = \frac{e}{m} \left(\mathbf{E} + \frac{1}{c} \mathbf{u} \times \mathbf{B} + \frac{1}{c} \mathbf{v} \times \mathbf{B}_0 \right), \tag{48}$$

$$\frac{\partial n}{\partial t} + \nabla \cdot (N \mathbf{v} + n \mathbf{u}) = 0, \tag{49}$$

where the perturbations in the electric ($\mathbf{E}$) and magnetic ($\mathbf{B}$) fields are given by the Maxwell equations

$$\nabla \times \mathbf{B} = \frac{4\pi}{c} \mathbf{J} + \frac{1}{c} \frac{\partial \mathbf{E}}{\partial t}, \tag{50}$$

$$\nabla \times \mathbf{E} = -\frac{1}{c} \frac{\partial \mathbf{B}}{\partial t}, \tag{51}$$

and

$$\mathbf{J} = \sum e (N \mathbf{v} + n \mathbf{u}). \tag{52}$$

The summation Eq. (52) is to be carried over both the species of the plasma. The cyclotron frequency is defined to be

$$\omega_c = \frac{e B_0}{m c}. \tag{53}$$

We shall now assume that all quantities have space and time dependence of the form $\exp i(-\omega t + \mathbf{k} \cdot \mathbf{r})$. Eqs. (48) and (49) then yield

$$n = \frac{N}{(\omega - \mathbf{k} \cdot \mathbf{u})} (\mathbf{k} \cdot \mathbf{v}) \tag{54}$$

and

$$-i (\omega - \mathbf{k} \cdot \mathbf{u})\, \mathbf{v} = \frac{e}{m} \left(\mathbf{E} + \frac{1}{c} \mathbf{u} \times \mathbf{B} \right) - \boldsymbol{\omega}_c \times \mathbf{v}. \tag{55}$$

The appearance of the factor $\omega - \mathbf{k} \cdot \mathbf{u}$ instead of ω is typical of a current-carrying plasma; the term $\mathbf{k} \cdot \mathbf{u}$ accounts just for the Doppler shift in the frequency ω due to the motion of the electrons or the ions. From Eqs. (51) and (55) we obtain

$$-i (\omega - \mathbf{k} \cdot \mathbf{u})(\boldsymbol{\omega}_c \cdot \mathbf{v}) = \frac{e}{m} (\boldsymbol{\omega}_c \cdot \mathbf{E}) + \frac{e}{m \omega} \boldsymbol{\omega}_c \cdot [\mathbf{u} \times (\mathbf{k} \times \mathbf{E})] \tag{56}$$

and

$$-i (\omega - \mathbf{k} \cdot \mathbf{u})(\boldsymbol{\omega}_c \times \mathbf{v}) = \frac{e}{m} (\boldsymbol{\omega}_c \times \mathbf{E}) + \frac{e}{m \omega} \boldsymbol{\omega}_c \times [\mathbf{u} \times (\mathbf{k} \times \mathbf{E})] - \boldsymbol{\omega}_c (\boldsymbol{\omega}_c \cdot \mathbf{v}) + \omega_c^2 \mathbf{v}. \tag{57}$$

Using the results (56) and (57) into Eq. (55), we obtain

$$\mathbf{v} = -\frac{e}{m} \frac{1}{\omega_c^2 - (\omega - \mathbf{k} \cdot \mathbf{u})^2} \Bigg[i (\omega - \mathbf{k} \cdot \mathbf{u}) \left\{ \mathbf{E} + \frac{1}{\omega} \mathbf{u} \times (\mathbf{k} \times \mathbf{E}) \right\} + \boldsymbol{\omega}_c \times \mathbf{E} + \frac{1}{\omega} \boldsymbol{\omega}_c \times \left\{ \mathbf{u} \times (\mathbf{k} \times \mathbf{E}) \right\} - i \frac{\boldsymbol{\omega}_c}{(\omega - \mathbf{k} \cdot \mathbf{u})} \left\{ (\boldsymbol{\omega}_c \cdot \mathbf{E}) + \frac{1}{\omega} \boldsymbol{\omega}_c \cdot [\mathbf{u} \times (\mathbf{k} \times \mathbf{E})] \right\} \Bigg]. \tag{58}$$

From Eqs. (52) and (54) we obtain for the current density due to oscillations

$$\mathbf{J} = \sum e N \left(\mathbf{v} + \mathbf{u} \frac{\mathbf{k} \cdot \mathbf{v}}{\omega - \mathbf{k} \cdot \mathbf{u}} \right). \tag{59}$$

Equations (50), (51), and (59) lead to

$$(\omega^2 - c^2 k^2)\, \mathbf{E} + c^2 \mathbf{k} (\mathbf{k} \cdot \mathbf{E}) + 4 \pi i \omega \sum e N \left(\mathbf{v} + \mathbf{u} \frac{\mathbf{k} \cdot \mathbf{v}}{\omega - \mathbf{k} \cdot \mathbf{u}} \right) = 0, \tag{60}$$

where $\mathbf{v}$ is given by Eq. (58). On substituting for $\mathbf{v}$ in accordance with Eq. (58) into Eq. (60) we obtain, in general, an equation of the form

$$\mathbf{R} \cdot \mathbf{E} = 0, \tag{61}$$

* The notation used here (u for the velocity in the steady state and v for the perturbation in the velocity) is different from that used in section II. This should, however, cause no confusion.

where **R** is a 3 × 3 Hermitian matrix. In order that Eq. (61) have a non-trivial solution, we must demand that the secular equation

$$\| \mathbf{R} \| = 0, \qquad (62)$$

be satisfied. This results in the required dispersion relation. We shall now discuss the implications of Eq. (62) in several special cases.

3.1 Oscillations in a Static Plasma

We shall first discuss the case of oscillations in a static plasma, i.e., where the mean fluid velocity vanishes everywhere. Setting $\mathbf{u} = 0$ in Eq. (58) and substituting the resulting expression into Eq. (60), we obtain an equation of the form (61). Taking **k** to be along the z-axis of a Cartesian system of co-ordinates and assuming that the magnetic field lies in the xz plane making an angle θ with the z-axis, the elements of the matrix **R** are given by

$$\left.\begin{aligned}
R_{11} &= \omega^2 - c^2k^2 - \sum \omega_p^2 + \sum \frac{\omega_p^2 \omega_c^2 \cos^2\theta}{\omega_c^2 - \omega^2} \\
R_{12} &= -R_{21} = \sum i\,\omega_p^2 \frac{\omega\,\omega_c \cos\theta}{\omega_c^2 - \omega^2} \\
R_{13} &= +R_{31} = -\sum \omega_p^2 \frac{\omega_c^2}{\omega_c^2 - \omega^2} \sin\theta\cos\theta \\
R_{22} &= \omega^2 - c^2k^2 - \sum \omega_p^2 + \sum \omega_p^2 \frac{\omega_c^2}{\omega_c^2 - \omega^2} \\
R_{23} &= -R_{32} = i \sum \omega_p^2 \frac{\omega\omega_c \sin\theta}{\omega_c^2 - \omega^2} \\
R_{33} &= \omega^2 - \sum \omega_p^2 + \sum \omega_p^2 \frac{\omega_c^2 \sin^2\theta}{\omega_c^2 - \omega^2}
\end{aligned}\right\}, \qquad (63)$$

where $\omega_p^2 = 4\pi Ne^2/m$.

3.11 No Magnetic Field Case

As the simplest illustrative example of Eq. (62), consider the case of electron oscillations. Setting $\omega_c = 0$ in Eq. (63), we obtain Eq. (64), see below on this page, where ω_p now denotes the electron plasma frequency. We thus obtain for longitudinal oscillations (**k** along **E**)

$$\omega^2 = \omega_p^2, \qquad (65)$$

and for transverse oscillations (**k** perpendicular to **E**)

$$\omega^2 = \omega_p^2 + c^2k^2, \qquad (66)$$

which are in accordance with Eqs. (8) and (17).

3.12 Propagation along the Magnetic Field

For propagation along the magnetic field, $\theta = 0$, and Eq. (61) takes the particularly simple form (cf. Eqs. (61) and (63)) of Eq. (67), see bottom of this page. For longitudinal oscillations we thus obtain the relation

$$\omega^2 = \sum \omega_p^2 = \omega_{pe}^2 \left(1 + \frac{m}{M}\right) \simeq \omega_{pe}^2, \qquad (68)$$

where ω_{pe} denotes the electron plasma frequency. The transverse oscillations are circularly polarized and are described by the equation

$$\left[\omega^2 - c^2k^2 - \sum \omega_p^2 \frac{\omega}{\omega \mp \omega}\right] E_\pm = 0, \qquad (69)$$

where

$$E_\pm = E_x \pm iE_y, \qquad (70)$$

the plus or minus sign corresponding to the right or left handed circularly polarized waves respectively. The oscillations are, therefore, governed by the dispersion relation

$$\omega^2 - c^2k^2 - \omega_{pe}^2 - \omega_{pi}^2 + \omega_{pe}^2 \frac{\omega_e}{\omega + \omega_e} - \omega_{pi}^2 \frac{\omega_i}{\omega - \omega_i} = 0. \qquad (71)$$

for the right handed circularly polarized waves. Here the electron and the ion plasma frequencies are denoted by ω_{pe} and ω_{pi} respectively, while the electron and ion cyclotron frequencies are denoted by ω_e and ω_i respectively. A relation similar to (71) applies to the left handed circularly polarized waves.

a. High Frequency Oscillations

If $\omega \gg \omega_i$, the dispersion relation (71) reduces to

$$\omega^2 - c^2k^2 - \omega_{pe}^2 \frac{\omega}{\omega + \omega_e} - \omega_{pi}^2 = 0. \qquad (72)$$

In the limit when $\omega \gg \omega_e$, Eq. (72) yields, correct to the lowest significant order in ω_e/ω,

$$\omega^2 = c^2k^2 + \omega_{pe}^2 \left[1 - \frac{\omega_e}{(\omega_{pe}^2 + c^2k^2)^{1/2}}\right]. \qquad (73)$$

It is clear that a necessary condition for the validity of this relation is that $\omega_e^2 \ll \omega_{pe}^2 + c^2k^2$.

$$\begin{vmatrix} \omega^2 - \omega_p^2 - c^2k^2 & 0 & 0 \\ 0 & \omega^2 - \omega_p^2 - c^2k^2 & 0 \\ 0 & 0 & \omega^2 - \omega_p^2 \end{vmatrix} \begin{vmatrix} E_x \\ E_y \\ E_z \end{vmatrix} = 0 \qquad (64)$$

$$\begin{vmatrix} \omega^2 - c^2k^2 + \sum \frac{\omega_p^2 \omega^2}{\omega_c^2 - \omega^2} & i \sum \omega_p^2 \frac{\omega\omega_c}{\omega_c^2 - \omega^2} & 0 \\ -i \sum \omega_p^2 \frac{\omega\omega_c}{\omega_c^2 - \omega^2} & \omega^2 - c^2k^2 + \sum \omega_p^2 \frac{\omega^2}{\omega_c^2 - \omega^2} & 0 \\ 0 & 0 & \omega^2 - \sum \omega_p^2 \end{vmatrix} \begin{vmatrix} E_x \\ E_y \\ E_z \end{vmatrix} = 0. \qquad (67)$$

b. Oscillations near the Electron Cyclotron Frequency

Another case of interest is the one when the frequency of oscillations is close to the electron cyclotron frequency. In this case we find that Eq. (72) leads to

$$\omega = -\omega_e \left[1 + \frac{\omega_{pe}^2}{\omega_e^2 - (c^2 k^2 + \omega_{pe}^2)}\right]. \qquad (74)$$

It is clear that the necessary condition for this approximation to be valid is that

$$\omega_{pe}^2 < | \omega_e^2 - c^2 k^2 |. \qquad (75)$$

We can write Eq. (72) in the form (for $\omega \gg \omega_i$)

$$\left(\frac{V}{c}\right)^2 = \frac{1 + (\omega_e/\omega)}{1 + (\omega_e/\omega) - (\omega_{pe}^2/\omega^2)}, \qquad (76)$$

where $V = \omega/k$ is the phase velocity of the wave. The behaviour of the phase velocity as a function of the frequency of oscillation is illustrated in Figs. 1—3 for some values of the field strength.

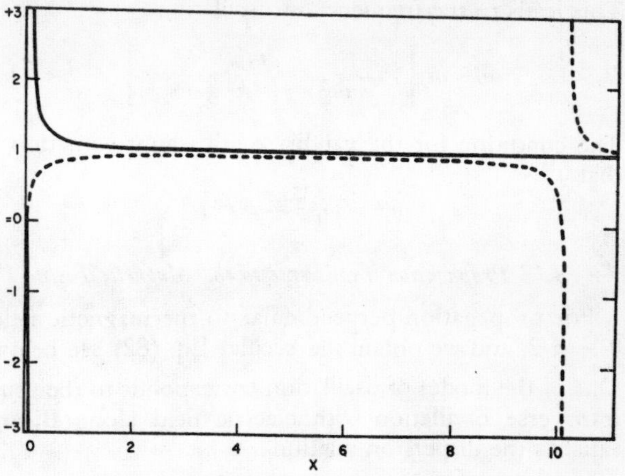

Fig. 3 The behavior of $Z = (V/c)^2$ as a function of $x = \omega/\omega_p$ for electron oscillations for propagation along the magnetic field for the case when $\omega_e = 10\,\omega_p$.

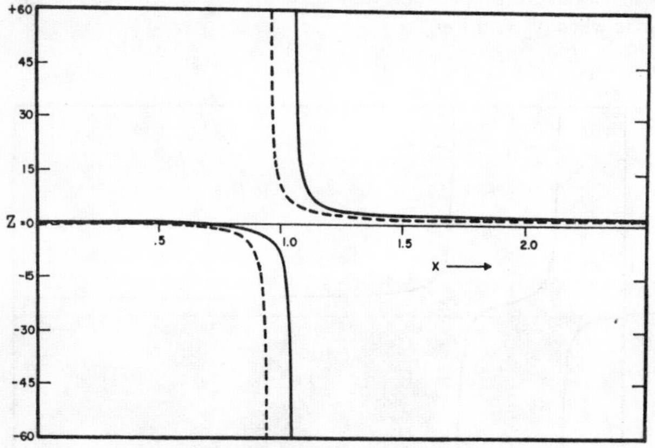

Fig. 1 The behavior of $Z = (V/c)^2$, where V is the phase velocity of the wave, as a function of $x = \omega/\omega_p$ for electron oscillations for propagation along the magnetic field for the case when $\omega_e = 0.1\,\omega_p$. The negative values of Z correspond to imaginary values of k, which correspond to absorption of waves in a bounded plasma.

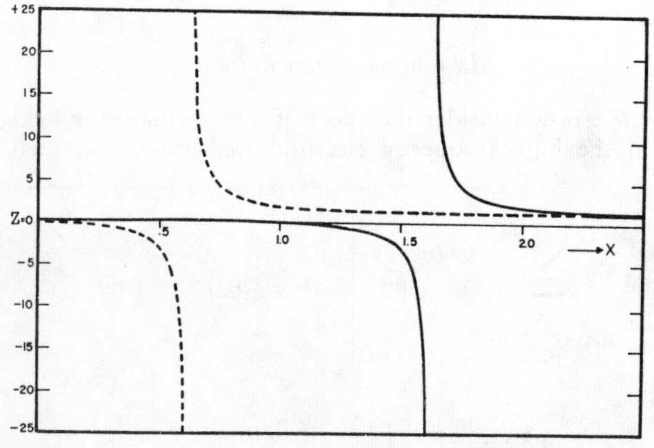

Fig. 2 The behavior of $Z = (V/c)^2$ as a function of $x = \omega/\omega_p$ for electron oscillations for propagation along the magnetic field for the case when $\omega_e = \omega_p$.

c. Oscillations much below the Ion Cyclotron Frequency

Now consider the low frequency oscillations such that the condition $\omega < \omega_i$ is satisfied. Then to the lowest significant order we can write Eq. (71) as

$$\omega^2 - c^2 k^2 + \omega_{pi}^2 \frac{\omega}{\omega_i}\left(1 + \frac{\omega}{\omega_i}\right) - \omega_{pe}^2 \frac{\omega}{\omega_e} = 0. \qquad (77)$$

Using the fact that $\omega_{pi}^2/\omega_i = \omega_{pe}^2/\omega_e$ and $\omega_{pi}^2/\omega_i^2 = c^2\, 4\pi NM/B_0^2$, Eq. (77) leads to

$$\omega^2 = \frac{c^2 k^2}{1 + (c^2/A^2)}, \qquad (78)$$

where

$$A = \frac{B_0}{(4\pi NM)^{1/2}} \qquad (79)$$

denotes the Alfvén speed. Eq. (78) is the dispersion relation of Aström for the extra-ordinary hydromagnetic wave. It must be emphasized here that the hydromagnetic wave, in principle, is just a special case, in the appropriate frequency region, of the well-known transverse electromagnetic waves.

In the limit when $c/A \gg 1$, Eq. (78) reduces to

$$\left(\frac{\omega}{k}\right)^2 = A^2; \qquad (80)$$

that is, the phase velocity of the wave is just the Alfvén speed. In the other limit when $c/A \ll 1$, we get

$$\omega^2 = c^2 k^2, \qquad (80a)$$

which corresponds to the usual electromagnetic modes.

d. Oscillations near the Ion Cyclotron Frequency

Let us now consider the case when $\omega \simeq \omega_i$. This implies that $\omega < \omega_e$, and the dispersion relation (71) reduces to

$$\omega^2 - c^2 k^2 - \omega_{pi}^2 - \omega_{pi}^2 \frac{\omega_i}{\omega - \omega_i} = 0. \qquad (81)$$

This leads to the frequency of oscillation

$$\omega \sim \omega_i \left[1 + \frac{\omega_{pi}^2}{\omega_i^2 - (c^2k^2 + \omega_{pi}^2)}\right]. \qquad (81\,a)$$

The condition for the validity of this approximation is that

$$\omega_i^2 \gg \omega_{pi}^2 + c^2k^2 .$$

3.13 Propagation Transverse to the Magnetic Field

For propagation perpendicular to the magnetic field, $\theta = \pi/2$, and we obtain the secular Eq. (82) see below. One of the modes of oscillation corresponds to the usual transverse oscillation with electric field along $\mathbf{B}_0$ and satisfies the dispersion relation

$$\omega^2 = c^2k^2 + \sum \omega_p^2 \simeq c^2k^2 + \omega_{pe}^2 . \qquad (83)$$

The other two modes of oscillation are determined as roots of the equation (84), see bottom of this page. Consider the case when $\omega \ll ck$. Then to the lowest significant order, the 22 element of this determinant must vanish. We thus obtain

$$1 + \frac{\omega_{pi}^2}{\omega_i^2 - \omega^2} + \frac{\omega_{pe}^2}{\omega_e^2 - \omega^2} = 0 . \qquad (85)$$

In the limit when $\omega_i \ll \omega \ll \omega_e \ll \omega_p$, Eq. (85) reduces to

$$-\frac{\omega_{pi}^2}{\omega^2} + \frac{\omega_{pe}^2}{\omega_e^2} = 0 . \qquad (86)$$

The frequency of oscillation is then determined by

$$\omega = \left(\frac{\omega_e^2\,\omega_{pi}^2}{\omega_{pe}^2}\right)^{1/2} = (\omega_e\,\omega_i)^{1/2} \qquad (87)$$

This frequency of oscillation is referred to as the *lower hybrid frequency*.

Now consider the limiting case where the conditions $\omega^2 \gg \omega_i^2$ and $\omega^2 \gg \omega_{pi}^2$ are satisfied. Eq. (85) then leads to

$$\omega = (\omega_e^2 + \omega_{pe}^2)^{1/2}. \qquad (88)$$

This frequency of oscillation is referred to as the *upper hybrid frequency*.

For the high frequency oscillations, $\omega \gg \omega_i, \omega_{pi}$, we may neglect the motion of the ions, and Eq. (84) leads to

$$\left(\omega^2 + \omega_{pe}^2 \frac{\omega^2}{\omega_e^2 - \omega^2}\right)\left(\omega^2 + \omega_{pe}^2 \frac{\omega^2}{\omega_e^2 - \omega^2} - c^2k^2\right) - \omega_{pe}^4 \frac{\omega^2\,\omega_e^2}{(\omega_e^2 - \omega^2)^2} = 0. \qquad (89)$$

The behaviour of the phase velocity as a function of the frequency corresponding to the roots of this equation are illustrated in Figs. 4—6 for some values of the field strength.

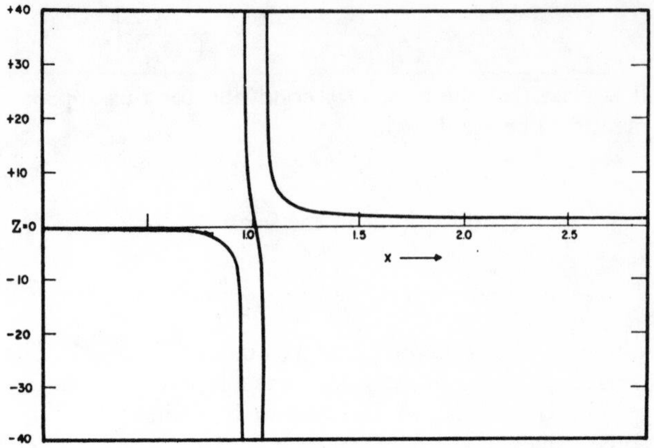

Fig. 4 The behavior of $Z = (V/c)^2$, where V denotes the phase velocity of the wave, as a function of $x = \omega/\omega_p$ for electron oscillations for propagation transverse to the magnetic field for the case when $\omega_e = 0.1\,\omega_p$.

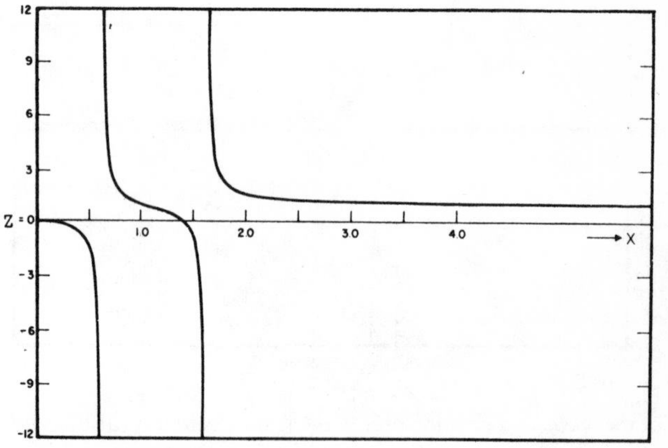

Fig. 5 The behavior of $Z = (V/c)^2$, where V denotes the phase velocity of the wave as a function of $x = \omega/\omega_p$ for electron oscillations for propagation transverse to the magnetic field for the case when $\omega_e = \omega_p$

3.14 Weak Magnetic Field

We now consider the effect of a weak magnetic field on the high frequency electron oscillations described

$$\begin{vmatrix} \omega^2 - \sum\omega_p^2 - c^2k^2 & 0 & 0 \\ 0 & \omega^2 - c^2k^2 + \sum \frac{\omega_p^2\omega^2}{\omega_c^2 - \omega^2} & +i\sum \omega_p^2 \frac{\omega\omega_c}{\omega_c^2 - \omega^2} \\ 0 & -i\sum \omega_p^2 \frac{\omega\omega_c}{\omega_c^2 - \omega^2} & \omega^2 + \sum \omega_p^2 \frac{\omega^2}{\omega_c^2 - \omega^2} \end{vmatrix} = 0 . \qquad (82)$$

$$\begin{vmatrix} \omega^2 - c^2k^2 + \sum \omega_p^2 \frac{\omega^2}{\omega_c^2 - \omega^2} & +i\sum \omega_p^2 \frac{\omega\omega_c}{\omega_c^2 - \omega^2} \\ -i\sum \omega_p^2 \frac{\omega\omega_c}{\omega_c^2 - \omega^2} & \omega^2 + \sum \omega_p^2 \frac{\omega^2}{\omega_c^2 - \omega^2} \end{vmatrix} = 0 . \qquad (84)$$

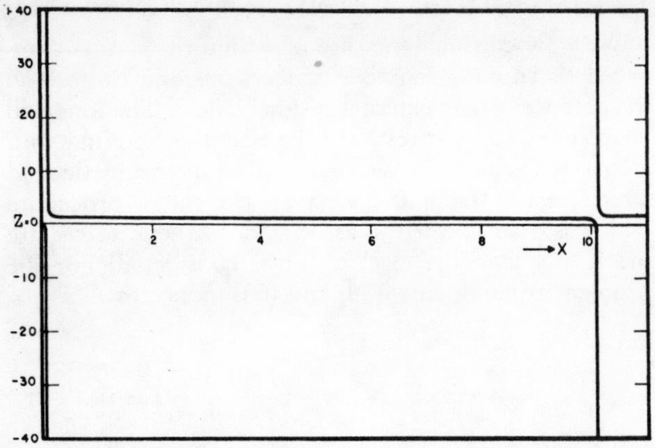

Fig. 6 The behavior of $Z = (V/c)^2$, where V denotes the phase velocity of the wave as a function of $x = \omega/\omega_p$ for electron oscillations for propagation transverse to the magnetic field for the case when $\omega_e = 10\,\omega_p$.

in § 2 for arbitrary direction of the magnetic field. The weak field approximation, specifically, implies that $\omega_e \ll \omega$. Retaining terms up to second order in ω_e/ω, the dispersion equation now becomes (cf. Eqs. (61) and (63)) Eq. (90) see bottom of this page, where we have put

$$\omega_0^2 = \omega_p^2 + c^2k^2; \tag{91}$$

ω_0 is the frequency of oscillation of the transverse wave in the absence of a magnetic field. Since we have assumed ω_e/ω to be small, to a first approximation, for the transverse oscillations, ω can be replaced by ω_0 in all elements of the matrix **R** except R_{11} and R_{22}. Then it is clear that R_{33} is the leading term in **R**, being of order c^2k^2 and Eq. (90) gives

$$c^2k^2E_z = 0\,. \tag{92}$$

Since $k \neq 0$, we must require that E_z vanish. Thus to first approximation in ω_e/ω, the longitudinal and transverse modes of oscillation remain uncoupled. Retaining terms up to first order in ω_e/ω, Eq. (90) reduces to

$$\begin{vmatrix} \omega^2 - \omega_0^2 & -i\omega_{pe}^2\dfrac{\omega_e}{\omega_0}\cos\theta \\ i\omega_{pe}^2\dfrac{\omega_e}{\omega_0}\cos\theta & \omega^2 - \omega_0^2 \end{vmatrix} \begin{Vmatrix} E_x \\ E_y \end{Vmatrix} = 0, \tag{93}$$

In order that this equation have a non-trivial solution, we must demand that the determinant of the co-efficients vanish; this leads to the dispersion relation

$$\omega^2 = \omega_0^2 \pm \omega_{pe}^2\frac{\omega_e}{\omega_0}\cos\theta\,. \tag{94}$$

These modes of oscillation are circularly polarized with $E_x = \pm iE_y$. It can be verified readily from Eqs. (90) and (94) that to first order in ω_e/ω, E_z vanishes.

To carry through the calculations consistent to the second order in ω_e/ω, we now substitute ω in accordance with Eq. (94) in all elements of the matrix **R** except R_{11} and R_{22} in Eq. (90). Retaining terms up to second order in ω_e/ω, we obtain

$$\omega^2 = \omega_0^2 + \frac{1}{2}\omega_{pe}^2\frac{\omega_e^2}{\omega_0^2}(1+\cos^2\theta) \pm \frac{\omega_{pe}^2\omega_e}{2\omega_0}\left[4\cos^2\theta\left\{1 \mp \frac{\omega_{pe}^2}{\omega_0^2}\frac{\omega_e}{\omega_0}\cos\theta + \frac{\omega_{pe}^4}{\omega_0^4}\frac{\omega_e^2}{\omega_0^2}\cos^2\theta\right\} + \left(\frac{\omega_e}{\omega_0}\right)^2\left\{(1-\cos\theta)^2 + \sin^2\theta\frac{\omega_{pe}^2}{c^2k^2}\left[2(1+\cos^2\theta) + \sin^2\theta\frac{\omega_{pe}^2}{c^2k^2}\right]\right\}\right]^{1/2}. \tag{95}$$

In particular, for $\theta = 0$, we obtain

$$\omega^2 = \omega_0^2 \pm \omega_{pe}^2\frac{\omega_e}{\omega_0} + \omega_{pe}^2\frac{\omega_e^2}{\omega_0^2}\left(1 \pm \frac{1}{2}\frac{\omega_{pe}^2}{\omega_0^2}\right), \tag{96}$$

and for $\theta = \pi/2$, Eq. (95) gives

$$\omega^2 = \omega_0^2 + \frac{1}{2}\omega_{pe}^2\frac{\omega_e^2}{\omega_0^2}\left[1 \pm \left(1 + \frac{\omega_{pe}^2}{c^2k^2}\right)\right]. \tag{97}$$

We now find that the longitudinal and transverse waves are coupled; their polarizations are given by

$$\frac{E_x}{E_y} = \mp i\left(1 \pm \frac{1}{2}\frac{\omega_{pe}^2}{\omega_0^2}\frac{\omega_e}{\omega_0}\cos\theta\right) \tag{98}$$

and

$$\frac{E_z}{E_y} = -i\frac{1}{c^2k^2}\omega_{pe}^2\frac{\omega_e}{\omega_0}\sin\theta \tag{99}$$

Let us now consider longitudinal oscillations which are characterized by the plasma frequency $\omega = \omega_{pe}$ in the absence of a magnetic field. To a first approximation we can put $\omega = \omega_{pe}$ in all elements of the matrix **R** except R_{33} and obtain the secular equation (100) below.

$$\begin{vmatrix} \omega^2 - \omega_0^2 - \omega_{pe}^2\dfrac{\omega_e^2}{\omega^2}\cos^2\theta & -i\omega_{pe}^2\dfrac{\omega_e}{\omega}\cos\theta & \omega_{pe}^2\dfrac{\omega_e^2}{\omega^2}\sin\theta\cos\theta \\ i\omega_{pe}^2\dfrac{\omega_e}{\omega}\cos\theta & \omega^2 - \omega_0^2 - \omega_{pe}^2\dfrac{\omega_e^2}{\omega^2} & -i\omega_{pe}^2\dfrac{\omega_e}{\omega}\sin\theta \\ \omega_{pe}^2\dfrac{\omega_e^2}{\omega^2}\sin\theta\cos\theta & +i\omega_{pe}^2\dfrac{\omega_e}{\omega}\sin\theta & \omega^2 - \omega_{pe}^2 - \omega_{pe}^2\dfrac{\omega_e^2}{\omega^2}\sin^2\theta \end{vmatrix} \begin{Vmatrix} E_x \\ E_y \\ E_z \end{Vmatrix} = 0, \tag{90}$$

$$\begin{vmatrix} -c^2k^2 - \omega_e^2\cos^2\theta & -i\omega_{pe}\omega_e\cos\theta & \omega_e^2\sin\theta\cos\theta \\ i\omega_{pe}\omega_e\cos\theta & -c^2k^2 - \omega_e^2 & -i\omega_{pe}\omega_e\sin\theta \\ \omega_e^2\sin\theta\cos\theta & i\omega_{pe}\omega_e\sin\theta & \omega^2 - \omega_{pe}^2 - \omega_e^2\sin^2\theta \end{vmatrix} = 0. \tag{100}$$

The electrostatic oscillations are characterized by the condition that $ck \gg \omega$. Thus the leading elements of the matrix are R_{11} and R_{22}, and to compute the corrections to the root thus obtained, it can be readily verified that it is sufficient to demand that the co-factor of R_{11} vanish. This yields the dispersion relation

$$\omega^2 = \omega_{pe}^2 \left[1 + \left(\frac{\omega_e^2}{\omega_{pe}^2} - \frac{\omega_e^2}{c^2 k^2}\right)\sin^2\theta\right] \qquad (101)$$

The correction terms are small as long as ω_e^2/ω_{pe}^2 and ω_e^2/c^2k^2 are both much less than unity.

It may be remarked here that for transverse oscillations the correction terms to ω^2, to lowest significant order, are of order ω_e/ω, while for longitudinal oscillations the correction terms, to the lowest significant order, are of order $(\omega_e/\omega)^2$.

3.15 Strong Magnetic Field

We shall now consider the case of a strong magnetic field which implies that $\omega_i/\omega \gg 1$. Retaining terms up to second order in (ω_c/ω), Eqs. (61) and (63) lead to (102), see bottom of page. In writing Eq. (102) we have used

$$\sum \frac{\omega_p^2}{\omega_c^2} = \frac{4\pi N M c^2}{B_0^2}\left(1 + \frac{m}{M}\right)$$
$$\simeq \frac{4\pi N M c^2}{B_0^2} = \frac{c^2}{A^2}, \qquad (103)$$

and

$$\frac{\omega_{pe}^2}{\omega_e} = \frac{\omega_{pi}^2}{\omega_i}. \qquad (104)$$

One of the roots of Eq. (102) is clearly given by

$$\omega^2 = \frac{c^2 k^2}{1 + (c^2/A^2)}, \qquad (105)$$

this is the dispersion formula of Aström for the extraordinary hydromagnetic wave. The characteristic frequencies of the other two modes are determined by the algebraic equation (assuming $c/A \gg 1$)

$$\frac{c^4}{A^4}\omega^4 - \frac{c^2}{A^2}\omega^2 (c^2 k^2 + \omega_{pe}^2) + c^2 k^2 \omega_{pe}^2 \cos^2\theta = 0. \quad (106)$$

The roots of this equation are given by

$$\omega^2 = \frac{A^2}{2c^2}\Big\{c^2 k^2 + \omega_{pe}^2$$
$$+ [c^2 k^2 + \omega_{pe}^2)^2 - 4 c^2 k^2 \omega_{pe}^2 \cos^2\theta]^{1/2}. \quad (107)$$

In hydromagnetic waves $\omega_{pe} \ll ck$, and Eq. (107) reduces to

$$\left(\frac{\omega}{k}\right)^2 = A^2; \qquad (108)$$

this is the ordinary hydromagnetic wave of Alfvén.

4. Instability in a Plasma Carrying Current

We now consider the case of a uniform plasma composed of an equal number of electrons and protons in the absence of any external magnetic field. The ions will be assumed to be at rest, and the electrons, moving with a constant velocity u. We shall neglect the magnetic field which results from the electron current, a procedure which is plausible if the associated magnetic forces are much less than the electric forces considered. For the problem at hand, Eqs. (58) and (60) reduce to

$$(\omega^2 - c^2 k^2)\,\mathbf{E} + c^2 \mathbf{k}\,(\mathbf{k}\cdot\mathbf{E})$$
$$+ 4\pi i\omega \Sigma\, eN\left(\mathbf{v} + \mathbf{u}\frac{\mathbf{k}\cdot\mathbf{v}}{\omega - \mathbf{k}\cdot\mathbf{u}}\right) = 0. \quad (109)$$

and

$$\mathbf{v} = \frac{ie}{m}\frac{1}{\omega - \mathbf{k}\cdot\mathbf{u}}\left[\mathbf{E} + \frac{1}{\omega}\mathbf{u}\times(\mathbf{k}\times\mathbf{E})\right]. \quad (110)$$

We first consider electrostatic oscillations only and take $\mathbf{k}$ to be in the direction of the electron stream. Eqs. (109) and (110) then lead to the dispersion relation

$$1 = \frac{\omega_{pi}^2}{\omega^2} + \frac{\omega_{pe}^2}{(\omega - ku)^2}, \qquad (111)$$

where ω_{pi} and ω_{pe} denote the ion and electron plasma frequencies respectively. It is now convenient to introduce the dimensionless parameters

$$x = \frac{\omega}{\omega_{pe}}, \quad y = \frac{ku}{\omega_{pe}}, \quad \text{and} \quad \varepsilon = \frac{m}{M} \qquad (112)$$

The dispersion relation (111) then takes the form

$$F(x,y) = \frac{1}{(x-y)^2} + \frac{\varepsilon}{x^2} = 1. \qquad (113)$$

A schematic plot of $F(x,y)$ as a function of x for $y = 1$ is shown Fig. 7 for a hydrogen plasma. If the line $F = 1$ lies above the minimum of the curve, then it is

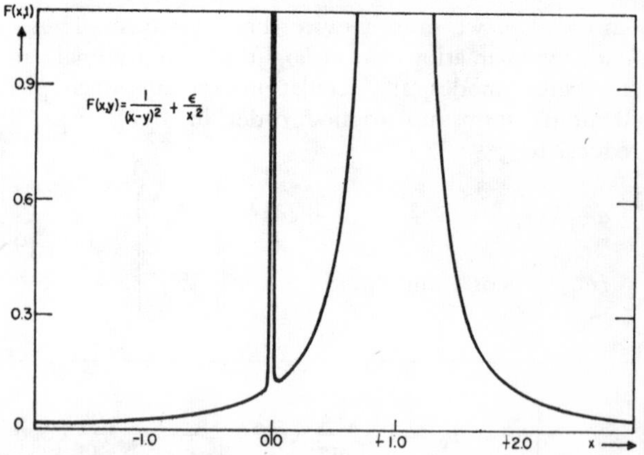

Fig. 7 The plot of $F(x,y)$ given by Eq. (113) as a function of x for $y = 1$ for a plasma composed of electrons and protons.

$$\begin{vmatrix} \omega^2 - c^2k^2 + \frac{c^2\omega^2}{A^2} - \omega_{pe}^2 \sin^2\theta & 0 & -\omega_{pe}^2 \sin\theta\cos\theta \\ 0 & \omega^2 - c^2k^2 + \frac{c^2}{A^2}\omega^2 & 0 \\ -\omega_{pe}^2\sin\theta\cos\theta & 0 & \omega^2 + \frac{c^2\omega^2}{A^2} - \omega_{pe}^2\cos^2\theta \end{vmatrix} = 0, \qquad (102)$$

clear that there exist four real roots of Eq. (113) and that all modes of oscillation are oscillatory. However, if the line $F=1$ lies below the minimum of the curve, then there are only two real roots and there must exist a pair of complex conjugate roots, one of which has a positive imaginary part and is, therefore, unstable. The minimum of the curve $F(x,y)$ is determined by the condition that, for a given y, $F(x,y)$ be stationary, i.e.,

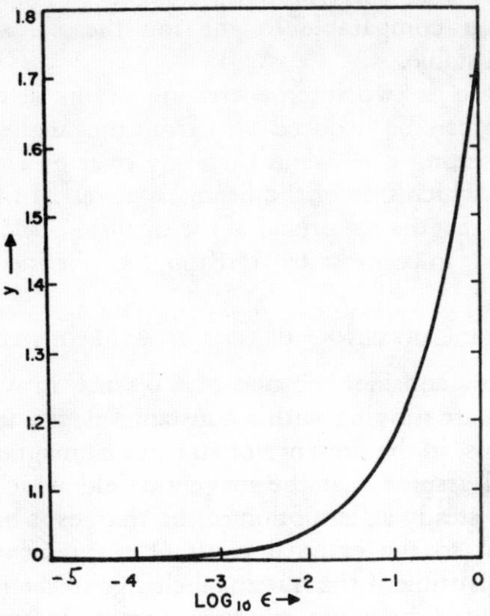

Fig. 8 The behavior of y_c given by Eq. (116) as a function of ε, the ratio of the negative to the positive ion mass.

$$\frac{\partial}{\partial x} F(x,y) = 0. \tag{114}$$

This leads to

$$x = \frac{\varepsilon^{1/3}}{1+\varepsilon^{1/3}} y \simeq \varepsilon^{1/3} y, \text{ if } \varepsilon \ll 1. \tag{115}$$

The value of y for which this minimum is just tangent to the line $F=1$ can be readily obtained by substituting this value of x into Eq. (113) and solving the resulting equation for y. Denoting these minimum values by x_c and y_c, we have

$$y_c = (1+\varepsilon^{1/3})^{3/2} . \tag{116}$$

The behaviour of y_c as a function of ε is illustrated in Fig. 8. If $y_c > y$, Eq. (113) admits four real roots. Thus a cold streaming plasma is *stable* to all perturbations having wavelengths smaller than the critical wavelength λ_c given by

$$\lambda_c = 2\pi \frac{u}{\omega_{pe}} \left(1+\varepsilon^{1/3}\right)^{-3/2} \tag{117}$$

$$\simeq 2\pi \frac{u}{\omega_{pe}} \left(1-\frac{3}{2}\varepsilon^{1/3}\right), \quad \text{if } \varepsilon \ll 1. \tag{118}$$

For values of y close to y_c, by Taylor's expansion, Eq. (113) can be written as (cf. Eq. (114))

$$(y-y_c)\, F_y(x_c, y_c) + \frac{1}{2}(x-x_c)^2 F_{xx}(x_c, y_c) = 0. \tag{119}$$

This leads to

$$x = x_c \pm i\varepsilon^{1/6} \left[\frac{\frac{2}{3}(y_c - y)}{(1+\varepsilon^{1/3})^{1/2}}\right]^{1/2} \tag{120}$$

it is clear that this expression is valid so long as

$$y_c - y \ll \frac{3}{2}\varepsilon^{1/3}. \tag{121}$$

Eq. (120) implies that

$$\text{Im}\,\frac{dx}{dy} \to \pm\infty \quad \text{as } y \to y_c. \tag{122}$$

For values of x close to the origin, and on the assumption that $x/y \ll 1$, an approximation which is legitimate for the unstable roots (cf. Eq. (116)), we obtain

$$x = \pm i\varepsilon^{1/2} y. \tag{123}$$

Equations (122) and (123) give the behaviour of x near x_c and the origin as a function of y. For the continuous range of values of y between 0 and y_c, Eq. (113) has been solved numerically, and the results are illustrated in Fig. 9 where the real and imaginary parts of x are plotted as a function of y.

The growth rate of maximum instability can be readily computed from Eq. (113) by observing that at the maximum

$$\text{Im}\,\frac{dx}{dy} = 0. \tag{124}$$

From Eq. (113) we obtain

$$\frac{dx}{dy} = \frac{1}{1-\varepsilon\left(\frac{y}{x}-1\right)^3} \tag{125}$$

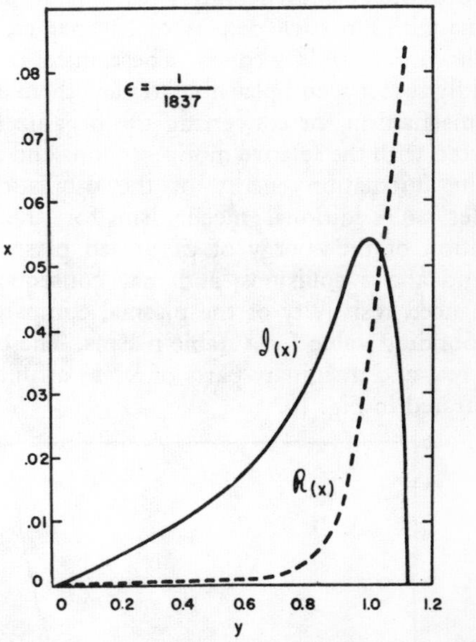

Fig. 9 The behavior of the real and imaginary part of the frequency of oscillation ($x = \omega/\omega_p$) as a function of the wave number of the disturbance ($k = \omega_p y/u$) for the unstable modes of oscillation.

Since Im dx/dy vanishes at the point in question, it follows that the denominator occurring in Eq. (125) must be real; we take

$$\frac{y}{x} - 1 = \alpha e^{-i\pi/3} \text{ at } y = y^*, \tag{126}$$

where α is a real positive number of order $\varepsilon^{-1/3}$. This choice of phase will be justified a posteriori. We use an asterisk to denote the value of any quantity corresponding to the maximum growth rate of instability. Substituting Eq. (126) into Eq. (113) and separating real and imaginary parts, we obtain

$$y^2 = 1 + \frac{1}{\alpha^3 (2+\alpha)} (1 + 2\alpha + 3\alpha^2) \qquad (127)$$

and

$$\varepsilon = \frac{1}{\alpha^3} \frac{1+2\alpha}{2+\alpha}. \qquad (128)$$

To the lowest significant order, Eq. (128) gives

$$\alpha = \left(\frac{2}{\varepsilon}\right)^{1/3}. \qquad (129)$$

Substituting this value of α into Eq. (127), we obtain to the lowest significant order

$$y^* = 1 + \frac{3}{2}\left(\frac{\varepsilon}{2}\right)^{2/3}. \qquad (130)$$

From Eqs. (126), (128), (129), and (130) we find that

$$x^* = \left(\frac{\varepsilon}{2}\right)^{1/3}\left[\frac{1}{2} + \frac{1}{2}\left(\frac{\varepsilon}{2}\right)^{1/3} - \frac{1}{4}\left(\frac{\varepsilon}{2}\right)^{2/3} + \ldots\right] + i\left(\frac{\varepsilon}{2}\right)^{1/3}\frac{3^{1/2}}{2}\left[1 + \frac{3}{4}\left(\frac{\varepsilon}{2}\right)^{2/3} + \ldots\right]. \qquad (131)$$

The maximum growth rate of instability, therefore corresponds to (for a hydrogen plasma)

$$\mathrm{Im}\, x^* = \mathrm{Im}\frac{\omega^*}{\omega_{pe}} \simeq \frac{3^{1/2}}{2}\left(\frac{\varepsilon}{2}\right)^{1/3} \simeq \frac{1}{18}. \qquad (132)$$

Therefore the smallest *e*-folding time is 18 ω_{pe}^{-1}. For a plasma with a particle density of 10^{14} per cc, this time is of the order 10^{-10} seconds. These instabilities grow so rapidly that it seems plausible to view them as providing a mechanism for converting the organized energy, associated with the relative motion of ions and electrons, into the fluctuation energy of the oscillations. This provides an additional mechanism for the effective dissipation of the energy of organized plasma motion over and above collisions, and may consequently lead to enhanced resistivity of the plasma, compared to the corresponding value for a stable plasma. The behaviour of the real and imaginary parts of x^* as a function of ε is illustrated in Fig. 10.

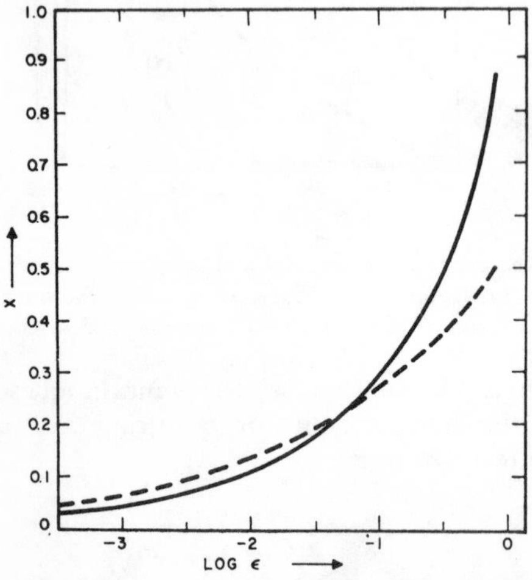

Fig. 10 The dependence of the maximum growth rate of instability as a function of ε is shown by the solid curve. The corresponding real part of the frequency is shown by the broken curve.

It may be emphasized here that these results are valid only so long as the phase velocities of the waves are much less than ion and electron thermal speeds. When this problem is examined from the standpoint of kinetic theory in part II, it will be seen that the thermal corrections transform certain stable regions in the $(u, \omega/k)$ plane into unstable regions, albeit with an exponentially small instability rate. Moreover, the region of the $(u, \omega/k)$ plane, corresponding roughly to the relative velocity $\mathbf{u}$ comparable to the ion thermal speed, is rendered stable.

The case of two interpenetrating beams of electrons (or ions) can be deduced also from the analysis given here by setting $\varepsilon = 1$ and by going over to a reference frame in which one of the beams is at rest. In this case one finds that the reciprocal of the smallest *e*-folding time is .866 ω_{pe} in contrast to (1/18) ω_{pe} as obtained earlier.

5. Plasma Carrying Current in a Magnetic Field

We now consider the case of a plasma, in which the electrons are moving with a constant velocity $\mathbf{u}$ relative to the ions, in the presence of an external magnetic field. We shall assume that the magnetic field which results from the steady state motion of the charges is negligible compared to the external constant magnetic field B_0. This is plausible if the fractional change in the magnetic field induced by these external currents is small over the wavelength of the perturbation in question. The equations for the problem at hand are (cf. Eqs. (58) and (60)):

$$(\omega^2 - c^2k^2)\,\mathbf{E} + c^2\mathbf{k}\,(\mathbf{k}\cdot\mathbf{E}) + 4\pi i\omega \sum eN\left[\mathbf{v} + \frac{\mathbf{u}\,(\mathbf{k}\cdot\mathbf{v})}{(\omega - \mathbf{k}\cdot\mathbf{u})}\right] = 0. \qquad (133)$$

and

$$\mathbf{v} = \frac{e}{m}\frac{i}{\omega}\frac{1}{\omega_c^2 - (\omega - \mathbf{k}\cdot\mathbf{u})^2}\Big\{\boldsymbol{\omega}_c\,(\boldsymbol{\omega}_c\cdot\mathbf{E}) - (\omega - \mathbf{k}\cdot\mathbf{u})^2\,\mathbf{E} + \frac{1}{(\omega - \mathbf{k}\cdot\mathbf{u})}[\boldsymbol{\omega}_c\,(\boldsymbol{\omega}_c\cdot\mathbf{k}) - \mathbf{k}\,(\omega - \mathbf{k}\cdot\mathbf{u})^2]\,(\mathbf{u}\cdot\mathbf{E}) + i\,(\omega - \mathbf{k}\cdot\mathbf{u})\,\boldsymbol{\omega}_c \times \mathbf{E} + i\,\boldsymbol{\omega}_c \times \mathbf{k}\,(\mathbf{u}\cdot\mathbf{E})\Big\}. \qquad (134)$$

We shall first restrict ourselves to the case when $\mathbf{B}_0$, $\mathbf{u}$, and $\mathbf{k}$ are along the z-axis. Then $\boldsymbol{\omega}_c \times \mathbf{k}$ vanishes and Eq. (134) reduces to

$$\mathbf{v} = \frac{e}{m}\frac{i}{\omega}\frac{1}{\omega_c^2 - (\omega - \mathbf{k}\cdot\mathbf{u})^2}\Big\{\left[\omega_c^2 - (\omega - ku)^2\right] E_z\, \mathbf{n} - (\omega - ku)^2\,(\mathbf{E} - \mathbf{n}\,\mathbf{n}\cdot\mathbf{E}) + \mathbf{k}\,\frac{\mathbf{u}\cdot\mathbf{E}}{(\omega - ku)}\left[\omega_c^2 - (\omega - ku)^2\right] + i\,(\omega - ku)\,\boldsymbol{\omega}_c \times \mathbf{E}\Big\}, \qquad (135)$$

where $\mathbf{n}$ denotes a unit vector along the z-axis. From Eqs. (133) and (135) we obtain for longitudinal oscillations

$$\left[\omega^2 - \sum_{+,-} \omega_p^2 \frac{\omega^2}{(\omega - ku)^2}\right] E_z = 0 \qquad (136)$$

and for transverse oscillations

$$\left[\omega^2 - c^2k^2 - \sum_{+,-} \omega_p^2 \frac{\omega - ku}{\omega - ku \mp \omega_c}\right] E_\pm = 0, \qquad (137)$$

where

$$E_{\pm} = E_x \pm iE_y \tag{138}$$

represents the electric vector for the right and left handed circularly polarized waves respectively. The upper sign in the denominator in Eq. (137) corresponds to E_+, while the lower sign corresponds to E_-.

When E_z does not vanish, we obtain for longitudinal oscillations the dispersion relation

$$\sum \omega_p^2 \frac{1}{(\omega - ku)^2} = 1. \tag{139}$$

It is to be observed from this expression that the longitudinal oscillations are unaffected by the presence of an external magnetic field (cf. § 4). Consequently, our earlier remarks are applicable in this case as well. For propagation along any arbitrary direction the present discussion of longitudinal oscillations is also valid if one replaces k by $k_{\|}$, the component of $\mathbf{k}$ along the magnetic field.

We shall now discuss the implications of the dispersion formula for the right handed circularly polarized wave only; a similar discussion applies to the left hand circularly polarized waves also and will not be given here. We have for the dispersion relation (cf. Eq. (137)):

$$\omega^2 - c^2 k^2 - \sum_{+,-} \omega_p^2 \frac{\omega - ku}{\omega - ku - \omega_c} = 0. \tag{140}$$

Denoting the stream velocity for the ions and electrons by u_i and u_e respectively, Eq. (140) takes the form

$$\omega^2 - c^2 k^2 - \omega_{pe}^2 \left(1 - \frac{\omega_e}{\omega - ku_e + \omega_e}\right) - \omega_{pi}^2 \left(1 + \frac{\omega_i}{\omega - ku_i - \omega_i}\right) = 0, \tag{141}$$

where, it may be recalled, ω_i and ω_e denote the ion and electron cyclotron frequencies respectively. Introducing the non-dimensional parameters

$$\left. \begin{aligned} x &= \frac{\omega}{\omega_{pe}}, \; y = \frac{ku}{\omega_{pe}}, \; \varepsilon = \frac{m}{M}, \\ z &= \frac{\omega_e}{\omega_{pe}}, \; \alpha = \frac{c}{u} y = \frac{ck}{\omega_{pe}} \end{aligned} \right\}, \tag{142}$$

we can write Eq. (141) as

$$F(x) = 1 + \varepsilon - x^2 + \alpha^2 - \varepsilon^2 \frac{z}{\varepsilon z - x + y_i} - \frac{z}{z + x - y_e} = 0. \tag{143}$$

We shall now discuss the implications of the relation (143).

Let us first consider the case when there is no stream. Eq. (143) then reduces to

$$F(x) = 1 + \varepsilon - x^2 + \alpha^2 - \varepsilon^2 \frac{z}{\varepsilon z - x} - \frac{z}{z + x} = 0. \tag{144}$$

The analysis of Eq. (144) is most readily effected by means of Fig. 11, where $F(x)$ is plotted schematically as a function of x. Observe that for large x, $F(x) \to -x^2$, $F(0) = \alpha^2$, and there are simple poles at $x = -z$ and $x = \varepsilon z$. Thus the curve $F(x)$ consists of three branches as indicated in Fig. 11 and there are clearly four real roots; consequently, all modes of oscillation are oscillatory and are *stable*.

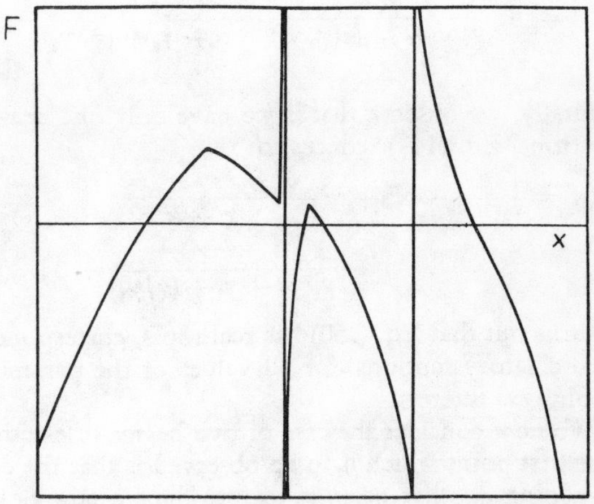

Fig. 11 A schematic plot of $F(x)$ given by Eq. (144) as a function of x. The singularities occur at the electron and ion cyclotron frequencies. The curve $F(x)$ intersects the x-axis at four points corresponding to four real roots.

5.1 Stream Instability (Transverse Oscillations)

We shall now consider the transverse oscillations for the case where we have two beams of fast electrons traversing the plasma. Suppose the fraction $1 - \beta$ of the electrons is moving with velocity $-\mathbf{u}_1$, and the fraction β is moving with velocity $\mathbf{u}_2$. The net current due to the electron streams is

$$\mathbf{J} = eN[-(1-\beta)\,\mathbf{u}_1 + \beta \mathbf{u}_2]. \tag{145}$$

In order that the net current due to the electron streams vanish, we must demand that

$$(1-\beta)\, u_1 = \beta u_2. \tag{146}$$

The corresponding results for the problem of one beam can be obtained immediately from these results by setting u_2 and β equal to zero. For the beam of relativistic electrons, the only modification in the dispersion relation is to replace the electron mass m by

$$m = \frac{m_0}{[1 - (u^2/c^2)]^{1/2}} = \gamma m_0, \tag{147}$$

where m_0 is the rest mass of the electrons. The dispersion relation now becomes

$$\omega^2 - c^2k^2 - \omega_{pi}^2\left(1 + \frac{\omega_i}{\omega - \omega_i}\right) - (1-\beta)\frac{\omega_{pe}^2}{\gamma_1}\left[1 - \frac{\omega_e/\gamma_1}{\omega + (\omega_e/\gamma_1) + ku_1}\right] - \beta\frac{\omega_{pe}^2}{\gamma_2}\left[1 - \frac{\omega_e/\gamma_2}{\omega + (\omega_e/\gamma_2) - ku_2}\right] = 0, \tag{148}$$

where ω_{pe} now denotes the electron plasma frequency defined with respect to the electron rest mass, and, it will be recalled, that $\mathbf{k}$ and $\mathbf{u}$ are both along $\mathbf{B}_0$. Introducing the dimensionless variable given in Eq. (142), we can write Eq. (148) in the form

$$F(x) = (1-\beta)\frac{1}{\gamma_1} + \frac{\beta}{\gamma_2} + \varepsilon - x^2 + \alpha^2 - \varepsilon^2 \frac{z}{\varepsilon z - x}$$
$$-(1-\beta)\frac{1}{\gamma_1}\frac{z/\gamma_1}{x + y_1 + (z/\gamma_1)} - \frac{z\beta/\gamma_2^2}{x - y_2 + (z/\gamma_2)} = 0. \tag{149}$$

Firstly, we observe that if we have only one beam of electrons, Eq. (149) reduces to

$$F(x) = \frac{1}{\gamma_1} + \varepsilon - x^2 + \alpha^2 - \varepsilon^2 \frac{z}{\varepsilon z - x}$$
$$-\frac{1}{\gamma_1^2}\frac{z}{x + y_1 + (z/\gamma_1)} = 0. \tag{150}$$

It turns out that Eq. (150) has real roots, corresponding to oscillatory motions, for all values of the parameters of physical interest.

We now consider the case of two beams of electrons. The first point which is to be observed is that the effect of adding another beam is to introduce a new pole as shown schematically in Fig. 12. As u_2 increases from its zero value, the additional root moves to the left in Fig. 12.

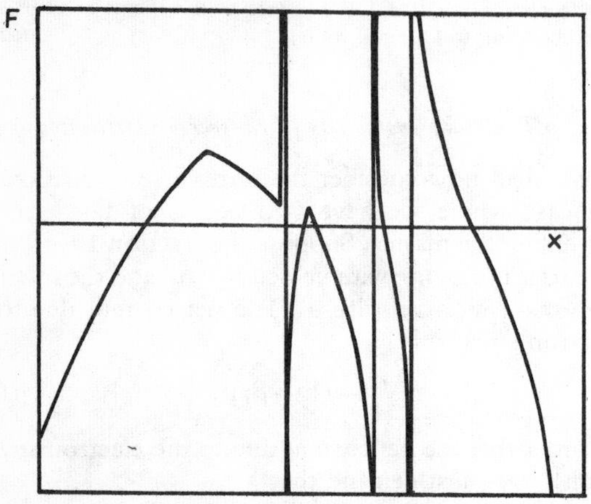

Fig. 12 A schematic plot of $F(x)$ given by Eq. (149) as a function of x. Note the additional branch of the curve introduced by the presence of interpenetrating beams of fast electrons. The curve $F(x)$ intersects the x-axis five times corresponding to all real roots.

When u_2 is so large that the gap introduced in the curve of Fig. 12 straddles the x-axis, two real roots are lost and a pair of complex conjugate roots are acquired. One of these must have a positive imaginary part and corresponds to instability. This is illustrated in Fig. 13.

When instability does occur it has a simple physical interpretation; namely, the condition that the gap straddles the x-axis is that

$$x - y_2 + (z/\gamma_2) \simeq 0. \tag{151}$$

This can be interpreted as saying that, in its rest frame, the electron beam sees the circularly polarized wave as having a frequency equal to the electron cyclotron frequency, and the in-phase rotating component of the electric field is resonant with the particle motion. Since instability occurs only when the gap straddles the x-axis, it is clear that for this to occur the new pole must lie between the electron and ion cyclotron frequencies, i.e., between $-z$ and εz.

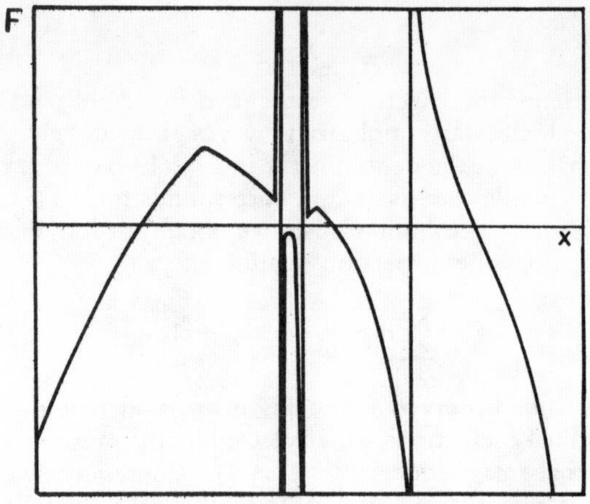

Fig. 13 A schematic plot of $F(x)$ given by Eq. (150) as a function of x for the case where the interpenetrating beams have velocities corresponding to unstable modes of oscillation. Observe that $F(x)$ now intersects the x-axis only three times, corresponding to three real roots and two complex roots.

5.11 *Oscillations much below the Ion Cyclotron Frequency*

We now consider the consequences on the hydromagnetic waves given by Eq. (78) of the introduction of beams of fast electrons such that the small gap straddles the real axis near the unperturbed root (denoted by subscript 1):

$$x_1 = -\alpha\left(1 + \frac{1}{\varepsilon z^2}\right)^{-1/2}. \tag{152}$$

Then for the case contemplated

$$F(x) = \varepsilon - x^2 + \alpha^2 - \varepsilon\left(1 - \frac{x}{\varepsilon z}\right)^{-1} + \frac{1}{\gamma_1}(1-\beta)$$
$$+\frac{1}{\gamma_2}\beta - (1-\beta)\frac{1}{\gamma_1}\left(1 + \frac{x + y_1}{z/\gamma_1}\right)^{-1}$$
$$-\frac{\beta}{\gamma_2^2}\frac{z}{x - y_2 + (z/\gamma_2)} = 0 \tag{153}$$

or

$$F(x) = -x^2 + \alpha^2 - \left(\frac{x}{z} + \frac{x^2}{\varepsilon z^2} + \ldots\right)$$
$$+(1-\beta)\frac{1}{\gamma_1}\left(\frac{x + y_1}{z/\gamma_1} + \ldots\right)$$
$$+\frac{\beta}{\gamma_2}\left[1 - \frac{z/\gamma_2}{x - y_2 + (z/\gamma_2)}\right] = 0, \tag{154}$$

$$= -x^2\left(1 + \frac{1}{\varepsilon z^2}\right) + \alpha^2 - \beta\frac{x - y_2}{z}$$
$$+\frac{\beta}{\gamma_2}\left[1 - \frac{z/\gamma_2}{x - y_2 + (z/\gamma_2)}\right] = 0, \tag{155}$$

where in writing Eq. (155) we have used the fact that

$$(1-\beta)y_1 = \beta y_2. \tag{156}$$

Making use of Eq. (152), we can write Eq. (155) as

$$F(x) = (x_1^2 - x^2)\left(1 + \frac{1}{\varepsilon z^2}\right) + \beta\left(\frac{1}{\gamma_2} - \frac{x}{z} + \frac{y_2}{z}\right)$$
$$-\frac{\beta z}{\gamma_2^2}\frac{1}{x - y_2 + (z/\gamma_2)} = 0. \tag{157}$$

For the case under consideration $x/\varepsilon z \ll 1$ and, further, since we are interested in the case when $x \sim x_1$, we may set

$$x_1^2 - x^2 \simeq -2x_1(x - x_1). \tag{158}$$

Eq. (157) then reduces to (assuming $x/z \ll 1$):

$$F(x) = -\left(1 + \frac{1}{\varepsilon z^2}\right) 2x_1(x - x_1) + \beta\left(\frac{1}{\gamma_2} + \frac{y_2}{z}\right) - \frac{\beta z}{\gamma_2^2[x - y_2 + (z/\gamma_2)]} = 0. \tag{159}$$

Letting

$$\left.\begin{aligned} p &= \left(1 + \frac{1}{\varepsilon z^2}\right) 2x_1, \\ q &= \beta\left(\frac{1}{\gamma_2} + \frac{y_2}{z}\right), \\ r &= -\frac{\beta z}{\gamma_2^2}, \end{aligned}\right| \tag{160}$$

Eq. (159) then leads to the following quadratic equation for x:

$$x^2 + x\left(-x_1 + \frac{z}{\gamma_2} - y_2 - \frac{q}{p}\right) + \left(x_1 + \frac{q}{p}\right)\left(y_2 - \frac{z}{\gamma_2}\right) - \frac{r}{p} = 0. \tag{161}$$

The roots of this equation are given by

$$x = +\frac{1}{2}\left(x_1 - \frac{z}{\gamma_2} + y_2 + \frac{q}{p}\right) \pm \frac{1}{2}\left[\left(x_1 + \frac{q}{p} - y_2 + \frac{z}{\gamma_2}\right)^2 + \frac{4r}{p}\right]^{1/2}. \tag{162}$$

Explicitly, we may write this as

$$\omega = +\frac{1}{2}\left[\omega_1 - \frac{\omega_e}{\gamma_2} + ku_2 + \beta\frac{[(1/\gamma_2) + (ku_2/\omega^\circ)]\,\omega^2_{pe}}{2|\omega_1|[1 + (4\pi NMc^2/B_0^2)]}\right] \pm \frac{1}{2}\left[\left\{\omega_1 + \frac{\omega_e}{\gamma_2} - ku_2 + \beta\frac{[(1/\gamma_2) + (ku_2/\omega_e)]\,\omega^2_{pe}}{2|\omega_1|[1 + (4\pi NMc^2/B_0^2)]}\right\}^2 - \frac{2\beta\omega_{pe}^2\omega_e/\gamma_2^2}{|\omega_1|[1 + (4\pi NMc^2/B_0^2)]}\right]^{1/2} \tag{163}$$

It is clear from this expression that the maximum instability rate occurs when the term in the braces vanishes; this is indeed the approximate criterion given in Eq. (151). The spread in velocity of the electron beam about that given in Eq. (151) for which there is instability is given by (cf. Eq. (163)):

$$k\Delta u_2 = \left[\frac{2\beta\omega_{pe}^2\omega_e/\gamma_2^2}{|\omega_1|[1 + (4\pi NMc^2/B_0^2)]}\right]^{1/2} \tag{164}$$

5.12 Oscillations near the Ion Cyclotron Frequency

Let us now consider the case when the physical parameters are such that in the absence of the beam the interesting root is given by Eq. (81) — namely, near the ion cyclotron frequency. For the case under consideration, $x \ll z$, and we shall assume that y_1 is of order x. Denoting the root in question by the subscript 2, we have (cf. Eq. (81))

$$x_2 = \varepsilon z\left(1 + \frac{\varepsilon}{\varepsilon^2 z^2 - \varepsilon - \alpha^2}\right). \tag{165}$$

Equation (149) can then be written in the form

$$F(x) = \varepsilon^2 z\left(\frac{1}{\varepsilon z - x_2} - \frac{1}{\varepsilon z - x}\right) + \frac{\beta}{\gamma_2} - \frac{\beta}{\gamma_2^2}\frac{z}{x - y_2 + (z/\gamma_2)} = 0, \tag{166}$$

$$\sim -\varepsilon^2 z\frac{x - x_2}{(\varepsilon z - x_2)^2} + \frac{\beta}{\gamma_2} - \frac{\beta}{\gamma_2^2}\frac{z}{x - y_2 + (z/\gamma_2)} = 0. \tag{167}$$

Setting

$$p_1 = \frac{\varepsilon^2 z}{(\varepsilon z - x_2)^2},\ q_1 = \frac{\beta}{\gamma_2},\ r_1 = \frac{\beta z}{\gamma_2^2}, \tag{168}$$

Eq. (167) leads to the quadratic

$$x^2 + x\left(-x_2 - y_2 + \frac{z}{\gamma_2} - \frac{q_1}{p_1}\right) + \left(y_2 - \frac{z}{\gamma_2}\right)\left(x_2 + \frac{q_1}{p_1}\right) + \frac{r_1}{p_1} = 0. \tag{169}$$

The roots of this equation are given by

$$x = +\frac{1}{2}\left(+x_2 + y_2 - \frac{z}{\gamma_2} + \frac{q_1}{p_1}\right) \pm \frac{1}{2}\left[\left(x_2 - y_2 + \frac{z}{\gamma_2} + \frac{q_1}{p_1}\right)^2 - \frac{4r_1}{p_1}\right]^{\frac{1}{2}}. \tag{170}$$

The maximum growth rate of instability occurs when

$$x_2 - y_2 + \frac{z}{\gamma_2} + \frac{q_1}{p_1} = 0, \tag{171}$$

which is again similar to the approximate criterion stated in Eq. (151). The spread in velocity about that given by Eq. (151) for which instability does occur is given by

$$k\Delta u_2 = \frac{4r_1}{p_1} = \frac{4\beta z(\varepsilon z - x_2)^2}{\gamma_2^2\,\varepsilon^2 z}. \tag{172}$$

The instabilities due to the presence of streams of electrons (or ions) may be responsible for microwave noise in the laboratory plasmas and the radio emission from astronomical objects.

6. Summary of Sections III 2 — III 5

We shall present here a summary of the dispersion relations for the various modes of oscillation of a plasma.

a) Static Plasma in the Absence of a Magnetic Field

(i) Longitudinal electron oscillations ($\omega^2 \gg k^2\Theta/m$)

$$\omega^2 = \omega_{pe}^2 + 3\frac{\Theta}{m}k^2 \tag{173}$$

(ii) Transverse electron oscillations ($\omega^2 \gg k^2\Theta/m$)

$$\omega^2 = \omega_{pe}^2 + c^2k^2 + k^2\frac{\Theta}{m}\frac{\omega_{pe}^2}{\omega_{pe}^2 + c^2k^2} \tag{174}$$

(iii) Longitudinal ion oscillations ($\Theta_i \ll \Theta_e$)

$$\omega^2 = \frac{1}{1 + (k\lambda_D)^{-2}}\omega_{pi}^2 + 3k^2\frac{\Theta_i}{M} \tag{175}$$

b) Static Plasma in a Magnetic Field, $\mathbf{k} \parallel \mathbf{B}_0$

(iv) High frequency oscillations $\omega \gg \omega_{e,i}$, $\omega_e^2 \ll \omega_{pe}^2 + c^2k^2$

$$\omega^2 = c^2 k^2 + \omega_{pe}{}^2 \left[1 - \frac{\omega_e}{(\omega_{pe}{}^2 + c^2 k^2)^{1/2}}\right] \quad (176)$$

(v) Oscillations near electron cyclotron frequency ($\omega_e{}^2 > \omega_{pe}^2 + c^2 k^2$)

$$\omega = -\omega_e \left[1 + \frac{\omega_{pe}{}^2}{\omega_e{}^2 - (c^2 k^2 + \omega_{pe}{}^2)}\right] \quad (177)$$

(vi) Oscillations much below the ion cyclotron frequency

$$\omega^2 = \frac{c^2 k^2}{1 + (c^2/A^2)} \quad (178)$$

(vii) Oscillations near the ion cyclotron frequency ($\omega_i{}^2 \gg \omega_{pi}{}^2 + c^2 k^2$)

$$\omega = \omega_i \left[1 + \frac{\omega_{pi}{}^2}{\omega_i{}^2 - (c^2 k^2 + \omega_{pi}{}^2)}\right] \quad (179)$$

c) Static Plasma in a Magnetic Field, $\mathbf{k} \perp \mathbf{B}$

(viii) Lower hybrid frequency ($\omega \ll ck$), $\omega_i < \omega < \omega_e < \omega_{pe}$

$$\omega = (\omega_e\, \omega_i)^{1/2} \quad (180)$$

(ix) Upper hybrid frequency, $\omega > \omega_i$, $\omega > \omega_{pi}$

$$\omega = (\omega_e{}^2 + \omega_{pe}{}^2)^{1/2} \quad (181)$$

d) Stream Instabilities

1. Longitudinal oscillations, in the presence of a stream of electrons with constant velocity **u**, are unstable to all perturbations (along **u**) having wavelengths greater than

$$\lambda_c = 2\pi \frac{u}{\omega_{pe}} \left[1 - \frac{3}{2}\left(\frac{m}{M}\right)^{-\frac{1}{3}}\right]. \quad (182)$$

Smallest *e*-folding time $= 18\, \omega_{pe}{}^{-1}$.
This instability is unaffected by the presence of a magnetic field along **u**.

2. Transverse oscillations, in the presence of two streams of relativistic electrons, are unstable near the Alfvén frequency and the ion cyclotron frequency, **k** and **u** being assumed to be along **B**.

7. Hydromagnetic Waves from Chew, Goldberger, and Low Theory

We have shown earlier that, for a low density plasma in a strong magnetic field, the kinetic equations for the plasma reduce to equations for a single fluid if we neglect the heat flow along the lines of force and/or assume the low temperature approximation. We shall now discuss the propagation of hydromagnetic waves using this formalism.

Consider, then, a spatially homogeneous plasma in static equilibrium in a uniform magnetic field, which we shall assume to be along the z-axis of a Cartesian system of co-ordinates, with the pressure tensor given by

$$\mathbf{P} = p_\perp \mathbf{I} + (p_\parallel - p_\perp)\, \mathbf{n}\,\mathbf{n}, \quad (183)$$

where **n** denotes a unit vector along the field lines. In the perturbed state, let the various quantities be denoted by

$$\mathbf{v}, \varrho + \delta\varrho, p_\perp + \delta p_\perp, p_\parallel + \delta p_\parallel, \mathbf{B} + \delta\mathbf{B}, \quad (184)$$

The equations governing the perturbed quantities are obtained by linearizing Eqs. (II-135)—(II-140). These are

$$\varrho \frac{\partial \mathbf{v}}{\partial t} = -\nabla \cdot \delta\mathbf{P} + \frac{1}{4\pi}(\nabla \times \delta\mathbf{B}) \times \mathbf{B}, \quad (185)$$

$$\frac{\partial}{\partial t}\delta\varrho = -\varrho\, \nabla \cdot \mathbf{v}, \quad (186)$$

$$\frac{\partial}{\partial t}\delta\mathbf{B} = \nabla \times (\mathbf{v} \times \mathbf{B}), \quad (187)$$

$$\delta p_\perp = p_\perp \frac{\delta B}{B} + p_\perp \frac{\delta\varrho}{\varrho}, \quad (188)$$

and

$$\delta p_\parallel = -2 p_\parallel \frac{\delta B}{B} + 3 p_\parallel \frac{\delta\varrho}{\varrho}, \quad (189)$$

where $\delta B = \mathbf{B} \cdot \delta\mathbf{B}/B$. Introducing the Lagrangian displacement $\boldsymbol{\xi}, \mathbf{v} = \partial\boldsymbol{\xi}/\partial t$, Eqs. (186) and (187) can be readily integrated to give

$$\delta\varrho = -\varrho \nabla \cdot \boldsymbol{\xi} \quad (190)$$

and

$$\delta\mathbf{B} = \nabla \times (\boldsymbol{\xi} \times \mathbf{B}), \quad (191)$$

where the constant of integration, by definition, has been set equal to zero. It follows readily from Eq. (191) that

$$\frac{\delta B}{B} = -\nabla_\perp \cdot \xi_\perp B, \quad (192)$$

where we use a subscript $\perp$ to denote the component of a quantity in the plane transverse to **B**. Thus

$$\nabla_\perp = \nabla - \mathbf{n}\mathbf{n} \cdot \nabla. \quad (193)$$

The component of a quantity along **B** will be denoted by the subscript $\|$. We shall assume that all the perturbed quantities behave like $\exp i(-\omega t + \mathbf{k} \cdot \mathbf{r})$. Using the foregoing results, Eqs. (188) and (189) reduce to

$$\delta p_\perp = -p_\perp (2\nabla_\perp \cdot \xi_\perp + i k_\parallel \xi_\parallel) \quad (194)$$

and

$$\delta p_\parallel = -p_\parallel (\nabla_\perp \cdot \xi_\perp + 3 i k_\parallel \xi_\parallel). \quad (195)$$

From the form of **P**, it follows that

$$\nabla \cdot \delta\mathbf{P} = \nabla_\perp \delta p_\perp + i(p_\parallel - p_\perp) k_\parallel \delta\mathbf{n} + \mathbf{n}[(p_\parallel - p_\perp)\nabla \cdot \delta\mathbf{n} + i k_\parallel \delta p_\parallel]. \quad (196)$$

The change $\delta\mathbf{n}$ in the unit vector along the lines of force is obtained readily from Eq. (191):

$$\delta\mathbf{n} = \mathbf{n} \cdot \nabla \xi_\perp + \cdot \quad (197)$$

Using the relation (197) into (196), we obtain

$$\nabla \cdot \delta\mathbf{P} = \nabla_\perp \delta p_\perp + (p_\perp - p_\parallel) k_\parallel{}^2 \xi_\perp + i k_\parallel [(p_\parallel - p_\perp)\nabla_\perp \cdot \xi_\perp + \delta p_\parallel]\, \mathbf{n}. \quad (198)$$

From Eq. (191) it follows readily that

$$(\nabla \times \delta\mathbf{B}) \times \mathbf{B} = B^2 (\nabla_\perp \nabla_\perp \cdot \xi_\perp - k_\parallel{}^2 \xi_\perp). \quad (199)$$

Using the foregoing results the equation of motion (185) splits up into the two equations

$$\left[\varrho\omega^2 + k^2\left(p_\parallel - p_\perp - \frac{B^2}{4\pi}\right)\right] \xi_\perp = \mathbf{k}_\perp \left[2(\mathbf{k}_\perp \cdot \xi_\perp)\left(p_\perp + \frac{B^2}{8\pi}\right) + k_\parallel p_\perp \xi\right], \quad (200)$$

and

$$(\varrho\omega^2 - 3p_{\parallel}k_{\parallel}^2)\,\xi = k_{\parallel}p_{\perp}(\mathbf{k}_{\perp}\cdot\xi_{\perp}). \tag{201}$$

On substituting for $\xi_{\parallel}$ in accordance with Eq. (201) into (200) and forming the scalar product with $\mathbf{k}_{\perp}$, we obtain the dispersion relation

$$\varrho\omega^2 + k_{\parallel}^2\left(p_{\parallel} - p_{\perp} - \frac{B^2}{4\pi}\right) - 2k_{\perp}^2\left(p_{\perp} + \frac{B^2}{8\pi}\right) = k_{\parallel}^2 p_{\perp}^2 \frac{k_{\perp}^2}{\varrho\omega^2 - 3p_{\parallel}k_{\parallel}^2} \tag{202}$$

If θ denotes the angle which the propagation vector makes with the z-axis,

$$k_{\parallel} = k\cos\theta, \qquad k_{\perp} = k\sin\theta. \tag{203}$$

After some simplifications, Eq. (202) reduces to the following quadratic equation for ω^2:

$$\omega^4 - \frac{\omega^2}{\varrho}k^2\left(\frac{B^2}{4\pi} + p_{\perp} + 2p_{\parallel}\cos^2\theta + p_{\perp}\sin^2\theta\right) + 3\frac{k^4}{\varrho^2}p_{\parallel}\cos^2\theta\left[\frac{B^2}{4\pi} + p_{\perp}(1+\sin^2\theta) - p_{\parallel}\cos^2\theta\right] - \frac{k^4}{\varrho^2}p_{\perp}^2\sin^2\theta\cos^2\theta = 0. \tag{204}$$

The roots of this equation are given by

$$\omega^2 = \frac{k^2}{2\varrho}\left(\frac{B^2}{4\pi} + p_{\perp} + 2p_{\parallel}\cos^2\theta + p_{\perp}\sin^2\theta\right) + \frac{k^2}{2\varrho}\left\{\left[\frac{B^2}{4\pi} + p_{\perp}(1+\sin^2\theta) - 4p_{\parallel}\cos^2\theta\right]^2 + 4p_{\perp}^2\sin^2\theta\cos^2\theta\right\}^{1/2} \tag{205}$$

For propagation along the lines of force, $\theta = 0$ and Eq. (205) leads to the following two modes of oscillation (distinguished by the subscripts 1 and 2):

$$\omega_1^2 = \frac{k^2}{\varrho}\left(\frac{B^2}{4\pi} + p_{\perp} - p_{\parallel}\right) \tag{206}$$

and

$$\omega_2^2 = \frac{3k^2}{\varrho}p_{\parallel}. \tag{207}$$

It is clear that the mode of oscillation corresponding to Eq. (206) is unstable if

$$p_{\parallel} > \frac{B^2}{4\pi} + p_{\perp}. \tag{208}$$

That is, if the distribution function for the ions and/or electrons is strongly peaked along the lines of force, the hydromagnetic waves propagating along the field lines are unstable.

For propagation transverse to the field lines, $\theta = \pi/2$ and we obtain

$$\omega^2 = \frac{2k^2}{\varrho}\left(\frac{B^2}{8\pi} + p_{\perp}\right). \tag{209}$$

The corresponding phase velocity of the wave is given by

$$v_p = \frac{\omega}{k} = \left(\frac{2P}{\varrho}\right)^{1/2}, \tag{210}$$

where $P = p_{\perp} + (B^2/8\pi)$ denotes the total transverse pressure.

For any arbitrary direction of propagation there exist unstable modes of oscillation for all θ's less than θ_c as determined by the equation

$$\frac{B^2}{4\pi} + p_{\perp}(1+\sin^2\theta_c) = \frac{p_{\perp}^2}{3p_{\parallel}}\sin^2\theta_c + p_{\parallel}\cos^2\theta_c. \tag{211}$$

As an example, if we take $p_{\perp} = B^2/8\pi$ and $p_{\parallel} = B^2/2\pi$, we find from Eq. (211) that $\theta_c = 26^0\,45'$.

It will be shown in part II of this survey that in the presence of a magnetic field, whenever the distribution function is anisotropic (i.e., $P_{\parallel} < P_{\perp}$ or $P_{\perp} < P_{\parallel}$), we have instabilities, although their e-folding times tend to be rather small.

8. Hydromagnetic Waves: General Theory

In our previous simplified discussion of hydromagnetic waves we neglected the effects of the finite temperature, viscosity, electrical conductivity, thermal conductivity, and other transport co-efficients of the plasma. These shall now be taken into account in order to exhibit the coupling of the hydromagnetic and sound waves, and to discuss the damping of these waves due to dissipative effects. However, for the sake of simplicity, we shall assume that the ion gyration frequency is much smaller than the effective collision frequency so that all the transport co-efficients may be taken to be isotropic. Eqs. (II-94)—(II-97) then form the basis of our discussion.

In the equilibrium state $\mathbf{U} = 0$ and $\mathbf{B} = B_0\hat{e}_z$, where B_0 is constant and p and ϱ are uniform. For small departures from the equilibrium state let the various quantities be denoted by

$$\mathbf{v},\ p + p_1,\ \ \varrho + \varrho_1,\ \text{ and } \mathbf{B}_0 + \mathbf{B}_1. \tag{212}$$

The equations governing the small departures are obtained by linearizing the equations of motion (II-94)—(II-97). These are:

$$\frac{\partial\varrho_1}{\partial t} + \varrho\nabla\cdot\mathbf{v} = 0, \tag{213}$$

$$\varrho\frac{\partial\mathbf{v}}{\partial t} = -\nabla p_1 + \frac{1}{4\pi}(\nabla\times\mathbf{B}_1)\times\mathbf{B}_0 + \mu\nabla^2\mathbf{v} + \frac{1}{3}\mu\nabla\nabla\cdot\mathbf{v}, \tag{214}$$

$$\frac{\partial\mathbf{B}_1}{\partial t} = \nabla\times(\mathbf{v}\times\mathbf{B}_0) + \frac{c^2}{4\pi\sigma_1}\nabla^2\mathbf{B}_1, \tag{215}$$

and

$$\frac{\partial p_1}{\partial t} = s^2\frac{\partial\varrho_1}{\partial t} + \frac{2}{3}\nabla\cdot(\lambda_1\nabla\Theta_1 + \nu_1\mathbf{D}_1), \tag{216}$$

where $s = (\gamma p/\varrho)^{1/2}$ denotes the sound speed and $\mathbf{D}_1$ is obtained from the linearized form of Eq. (II-89). Thus

$$\mathbf{D}_1 = \frac{1}{\sigma_1}\left(\frac{c}{4\pi}\nabla\times\mathbf{B}_1 - \varkappa\nabla\Theta_1\right). \tag{217}$$

The temperature and the pressure are connected by the relation $\Theta = Mp/\varrho$; the linearized form of this gives

$$\Theta_1 = \frac{M}{\varrho}\left(p_1 - p\frac{\varrho_1}{\varrho}\right). \tag{218}$$

Introducing $\boldsymbol{\xi}$, the Lagrangian displacement of an element of the fluid, and assuming that all quantities behave like exp $i(-\omega t + \mathbf{k}\cdot\mathbf{r})$, after some straightforward reductions Eqs. (213), (215), and (216) lead to

$$\varrho_1 = -\varrho \nabla \cdot \boldsymbol{\xi}, \tag{219}$$

$$\mathbf{B}_1 = \alpha \nabla \times (\boldsymbol{\xi} \times \mathbf{B}_0), \tag{220}$$

and

$$p_1 = \varphi s^2 \varrho_1, \tag{221}$$

where

$$\frac{1}{\alpha} = 1 + \frac{i k^2 c^2}{4\pi \sigma_1 \omega} \tag{222}$$

and

$$\varphi = \frac{1 + \frac{2}{3} i [\lambda_1 - (\nu_1 \varkappa_1/\sigma_1)][k^2 M/(\gamma\, \omega \varrho)]}{1 + \frac{2}{3} i [\lambda_1 - (\nu_1 \varkappa_1/\sigma_1)][k^2 M/(\varrho\, \omega)]}. \tag{223}$$

It must be emphasized here that in writing the foregoing expressions we have assumed the various transport co-efficients to be isotropic. However, this may not be true, in general, for oscillating electromagnetic fields.

Using the foregoing results in the equation of motion (214), we obtain

$$\left(\omega^2 + i\omega \frac{\mu}{\varrho} k^2\right) \boldsymbol{\xi} = \left(s^2 \varphi - \frac{1}{3} i \omega \frac{\mu}{\varrho}\right) \mathbf{k}\mathbf{k}\cdot\boldsymbol{\xi} + \alpha A^2 \{\mathbf{k} \times [\mathbf{k} \times (\boldsymbol{\xi} \times \mathbf{n})]\} \times \mathbf{n}, \tag{224}$$

where $\mathbf{n}$ is a unit vector along $\mathbf{B}_0$ and A is the usual Alfvén speed. Assuming that $\mathbf{k}$ lies in the (xz) plane making an angle θ with the z-axis, Eq. (224) leads to the following equations for the different components of $\boldsymbol{\xi}$:

$$\left(\omega^2 - \alpha A^2 k^2 \cos^2\theta + \frac{i\mu}{\varrho} k^2 \omega\right) \xi_y = 0, \tag{225}$$

$$\left[\omega^2 - \alpha A^2 k^2 + i \frac{\mu}{\varrho} k^2 \omega - \left(s^2 \varphi - \frac{i\mu}{3\varrho}\omega\right) k^2 \sin^2\theta\right] \xi_x - \left(\varphi s^2 - i \frac{\omega \mu}{3 \varrho}\right) k^2 \sin\theta \cos\theta\, \xi_z = 0, \tag{226}$$

and

$$-\left(\varphi s^2 - \frac{i\omega\mu}{3\varrho}\right) k^2 \sin\theta\cos\theta\, \xi_x + \left[\omega^2 + \frac{i\mu}{\varrho}\omega k^2 - \left(\varphi s^2 - \frac{i\mu}{3\varrho}\omega\right) k^2 \cos^2\theta\right] \xi_z = 0. \tag{227}$$

8.1 Absence of dissipation

Let us first consider the limiting case of an ideal hydromagnetic fluid for which all the transport co-efficients vanish. In this limiting situation $\alpha = 1$, $\varphi = 1$, and $\mu = 0$. Eq. (225) then leads to

$$\omega = \pm A k \cos\theta; \tag{228}$$

these modes of oscillation remain unaffected by the finite plasma pressure. For Eqs. (226) and (227) to have a non-trivial solution, we must have (setting $\alpha = 1$, $\varphi = 1$, $\mu = 0$):

$$\begin{vmatrix} \omega^2 - A^2 k^2 - s^2 k^2 \sin^2\theta & -s^2 k^2 \sin\theta\cos\theta \\ -s^2 k^2 \sin\theta\cos\theta & \omega^2 - s^2 k^2 \cos^2\theta \end{vmatrix} = 0. \tag{229}$$

This leads to the following quadratic for ω^2:

$$\omega^4 - \omega^2 (A^2 + s^2) k^2 + A^2 s^2 k^4 \cos^2\theta = 0. \tag{230}$$

The roots of this equation are given by

$$\omega^2 = \frac{1}{2}\left\{(A^2 + s^2) k^2 \pm k^2 (A^2 + s^2)\left(1 - \frac{4 s^2 A^2 \cos^2\theta}{(s^2 + A^2)^2}\right)^{1/2}\right\}. \tag{231}$$

In the case of a strong magnetic field, $s/A \ll 1$, and Eq. (231) leads to the following roots (distinguished by the subscripts 1 and 2):

$$\omega_1^2 = k^2 (A^2 + s^2 \sin^2\theta) \tag{232}$$

and

$$\omega_2^2 = k^2 s^2 \cos^2\theta. \tag{233}$$

In the case of a weak magnetic field, $A/s \ll 1$, and Eq. (231) leads to

$$\omega_1^2 = k^2 (s^2 + A^2 \sin^2\theta) \tag{234}$$

and

$$\omega_2^2 = k^2 A^2 \cos^2\theta. \tag{235}$$

The principal result which stems from including the finite plasma pressure is that the hydromagnetic waves remain unaffected only if the motion of the material (i.e., $\boldsymbol{\xi}$) is normal to the plane containing the magnetic field and the propagation vector; otherwise the disturbance breaks up into coupled hydromagnetic waves and sound waves. The chief application of this result is to waves originating in the surface layers of a sunspot where A may be comparable to s. These remarks may be of some significance also in laboratory plasma diagnostics.

That the ω^2 are real in the case of ideal hydromagnetics also follows from the self adjointness of the equations of motion which may, in general, be written in the form

$$-\omega^2 \varrho\, \boldsymbol{\xi} = \mathbf{F}(\boldsymbol{\xi}), \tag{236}$$

where $\mathbf{F}$ is a linear operator acting on $\boldsymbol{\xi}$. The self adjointness of $\mathbf{F}$ immediately leads to the conclusion that ω^2 is real. Consequently, the criterion for stability is that there be no negative characteristic value ω^2. Also, it can be shown easily that a necessary and sufficient condition for this circumstance is that the potential energy

$$\frac{1}{2}\int d^3\mathbf{x}\, \boldsymbol{\xi}\cdot\mathbf{F}(\boldsymbol{\xi}) \tag{236a}$$

always be positive. This latter condition is a statement of the energy principle governing the stability of ideal hydromagnetic system. This criterion, while derived on the assumption of collision-dominated plasma, can be demonstrated to give a lower bound on stability as compared with the conclusions of the theories based on the collisionless Boltzmann equation in the limit of a strong magnetic field.

8.2 Effects of dissipation

We now consider the effects of dissipation on the various modes of oscillation discussed in the preceding section. Eq. (225) gives

$$\omega^2 = A^2 k^2 \cos^2\theta \left(1 + i\frac{c^2 k^2}{4\pi\sigma_1\omega}\right)^{-1} - \frac{i\mu}{\varrho} k^2 \omega. \qquad (237)$$

If $c^2k^2/4\pi\sigma_1\omega$ and $\mu\omega/\varrho A^2$ are both much less than unity, to the lowest significant order Eq. (237) yields

$$\omega = Ak\cos\theta - \frac{1}{2} i k^2 \left(\frac{c^2}{4\pi\sigma_1} + \frac{\mu}{\varrho}\right). \qquad (238)$$

We now consider Eqs. (226) and (227). In order that these admit a non-trivial solution, Eq. (239) see bottom of this page.

On the assumption that $c^2k^2/4\pi\sigma_1\omega$, $\mu k^2/\varrho\omega$, and $[\lambda_1 - (\nu_1\varkappa_1/\sigma_1)]\,[k^2M/\omega\varrho]$ are all much less than unity, we obtain in the strong field case ($s/A \ll 1$):

$$\omega_1^2 = k^2 A^2 \left\{1 + \frac{s^2}{A^2}\sin^2\theta - \frac{ik}{A}\left[\frac{c^2}{4\pi\sigma_1} + \frac{\mu}{\varrho}(1+\sin^2\theta) + \frac{2}{3}\frac{s^2}{A^2}\left(\lambda_1 - \frac{\nu_1\varkappa_1}{\sigma_1}\right)\frac{M}{\varrho}\frac{\gamma-1}{\gamma}\right]\right\} \qquad (240)$$

and

$$\omega_2^2 = k^2 \left\{s^2\cos^2\theta - ikA\left[\frac{\mu}{\varrho}(1+\cos^2\theta) + \frac{2}{3}\frac{s^2}{A^2}\left(\lambda_1 - \frac{\nu_1\varkappa_1}{\sigma_1}\right)\frac{M}{\varrho}\frac{\gamma-1}{\gamma}\right]\right\}. \qquad (241)$$

Under the same approximations for the weak field case we obtain

$$\omega_1^2 = k^2 s^2 \left\{1 + \frac{A^2}{s^2}\sin^2\theta - \frac{ik}{s}\left[\frac{4}{3}\frac{\mu}{\varrho} + \frac{2}{3}\frac{s^2}{A^2}\left(\lambda_1 - \nu_1\frac{\varkappa_1}{\sigma_1}\right)\frac{M}{\varrho}\frac{\gamma-1}{\gamma}\right]\right\} \qquad (242)$$

and

$$\omega_2^2 = k^2\left(A^2\cos^2\theta + \frac{i\mu}{\varrho} sk\right). \qquad (243)$$

It is clear from Eqs. (240) and (241) that the damping of the hydromagnetic waves is

$$\exp\left\{-\frac{k^2}{2}\left[\frac{c^2}{4\pi\sigma_1} + \frac{\mu}{\varrho} + \frac{2}{3}\frac{s^2}{A^2}\left(\lambda_1 - \frac{\nu_1\varkappa_1}{\sigma_1}\right)\frac{M}{\varrho}\frac{\gamma-1}{\gamma}\right]\right\}. \qquad (244)$$

Since $s/A \ll 1$, we may write this approximately as

$$\exp\left[-\frac{1}{2}k^2\left(\frac{c^2}{4\pi\sigma_1} + \frac{\mu}{\varrho}\right)\right]. \qquad (245)$$

This suggests that only the resistivity and the viscosity of the medium are significant for the dissipation of hydromagnetic waves. In order that these waves be realized in any physical situation, it is essential that the time required for their amplitudes to be reduced by a factor of e^{-1} of their initial amplitudes be much larger than one period of oscillation of the wave. Thus we must have

$$\frac{2}{k^2}\left(\frac{c^2}{4\pi\sigma_1} + \frac{\mu}{\varrho}\right)^{-1} > \frac{1}{kA}. \qquad (246)$$

Since $k = 2\pi/\lambda$, this relation implies that the wavelength of the disturbance must be greater than the critical wavelength λ_c given by

$$\lambda_c = \frac{\pi}{A}\left(\frac{c^2}{4\pi\sigma_1} + \frac{\mu}{\varrho}\right). \qquad (247)$$

IV. Oscillations of Bounded and Non-Uniform Plasmas

1. Oscillations of a Cylindrical Plasma

We shall now investigate the oscillations of a cylindrical plasma immersed in a uniform external magnetic field which will be assumed to be along the z-axis. In the equilibrium state the plasma is at rest and the electron charge density is neutralized by the ion charge density. We shall assume that the plasma is so dilute that direct interparticle collisions are negligible and that particles interact through long range electromagnetic interactions only. For the sake of simplicity we may, therefore, neglect the plasma pressure. For small departures from the state of static equilibrium the equations of motion for the electrons and ions, assumed singly charged, are

$$m\frac{\partial \mathbf{v}_e}{\partial t} = -e\left(\mathbf{E} + \frac{1}{c}\mathbf{v}_e \times \mathbf{B}_0\right) \qquad (1)$$

$$M\frac{\partial \mathbf{v}_i}{\partial t} = e\left(\mathbf{E} + \frac{1}{c}\mathbf{v}_i \times \mathbf{B}_0\right), \qquad (2)$$

together with Maxwell equations

$$\nabla \times \mathbf{B} = \frac{4\pi}{c}\mathbf{J} \quad \text{and} \quad \nabla \times \mathbf{E} = -\frac{1}{c}\frac{\partial \mathbf{B}}{\partial t}, \qquad (3)$$

where

$$\mathbf{J} = eN(\mathbf{v}_i - \mathbf{v}_e). \qquad (4)$$

We have neglected the displacement current as we are interested only in low frequency oscillations satisfying the condition $\omega \ll ck$. From the definitions of the mass density and the mean mass velocity, we obtain

$$\frac{1}{Ne^2}\frac{\partial \mathbf{J}}{\partial t} = \left(\frac{1}{M} + \frac{1}{m}\right)\mathbf{E} + \frac{1}{c}\left(\frac{1}{M}\mathbf{v}_i + \frac{1}{m}\mathbf{v}_e\right) \times \mathbf{B}_0 \simeq \frac{1}{m}\left(\mathbf{E} + \frac{1}{c}\mathbf{v}_e \times \mathbf{B}_0\right), \qquad (5)$$

and

$$\varrho\frac{\partial \mathbf{v}}{\partial t} = \frac{1}{c}\mathbf{J} \times \mathbf{B}_0, \qquad (6)$$

neglecting terms of order m/M. We now need a relation connecting $\mathbf{v}_e$, $\mathbf{v}$, and $\mathbf{J}$. From the definitions of $\mathbf{J}$ and $\mathbf{v}$ we readily obtain

$$\mathbf{v}_e \simeq \mathbf{v} - \frac{1}{Ne}\mathbf{J}. \qquad (7)$$

From Eqs. (5) and (7) we get

$$4\pi\omega_{pe}^{-2}\frac{\partial \mathbf{J}}{\partial t} = \mathbf{E} + \frac{1}{c}\mathbf{v} \times \mathbf{B}_0 - \frac{1}{cNe}\mathbf{J} \times \mathbf{B}_0. \qquad (8)$$

$$\begin{vmatrix} \omega^2 - \alpha A^2 k^2 + i\frac{\mu}{\varrho}k^2\omega - \left(\varphi s^2 - \frac{i}{3}\frac{\mu}{\varrho}\omega\right)k^2\sin^2\theta & -\left(\varphi s^2 - \frac{i\omega\mu}{3\varrho}\right)k^2\sin\theta\cos\theta \\ -\left(\varphi s^2 - \frac{i}{3}\omega\frac{\mu}{\varrho}\right)k^2\sin\theta\cos\theta & \omega^2 + \frac{i\mu}{\varrho}k^2\omega - \left(\varphi s^2 - \frac{i}{3}\frac{\mu}{\varrho}\omega\right)k^2\cos^2\theta \end{vmatrix} = 0. \qquad (239)$$

As we are interested in frequencies of oscillation much below the electron cyclotron frequency, we may drop the term on the left hand side of Eq. (8) and obtain for Ohm's law:

$$\mathbf{E} + \frac{1}{c}\mathbf{v} \times \mathbf{B}_0 - \frac{1}{cNe}\mathbf{J} \times \mathbf{B}_0 = 0. \quad (9)$$

From Eqs. (3) and (9) we then obtain

$$\frac{\partial \mathbf{B}}{\partial t} = \nabla \times \left(\mathbf{v} \times \mathbf{B}_0 - \frac{1}{Ne}\mathbf{J} \times \mathbf{B}_0\right). \quad (10)$$

Equations (6) and (10) form the basis of the characteristic value problem which must be solved subject to appropriate boundary conditions. We now assume that the t, θ, and z dependence of all quantities has the form $\exp i(-\omega t + m\theta + kz)$. Equations (6) and (10) then lead to

$$-\frac{\omega^2}{A^2}\mathbf{B} = \nabla \times \left\{[(\nabla \times \mathbf{B}) \times \mathbf{n}] \times \mathbf{n} + i\frac{\omega}{\omega_i}(\nabla \times \mathbf{B}) \times \mathbf{n}\right\} \quad (11)$$

where A denotes the Alfvén velocity and $\mathbf{n}$ is a unit vector along $\mathbf{B}_0$. On carrying out the normal mode analysis, we obtain the following equations for the various components of $\mathbf{B}$:

$$B_r = -\Lambda i k\left[-\frac{m}{r}\Omega\frac{\omega^2}{A^2}B_z + \left(k^2 - \frac{\omega^2}{A^2} - k^2\Omega^2\right)\frac{dB_z}{dr}\right], \quad (12)$$

$$B_\theta = \Lambda\left[\frac{mk}{r}\left(k^2 - \frac{\omega^2}{A^2} - \Omega^2 k^2\right)B_z - k\Omega\frac{\omega^2}{A^2}\frac{dB_z}{dr}\right], \quad (13)$$

and

$$\frac{1}{r}\frac{d}{dr}r\frac{dB_z}{dr} + \left(\chi^2 - \frac{m^2}{r^2}\right)B_z = 0, \quad (14)$$

where

$$\frac{1}{\Lambda} = \left(k^2 - \frac{\omega^2}{A^2}\right)^2 - k^4\Omega^2, \quad (15)$$

$$\chi^2 = -\frac{1}{\Lambda}\frac{1}{k^2 - (\omega^2/A^2) \cdot k^2\Omega^2}, \quad (16)$$

and $\Omega = \omega/\omega_i$. The solution of Eq. (14) which is regular on the axis of the cylinder is given by

$$B_z = B_1 J_m(\chi r), \quad (17)$$

where B_1 is an arbitrary multiplicative constant. Having determined B_z, B_r, and B_θ are readily obtained from Eqs. (12) and (13). This determines the perturbation in the magnetic field inside the plasma.

1.1 The Perturbation in the Vacuum Field

The vacuum magnetic field satisfies the equations

$$\mathbf{B} = \nabla\psi \quad \text{and} \quad \nabla^2\psi = 0. \quad (18)$$

The solution of Eq. (18) which is bounded at infinity is given by

$$\psi = B_2 K_m(kr), \quad (19)$$

where B_2 is another constant, $K_m(x)$ is the Bessel function of purely imaginary argument (the notation is that of Watson), and we have suppressed the factor $\exp i(m\theta + kz)$.

1.2 The Boundary Conditions

The boundary conditions which must be satisfied at the perturbed boundary of the plasma are

$$\Delta(\mathbf{B} \cdot \mathbf{n}) = 0, \quad (20)$$

and

$$\Delta\left(\frac{\mathbf{B}^2}{8\pi}\right) = 0, \quad (21)$$

where $\Delta(X)$ denotes the jump experienced by the quantity X at the interface. The linearized forms of these equations are

$$B_r^p = B_r^v \quad (r = R) \quad (22)$$

and

$$B_z^p = B_z^v \quad (r = R), \quad (23)$$

where have now used the superscripts p and v to indicate the quantities referring to the plasma and vacuum respectively. Using these boundary conditions, and after some straightforward reductions, we obtain the dispersion relation

$$k^2\Lambda\left[-m\Omega\frac{\omega^2}{A^2} + \left(k^2 - \frac{\omega^2}{A^2} - \Omega^2 k^2\right)\chi R\frac{J'_m(\chi R)}{J_m(\chi R)}\right] = \frac{kRK'_m(kR)}{K_m(kR)}, \quad (24)$$

For a specified k, A, and, Ω Eqs. (15) and (16) can be solved to give ω in terms of χ. When the ω thus obtained is substituted into Eq. (24), it admits an infinite number of discrete roots for χ for prescribed values of k, A, and Ω; denote these roots by χ_n. The dispersion relation then takes the form

$$\frac{\omega^2}{\omega_i^2} = \left(1 - \frac{\omega^2}{k^2A^2}\right)\left(1 - \frac{\omega^2}{A^2}\frac{1}{k^2 + \chi_n^2}\right). \quad (25)$$

1.21 Low frequency oscillations

Consider first the case when $\omega/\omega_i \ll 1$. Then Eq. (25) yields the roots

$$\omega^2 = k^2A^2 \quad (26)$$

and

$$\omega^2 = A^2(k^2 + \chi_n^2), \quad (27)$$

which correspond to the ordinary and the extra-ordinary hydromagnetic waves.

1. 22 Oscillations near the ion cyclotron frequency

We now consider the case when $\omega/kA \ll 1$. Eq. (25) then yields

$$\omega^2 = \omega_i^2\left[1 - \frac{\omega_i^2}{k^2A^2} - \frac{\omega_i^2}{A^2(k^2 + \chi_n^2)}\right]. \quad (28)$$

These oscillations are referred to as *ion cyclotron oscillations.*

In ion cyclotron oscillations the ion velocities are circularly polarized and the sense of rotation is the same as that for a free ion moving in a magnetic field. The electric field is elliptically polarized. One may decompose this electric field into two circularly polarized components, one of which will have the same sense of rotation as the ion motion in the wave. However, the ion velocity is 90^0 out of phase with that component of the electric

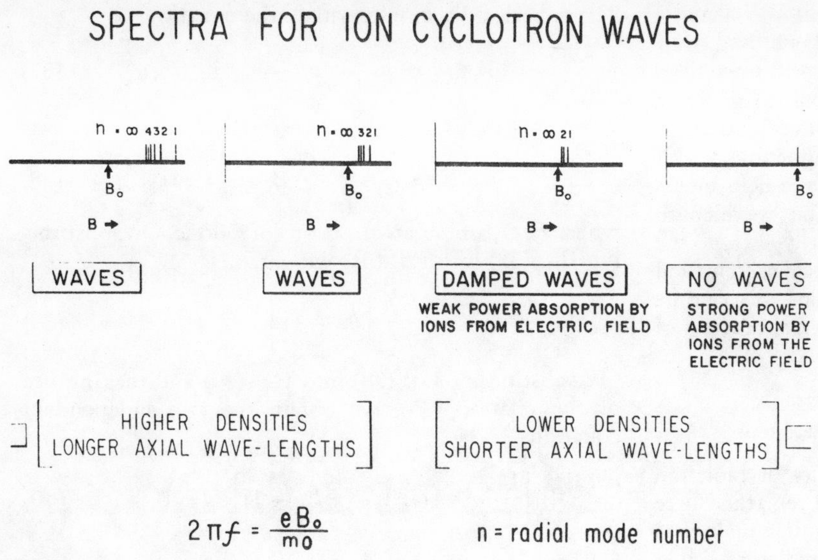

Fig. 14

field which rotates in the same sense as the ion. Consequently, there is no absorption of energy by the ions from the waves.

However, in the foregoing discussion we have not taken into account the thermal motion of the ions, and/or we have neglected also the collisions (short range) between the ions and electrons or the like particles. In either case damping of the ion cyclotron waves will result; in the former case we have Landau damping and in the latter case we have the usual collisional damping. When damping occurs there appears a component of the elliptically polarized electric field which is in phase with the ion motions. This leads to absorption of energy by the ions from the electric field of the wave. Consequently, this phenomenon is of fundamental interest in connection with the heating of the plasma.

In the experimental situation one has the plasma in a magnetic field and one superposes on this a transverse electric field which oscillates at the ion cyclotron frequency. As the ion motion is in phase with the electric field, energy is fed into ion motion, and the ions will move in a spiral of increasing radius.

At higher densities, say 10^{13} ions/cm^3, this single particle picture is no longer valid. Ion currents induce an electric field which has a decelerating effect on the ions, and heating a moderately dense plasma at the ion cyclotron frequency becomes rather inefficient. However, if we keep the frequency of the oscillating electric field fixed, but go to slightly stronger magnetic field, we find the existence of natural oscillations of the plasma. These natural oscillations, which we call "*ion cyclotron waves,*" are, in fact, the short-wave, low-density limit for the extra-ordinary hydromagnetic waves described by Alfvén and Aström.

Fig. 14 shows the spectra for ion cyclotron waves. The resonances are indicated as lines and are plotted against magnetic field strength. We first look at the picture denoted by "no waves." Here we have low densities and, as a consequence, single particle accelerations of the ions in the electric field. The ions move in growing spiral orbits and there is strong power absorption by the ions from the electric field. There are no waves at this very low density limit.

For moderately high densities (Fig. 14) there are ion cyclotron waves. The different vertical lines indicate the different modes of oscillation, and for the high density condition all of these modes occur at magnetic fields considerably stronger than the cyclotron field B_0. Once the ion cyclotron wave has been set up, the ions do not absorb energy from the electric fields. Therefore, there is no damping of the wave.

The second picture in Fig. 14 shows the spectrum for ion cyclotron waves for somewhat lower densities. The various modes now occur at magnetic field values which are somewhat closer to B_0. There is still no damping of the waves. In the third picture the density is quite low and the modes now occur at magnet ic fields very close to B_0. This is an intermediate case between the ion cyclotron wave resonance and the single particle resonance. For this condition we have waves, but the ions begin to move in growing spiral orbits and pick up energy from the electric field. In this case we have ion cyclotron waves which are slightly damped.

The transition from the undamped waves to the slightly damped waves is particularly interesting because it provides a method for thermalizing ion cyclotron waves, that is, for transforming the wave energy quickly into heat. It turns out that it is equally valid to talk of wavelengths instead of densities, and it is the short wavelengths which are damped. To illustrate a plasma heating scheme, we make an analogy to ocean waves running up on a beach. A cross section of an ocean beach is shown in Fig. 15. The waves are moving in toward the shore and, because the water is getting more and more shallow, the wave length of the ocean waves

A MAGNETIC BEACH
FOR THE THERMALIZATION OF ION CYCLOTRON WAVES

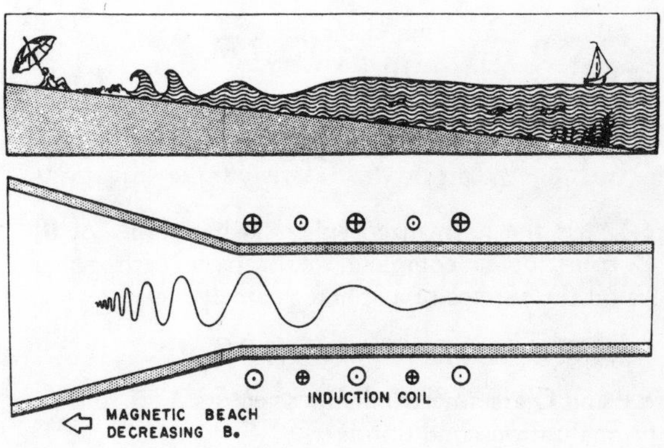

Fig. 15

becomes shorter and shorter. Finally, in the shallow water the waves are unable to propagate and they "break;" the wave energy is transformed into heat. Similarly, one might use an induction coil to generate rather long wavelength ion cyclotron waves and allow these waves to propagate along the magnetic lines of force through a region where the magnetic field tapers off and becomes somewhat weaker. The wavelength becomes shorter and shorter and, finally, when the wavelength is sufficiently short the waves damp out and the wave energy goes into heating the ions. It woud be in this "magnetic beach" region that the real heating of the gas would take place.

2. Radiation by Plasma Oscillation

We now wish to exhibit the possibility of radiation by plasma oscillations. Firstly, it may be remarked here that this problem is mathematically quite analogous to the scattering of electromagnetic radiation by a dielectric. Consider, then, a simple equilibrium configuration in which the ions are held fixed with a uniform density N and the electrons, whose thermal motions will be neglected, are distributed likewise inside a sphere of radius R. From the linearized equation of motion

$$m\frac{\partial^2 \xi}{\partial t^2} = -e\mathbf{E} \tag{29}$$

and the linearized Maxwell equations, we readily obtain

$$c^2 \nabla \times \nabla \times \mathbf{E} = (\omega^2 - \omega_p^2)\,\mathbf{E}, \tag{30}$$

where we have assumed the time dependence to be of the form exp $(-i\omega t)$, and ω_p denotes the electron plasma frequency. From Eq. (30) it follows that

$$\nabla \cdot \left[(\omega^2 - \omega_p^2)\,\mathbf{E}\right] = 0. \tag{30a}$$

Inside the sphere ω_p is constant; consequently, if $\omega^2 \neq \omega_p^2$ Eq. (30a) leads to

$$\nabla \cdot \mathbf{E} = 0 \tag{31}$$

for both inside and outside the plasma.

Because of the symmetry of the problem, it is convenient to seek a solution of Eq. (30) in terms of vector spherical harmonics:

$$\mathbf{A} = \hat{e}_r Y_l^m(\theta, \varphi,), \tag{32}$$

$$\mathbf{B} = \frac{r}{[l(l+1)]^{1/2}} \nabla Y_l^m(\theta, \varphi), \tag{33}$$

and

$$\mathbf{C} = \frac{1}{[l(l+1)]^{1/2}} \nabla \times \left[\mathbf{r}\, Y_l^m(\theta, \varphi)\right], \tag{34}$$

where $Y^m{}_l$ is the normalized spherical harmonic. **A**, **B**, and **C** constitute a complete set of basic orthogonal vectors on the surface of a sphere; namely,

$$\iint \mathbf{P}(l, m; \theta, \varphi) \cdot \mathbf{Q}(l, m; \theta, \varphi)\, d\Omega = 0, \tag{35}$$

where **P** and **Q** are any two distinct vectors **A**, **B**, and **C**. The normalization condition is

$$\iint \mathbf{P}(l_1, m_1; \theta, \varphi) \cdot \mathbf{P}(l_2 m_2; \theta, \varphi)\, d\Omega = \delta_{l_1 l_2} \delta_{m_1 m_2}. \tag{36}$$

The spherical harmonics satisfy the equation

$$\nabla^2 Y_l^m(\theta, \varphi) = -\frac{1}{r^2} l(l+1)\, Y_l^m(\theta, \varphi). \tag{37}$$

We now write

$$\mathbf{E} = \frac{F}{r^2}\mathbf{A} + \frac{G}{r}\mathbf{B} + \frac{H}{r}\mathbf{C}, \tag{38}$$

where F, G, and H are functions of r alone. On substituting Eq. (38) into Eq. (31) we obtain

$$\frac{dF}{dr} = \left[l(l+1)\right]^{1/2} G. \tag{39}$$

On substituting Eq. (38) into Eq. (30) and making use of the relation (35), we obtain the two independent equations

$$\frac{d^2 H}{dr^2} + \left[\frac{1}{c^2}(\omega^2 - \omega_p^2) - \frac{1}{r^2} l(l+1)\right] H = 0 \tag{40}$$

and

$$\frac{dG}{dr} + \frac{1}{[l(l+1)]^{1/2}} \left[\frac{1}{c^2}(\omega^2 - \omega_p^2) - \frac{1}{r^2} l(l+1)\right] F = 0. \tag{41}$$

The problem, then, is to solve Eqs. (39)—(41) subject to appropriate boundary conditions.

2.1 *The boundary conditions*

From Eq. (30a) it follows upon integration across the interface that we must have

$$(\omega^2 - \omega_p^2)\, \mathbf{E}_1 \cdot \mathbf{n} = \omega^2\, \mathbf{E}_2 \cdot \mathbf{n}, \tag{42}$$

where the subscripts 1 and 2 refer to the plasma and vacuum sides respectively and **n** denotes the unit outward normal to the surface. Since only **A** has a radial component, it follows from Eq. (42) that

$$(\omega^2 - \omega_p^2)\, F_1 = \omega^2 F_2 \quad \text{at } r = R. \tag{43}$$

It follows from $c\nabla \times \mathbf{E} = -\partial \mathbf{B}/\partial t$ that the tangential components of **E** are continuous at the interface. This requires that

$$G_1 = G_2 \quad \text{at } r = R, \tag{44}$$

and

$$H_1 = H_2 \quad \text{at } r = R. \tag{45}$$

Integrating Eq. (40) across the interface, we get

$$\frac{dH_1}{dr} = \frac{dH_2}{dr} \quad \text{at } r = R. \tag{46}$$

The conditions (45) and (46) may be combined to read

$$\frac{d}{dr} \ln H_1 = \frac{d}{dr} \ln H_2. \tag{47}$$

2.2 *Solution of the problem*

The solution of Eq. (40), which is regular at the center of the sphere, is given by

$$H = H_i r^{(1/2)} J_{l+1/2}(k_1 r), \tag{48}$$

where

$$k_1^2 = \frac{1}{c^2}(\omega^2 - \omega_p^2) \tag{49}$$

and H_i is an arbitrary multiplicative constant. It can be seen readily from Eqs. (39) and (41) that F satisfies the same equation as H; consequently, a similar solution holds for F. G is then determined by Eq. (39).

2.3 The case of a perfectly conducting boundary

An interesting situation which may approximate cavity resonators is the one where the plasma is enclosed by perfectly reflecting walls. The boundary conditions to be imposed in this case are that E_θ and E_φ vanish at $r = R$. This requires that

$$J_{l+1/2}(k_1 R) = 0. \tag{50}$$

Let the roots of Eq. (50) be denoted by $j_{l,m}$. From Eqs. (49) and (50) we than obtain the dispersion relation

$$\omega^2 = \omega_p^2 + \frac{c^2}{R^2} j^2_{l,m}. \tag{51}$$

It may be remarked here that as $R \to \infty$, $\omega \to \omega_p$, the natural plasma frequency.

2.4 The case of free boundary

In the case of a free boundary, the inside solution must be matched to the one outside with due regard to the boundary conditions. The equations governing the vacuum field can be obtained readily from Eqs. (40) and (41) by setting $\omega_p^2 = 0$. Thus H satisfies the equation

$$\frac{d^2 H}{dr^2} + \left[k_2^2 - \frac{l(l+1)}{r^2}\right] H = 0, \tag{52}$$

where $k_2 = \omega/c$. The solution of Eq. (52) is given by

$$H = r^{1/2}[H_0 H^{(1)}_{l+1/2}(k_2 r) + H_{01} H^{(2)}_{l+1/2}(k_2 r)], \tag{53}$$

where $H_\nu^{(1)}$ and $H_\nu^{(2)}$ are the two kinds of Hankel functions whose asymptotic forms are given by ($k_2 r \gg 1$)

$$H_\nu^{(1)}(z) \sim \left(\frac{2}{\pi z}\right)^{1/2} e^{i[z-(\pi/4)(2\nu+1)]} \tag{54}$$

and

$$H_\nu^{(2)}(z) \sim \left(\frac{2}{\pi z}\right)^{1/2} e^{-i[z-(\pi/4)(2\nu+1)]}. \tag{55}$$

In Eq. (53) H_0 and H_{01} are constants of integration. We have assumed the time dependence of the wave to be of the form exp $-i\omega t$. Therefore, in order that at large distances from the sphere we have only an outgoing wave, we must set $H_{01} = 0$. Thus the permissible solution is

$$H = H_0 r^{1/2} H^{(1)}_{l+1/2}(k_2 r). \tag{56}$$

Applying the boundary condition (47), we then obtain

$$\frac{d}{dr} \ln J_{l+1/2}(k_1 r) = \frac{d}{dr} \ln H^{(1)}_{l+1/2}(k_2 r). \tag{57}$$

We now restrict ourselves to the special case where $k_1 R \gg 1$ and $k_2 R \gg 1$. We may then use the asymptotic expansion

$$J_\nu(z) \sim \left(\frac{2}{\pi z}\right)^{1/2} \cos\left[z - \frac{\pi}{4}(2\nu+1)\right] \tag{58}$$

and Eq. (54) for $H_\nu^{(1)}$. Eq. (57) then leads to

$$-k_1 \tan\left[k_1 R - \frac{\pi}{2}(l+1)\right] = i k_2. \tag{59}$$

Using the relation

$$\text{arc tan } z = \frac{1}{2i} \ln \frac{1+iz}{1-iz}, \tag{60}$$

we obtain from Eq. (59)

$$\frac{R}{c}(\omega^2 - \omega_p^2)^{1/2} = \frac{\pi}{2}(2n+l+2) + \frac{1}{2i} \ln \frac{\omega + (\omega^2 - \omega_p^2)^{1/2}}{\omega - (\omega^2 - \omega_p^2)^{1/2}}. \tag{61}$$

The notion of a radiative solution implies that, at a fixed point in space, the amplitude of the perturbation should die out asymptotically in time on account of a finite amount of energy available for radiation in any admissible initial perturbation of the plasma. This implies that ω has a negative imaginary part. We consider oscillations close to the plasma frequency and set

$$\omega = \omega_p + \delta - i\gamma, \tag{62}$$

where γ is positive, and δ and γ are both assumed small. On substituting Eq. (62) into Eq. (61) and retaining terms to the lowest significant order, we obtain

$$\frac{\delta}{\gamma} = \frac{c}{2\omega_p R}\left(\omega_p^2 \frac{R^2}{c^2} - 1\right) \tag{63}$$

and

$$2\gamma\left[2\frac{R}{c} + \frac{c}{2\omega_p^2 R}\left(\omega_p^2 \frac{R^2}{c^2} - 1\right)^2\right] = \left[\pi\left(n+1+\frac{l}{2}\right)\right]^2. \tag{64}$$

We now consider the physically interesting situation where the time taken by the wave to traverse the radius of the sphere is much larger than the period of a plasma oscillation. That is,

$$\frac{R}{c}\omega_p = \frac{\tau_t}{\tau_p} \gg 1, \tag{65}$$

where

$$\tau_t = \frac{R}{c} \text{ and } \tau_p = \frac{1}{\omega_p}. \tag{66}$$

From Eqs. (63) and (64) we obtain to the lowest significant order

$$\gamma = \omega_p \left(\frac{\tau_p}{\tau_t}\right)^3 \left[\pi\left(n+1+\frac{l}{2}\right)\right]^2 \tag{67}$$

and

$$\delta = \frac{1}{2}\omega_p \left(\frac{\tau_p}{\tau_t}\right)^2 \left[\pi\left(n+1+\frac{l}{2}\right)\right]^2. \tag{68}$$

This establishes the possibility of radiation by plasma oscillations. However, it is not possible to determine the intensity of the radiation emitted within the framework of the linearized theory presented here and in the absence of any knowledge of the excitation mechanism for the oscillations.

In the preceding calculations it was tacitly assumed that $\omega^2 \neq \omega_p^2$. There are, however, situations for which

$\omega^2 = \omega_p^2$. It will be recalled from § 2 of Section III that within any region of a cold plasma of uniform density one can construct arbitrary wave packets of longitudinal waves characterized by

$$\nabla \times \mathbf{E} = 0 \text{ and } \nabla \cdot \mathbf{E} \neq 0\,, \tag{69}$$

which are non-dispersive and which do not couple to the radiation field characterized by

$$\nabla \cdot \mathbf{E} = 0. \tag{70}$$

The longitudinal oscillations, of course, can exist also in the interior of the sphere considered here, but clearly they do not radiate.

Those radiating modes involving the functions F and G, discussed previously, are associated, however, with a fluctuating surface density and do radiate.

The sharp transition between plasma and vacuum assumed here is merely a convenient mathematical device for representing a rapid, but continuous, transition in density. Clearly the radiation associated with the fluctuating surface charge can be viewed as arising from a coupling between longitudinal and transverse fields induced by the density gradient. In fact, one can verify readily that for the case where the density is a function of position, the decomposition into solenoidal and irrotational waves is no longer possible. For the general case, however, the calculations become much more difficult and the radiation associated with charge separation has, as yet, been explored only incompletely.

3. Oscillations in Non-Uniform Plasmas

We now consider the longitudinal electron oscillations in non-uniform plasmas in which temperature and/or density gradients are maintained by some agency. The model we take for the steady state is one in which the electron velocity distribution is assumend to be isotropic against a fixed background of positive ions, resulting in an electric field which balances the pressure forces in the equilibrium state. The force balance condition is, then,

$$\nabla p = -N e \mathbf{E}, \tag{71}$$

where $p\ (= N\Theta)$ and $\mathbf{E}$ denote the pressure and the electric field in equilibrium respectively. It is also assumed that there is no magnetic field. If we assume Θ to be constant, Eq. (71) can be integrated to give

$$N = N_0 \exp \frac{e\varphi}{\Theta}, \tag{72}$$

where φ is the electrostatic potential given by $\mathbf{E} = -\nabla\varphi$ and N_0 is a constant. Eq. (72) is the well known density law for an isothermal atmosphere. On the other hand, if we assume N to be constant, Eq. (71) gives the energy integral

$$\mathfrak{E} = \Theta - e\varphi. \tag{73}$$

In general, it follows from Eq. (71) that

$$p = f(N), \tag{74}$$

where f is an arbitrary function of its argument.

The equations governing the small departures from the state of equilibrium are (cf. Eqs. (II-47), (II-48), and (II-119))

$$\frac{\partial n}{\partial t} + \nabla \cdot (N\mathbf{v}) = 0, \tag{75}$$

$$mN \frac{\partial \mathbf{v}}{\partial t} = -\nabla \cdot \mathsf{p}_1 - n e\mathbf{E} - Ne\mathbf{E}_1, \tag{76}$$

and

$$\frac{\partial}{\partial t}\mathsf{p}_1 + \nabla \cdot (\mathbf{v}p)\,\mathbf{I} + p\nabla\mathbf{v} + p(\nabla\mathbf{v})^T = 0, \tag{77}$$

where n denotes the perturbation in the electron density and p_1, the perturbation in the stress tensor. The perturbation in the electric field $\mathbf{E}_1$ for the longitudinal oscillations under consideration is given by the Poisson equation

$$\nabla \cdot \mathbf{E}_1 = -4\pi e n. \tag{78}$$

Introducing $\boldsymbol{\xi}$, the Lagrangian displacement of an element of the fluid, Eqs. (75), (77), and (78) can be integrated to give

$$n = -\nabla \cdot (N\boldsymbol{\xi}), \tag{79}$$

$$\mathsf{p}_1 = -\nabla \cdot (\boldsymbol{\xi}p)\,\mathbf{I} - p\,(\nabla\boldsymbol{\xi}) - p\,(\nabla\boldsymbol{\xi})^T, \tag{80}$$

and

$$\mathbf{E}_1 = 4\pi e N\boldsymbol{\xi}. \tag{81}$$

Using the foregoing results in Eq. (76) we obtain

$$mN\frac{\partial^2\boldsymbol{\xi}}{\partial t^2} = p\nabla\left[\frac{1}{p}\nabla\cdot(p\boldsymbol{\xi})\right] + \frac{1}{p}\nabla p\,(\boldsymbol{\xi}\cdot\nabla p)$$
$$-\frac{1}{N}f'\nabla N(\boldsymbol{\xi}\cdot\nabla N) + \nabla\cdot[p\nabla\boldsymbol{\xi} + p\,(\nabla\boldsymbol{\xi})^T] - mN\omega_p^2\boldsymbol{\xi}. \tag{82}$$

$$\times\ f' = \frac{\nabla P}{\nabla N}$$

We now multiply Eq. (82) by $\boldsymbol{\xi}^*$ and integrate over the volume of the plasma. Assuming that $\boldsymbol{\xi}$ vanishes at the boundary, Eq. (82) leads to

$$\omega^2\int mN|\boldsymbol{\xi}|^2\,d\tau = \int\left\{\left[\frac{1}{p^{1/2}}|\nabla\cdot(p\boldsymbol{\xi})|\right]^2 - \left[\frac{1}{p^{1/2}}|\boldsymbol{\xi}\cdot\nabla p|\right]^2\right.$$
$$\left. + \left[\left(\frac{f'}{N}\right)^{1/2}|\boldsymbol{\xi}\cdot\nabla N|\right]^2 + 2p(\nabla\boldsymbol{\xi})_{\text{sym}} : \nabla\boldsymbol{\xi}^* + mN\omega_p^2|\boldsymbol{\xi}|^2\right\}d\tau. \tag{83}$$

Now all the terms except the second on the right hand side of Eq. (83) are positive definite. Thus the system will be unstable only if the second term is the dominant one on the right hand side of Eq. (83).

3.1 *Density gradients*

Let us first specialize to the case where there exist density gradients in a plasma at uniform temperature. Then $P = N\Theta$, where Θ is a constant and the second and the third terms on the right hand side of Eq. (83) cancel each other. Consequently, ω^2 is always positive definite and the system is *stable*.

3.2 *Temperature gradients*

We now consider the case when $\Theta = \Theta\,(\mathbf{x})$ and N is constant. Then the third term on the right hand side of Eq. (83) vanishes. For instability to occur the second term must be capable of having a large negative value compared to the fifth term. In order of magnitude, if h denotes the characteristic scale of variation of Θ, then for instability we must have

$$mN\omega_p^2 < \frac{N\Theta}{h^2}. \tag{84}$$

Eq. (84) can be written in the form

$$h^2 < \frac{\Theta}{m\omega_p^2} = \lambda_D^2. \tag{85}$$

Thus, for instability to occur we must have significant temperature gradients over lengths smaller than the Debye length. However, at such small lengths the macroscopic theory is inapplicable.

We may thus conclude that electron oscillations in non-uniform plasmas with arbitrary density or temperature gradients are macroscopically stable.

V. Non-Linear Oscillations

We now consider large amplitude electron oscillations in a uniform plasma and, for the sake of simplicity, restrict ourselves to one-dimensional oscillations only. Furthermore, we neglect the thermal motions of the electrons. Let x_0 denote the equilibrium position of an electron and $X(x_0)$ denote its displacement (not necessarily small) from the equilibrium position. The displaced position of the electron is then given by

$$x = x_0 + X(x_0). \tag{1}$$

In moving the distance $X(x_0)$ the electrons in the x_0 plane pass over an amount of positive charge eNX per unit area, where N denotes the equilibrium density of the electrons. If the ordering of the electrons in the x-direction is not changed, then all electrons which were originally on the positive side of a given electron remain on the positive side, while all those which were on the negative side remain on the negative side. We shall assume that the system is of infinite extent and that no charge enters or leaves the system at infinity. The equation of motion of an electron is given by

$$m\frac{d^2X}{dt^2} = -eE, \tag{2}$$

where, by Gauss's theorem, the electric field is given by

$$E = 4\pi NeX. \tag{3}$$

From Eqs. (2) and (3) we obtain for the equation of motion

$$\frac{a^2X}{dt^2} = -\omega_p^2 X. \tag{4}$$

where $\omega_p^2 = 4\pi Ne^2/m$. The general solution of Eq. (4) is given by

$$X = X_1(x_0)\sin\omega_p t + X_2(x_0)\cos\omega_p t, \tag{5}$$

where $X_1(x_0)$ and $X_2(x_0)$ are some arbitrary functions of x_0. Thus each electron executes simple harmonic motion about its equilibrium position, independent of its amplitude and the motion of the neighboring electrons so long as the ordering of the electrons is maintained.

The condition that the ordering is maintained can be readily derived in the following manner. Let $x_0 + X$ denote the displaced position of an electron originally at x_0, while $x_0 + \Delta x_0 + X + \Delta X_0$ denotes the displaced position of an electron originally at $x_0 + \Delta x_0$. In order that the ordering be maintained, it is clear that $\Delta x_0 + \Delta X > 0$; we thus obtain

$$\frac{\partial X}{\partial x_0} > -1 \tag{6}$$

as the required condition.

An interesting special solution to Eq. (4) arises when

$$X_1 = 0 \text{ and } X_2 = A\sin kx_0, \tag{7}$$

where A is a constant and k denotes the wave number of the disturbance in the x-direction. The solution of Eq. (4) is then given by

$$x = x_0 + A\sin kx_0 \cos\omega_p t \tag{8}$$

and

$$E = 4\pi NeA\sin kx_0\cos\omega_p t. \tag{9}$$

At $t = 0$ Eqs. (8) and (9) reduce to

$$x = x_0 + A\sin kx_0 \tag{10}$$

and

$$E = 4\pi NeA\sin kx_0. \tag{11}$$

We may solve Eq. (10) for x_0 as a function of x (this is most simply done numerically) and thus obtain E as a function of x. The ratio E/E_{max} is plotted in Fig. 16 as a function of x for various values of A. For small values of A the curves are essentially sine waves. For large values of A one gets a multiple valued curve which is, of course, meaningless. What has happened is that the ordering of the electrons has been destroyed. The crest of the wave falls into the trough and we have a wave breaking process somewhat similar to the breaking of water-waves, and we may expect the waves to be dissipated by this breaking mechanism converting the wave energy into the thermal energy of the electrons.

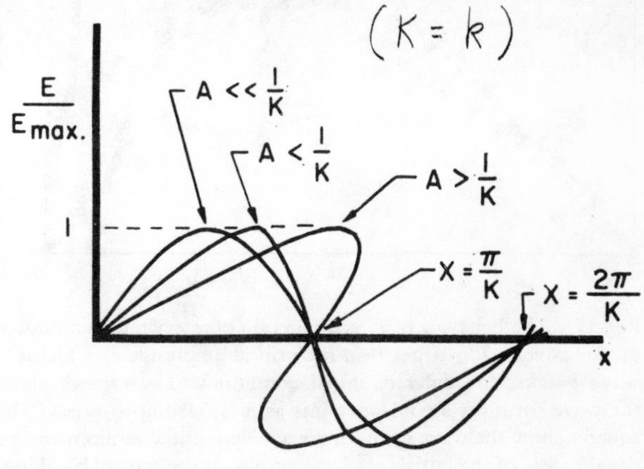

Fig. 16 The behavior of $E/E_{max.}$ as a function of x for various values of A at time $t = 0$.

A convenient mechanical model which exhibits the breaking process is a series of elastic pendulums constrained to move along a straight line. For small displacements the pendulums swing independently of each other. However, if the amplitude of the displacement becomes large, the bobs of the pendulums strike one another, destroying their periodic motion.

The breaking of large amplitude waves has been investigated by Dawson for the one dimensional case under various initial conditions. Firstly, consider the case when the initial displacement vanishes and the initial velocity is given by

$$V = V_0 \sin k x_0. \tag{12}$$

From Eqs. (6), (8), and (12) it follows that the critical breaking amplitude is

$$V_c = \omega_p / k. \tag{13}$$

In his numerical calculations Dawson investigated the case when the amplitude of the wave was taken to be 7% larger than the critical amplitude given by Eq. (13).

Secondly, we consider the case when, in addition to the initial velocity given by Eq. (12), there is superimposed on the particles a certain amount of random motion. The random motion was taken to be

$$V_{th} = V_{ot} \exp(-V^2/V_0^2) \tag{14}$$

whre V_{ot} is a constant which is proportional to the thermal energy. The effect of thermal motions on the breaking of waves is exhibited in Fig. 17 for the case where the thermal energy is 4% of the wave energy The lower curve in Fig. 17 shows the wave form for the wave at a time two plasma oscillations later. It is clear from this curve that the amplitude of the wave has reduced considerably and that the wave energy is being converted into the thermal energy of the electrons.

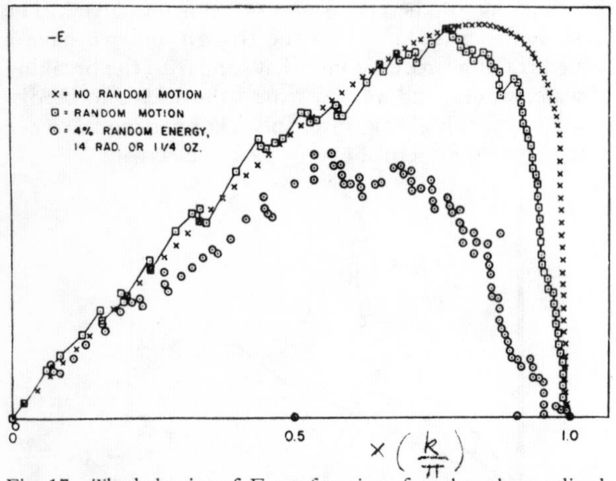

Fig. 17 The behavior of E as a function of x when the amplitude of the wave is 7% larger than the critical amplitude at which the wave breaks, for different initial conditions. The crosses show the wave form for a cold wave just as it is starting to break. The squares show the wave form for a wave with initial random energy equal to 4% of the initial wave energy, also at the start of breaking. The circles show the wave form for a warm wave two plasma periods later.

Fig. 18 shows the velocities of 270 pendulums after three oscillations for an initially cold wave. It is apparent that most of the particle velocities lie on a sine wave. However, there exist a number of particles with very

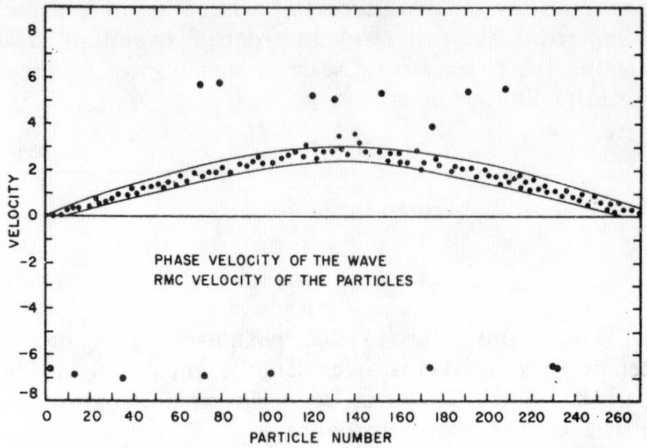

Fig. 18 The velocities of the particles after three oscillations.

high velocities, both positive and negative. These are particles which managed to get in just the right phase with the wave so as to ride it, and they account for the major loss in the energy of the wave.

In order to get a quantitative idea of the energy loss of the wave, we Fourier-analyze the displacement and the velocity in terms of the equilibrium position, i.e.,

$$X(x_i) = \sum_{n=1}^{N} A_n \sin \frac{n\pi x_i}{L} \tag{15}$$

and

$$V(x_i) = \sum_{n=1}^{N} B_n \sin \frac{n\pi x_i}{L}, \tag{16}$$

where L denotes the linear dimension of the system. The Fourier co-efficients A_n and B_n are given by

$$A_n = \frac{2}{N+1} \sum_{n=1}^{N} X(x_i) \sin \frac{n\pi x_i}{L}, \tag{17}$$

and

$$B_n = \frac{2}{N+1} \sum_{n=1}^{N} V(x_i) \sin \frac{n\pi x_i}{L}. \tag{18}$$

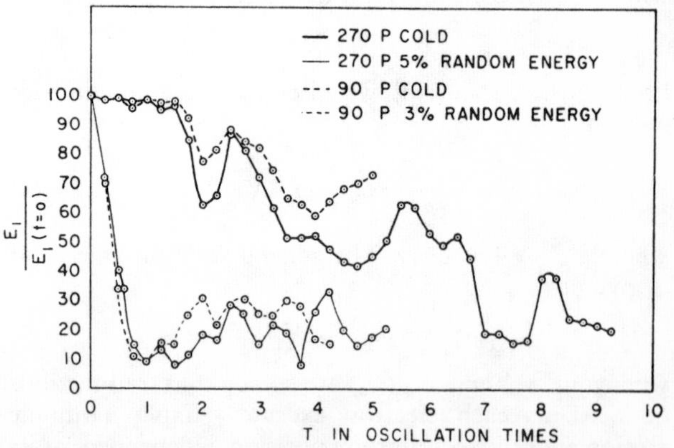

Fig. 19 The % of the energy in the first harmonic to its initial value for a number of different cases.

For the Fourier analysis it is convenient to use the equilibrium position rather than the actual physical position since for such a choice there is no coupling between the different modes without breaking. The results of the Fourier analysis are shown in Figs. 19 and 20. Fig. 19 shows the % of the energy in the first harmonic to its initial value (for a number of different cases) as a function of time. The cold wave loses very little energy during the first oscillation and a half, after which there is an almost continuous decrease in energy. As is clear from the diagram, the presence of a small amount of random motion causes the wave energy to drop to about 10% of its initial value over a period of one oscillation.

The absolute values of the amplitudes of the various Fourier modes for the case of forty-five pendulums without any random motion is shown in Fig. 20 after 2.25 oscillations. As is clear from the figure, there is no tendency to feed energy from the fundamental into any one of the higher modes. The curve is flat (with only small fluctuations superimposed on it) all the way out; only the fundamental has appreciably more energy than the rest of the modes. The energy of the wave seems to go into individual particles rather than into Fourier modes.

One may expect the system to exhibit a Poincaré cycle and return to its initial state after a sufficiently long interval of time. Simple probabilistic arguments indicate that this interval of time will indeed be very long even for a small number of charge sheets. For example, such arguments indicate that a system of five sheets should spend approximately 1/400 of the time in a state for which the energy of the fundamental is more than 95% of the total energy. A system of nine sheets would spend only one part in 1.6×10^5 of its time in such a state.

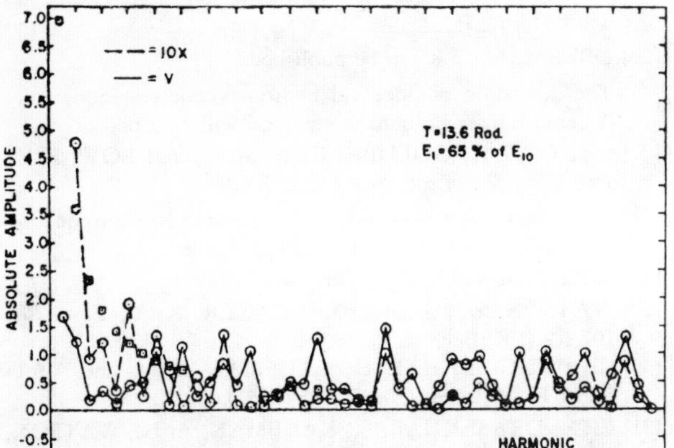

Fig. 20 The absolute values of the amplitudes for various Fourier modes for the case of forty-five particles per half wave length after 2.25 oscillations.

The recurrence time was investigated by Dawson following systems of five sheets and nine sheets for about sixty oscillations. The systems were started in the fundamental mode with amplitudes larger than the breaking amplitude. It was found that on the average there were five crossings per sheet for the five-sheet case, and ten crossings per sheet for the nine-sheet case, in one-half an oscillation time. The state of the system was sampled for 120 values of the time. It was found that the five-sheet system returned to a state in which the fundamental had 95% of the energy once during this time, while the nine-sheet system returned to a state in which the fundamental had half the energy once during this time. Fig. 21 shows the sum of 120 time-averaged velocity distribution functions for the nine-particle system. The smooth curve in Fig. 21 shows what would be expected if the motion was roughly ergodic. These results seem compatible with the probabilistic estimates.

The foregoing discussion indicates that the breaking of waves can be an effective mechanism for the dissipation of wave energy into the thermal energy of electrons and that the presence of a small amount of random motion can greatly enhance this mechanism.

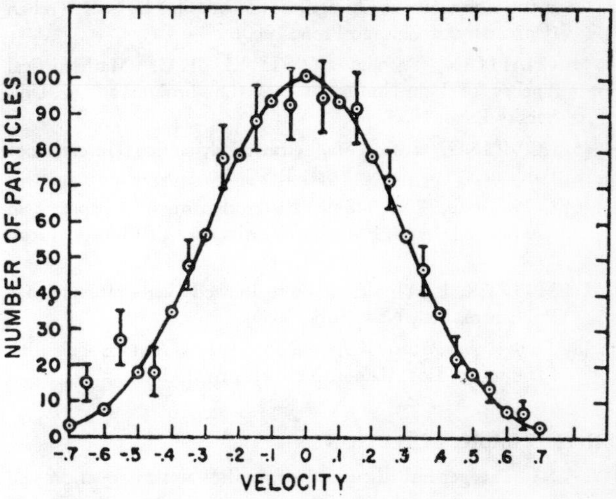

Fig. 21 The velocity spectrum of the particles.

Acknowledgements

It is a pleasure to express our indebtedness to Professor Lyman Spitzer, Jr. for his reading of the manuscript, and criticism. We are grateful to: Dr. C. R. Oberman for communicating to us his results on the low temperature approximation; to Dr. C. R. Oberman and Dr. J. Dawson for communicating to us their results on the radiation by plasma oscillations in a uniform sphere, prior to publication; to Dr. R. M. Kulsrud for reading Section I and the first part of Section II; to Dr. T. Stix for reading the first part of Section IV; and to Dr. M. Weenink for checking some of the calculations. We would also like to express our gratitude to Mrs. H. Selberg for her excellent execution of the numerical computations which were needed for the graphs. Finally, our thanks are due also to Mrs. Isabelle Murphy for capably carrying out the arduous task of typing the manuscript.

Bibliographical Notes

I. INTRODUCTION

It is of historical interest to note that the problem of plasma oscillations was first considered by Lord Rayleigh in connection with the electrical vibration and the constitution of the atom.

[1] LORD RAYLEIGH, *Phil Mag.* **11,** 117 (1906). See also *Scientific Papers of Lord Rayleigh*, Vol. V, p. 287.

Rayleigh's formulation of the problem was in the following terms:

"... The cloud of electrons may then be assimilated to a fluid whose properties, however, must differ in many respects from those with which we are most familiar. We suppose that the whole quantities of positive and negative are equal. The difference between them is that the positive are constrained to remain undisplaced while the negative are free to move. In equilibrium, the negative distributes itself with uniformity throughout the sphere occupied by the positive, so that the total density is everywhere zero. There is then no force at any point; but if the negative be displaced, a force is usually called into existence ..."

The following general references may be noted.

[2] ALFVÉN, H., Cosmical Electrodynamics (Oxford: at the Clarendon Press, 1950).

[3] CHANDRASEKHAR, S., Plasma Physics—a course given at the University of Chicago, notes compiled by S. K. Trehan (University of Chicago Press, 1960).

[4] CHAPMAN, S., and COWLING, T. G., Mathematical Theory of Non-Uniform Gases (Cambridge: at the University Press, 1953).

[5] COWLING, T. G., Magnetohydrodynamics (Interscience Publishers, Inc., New York, 1957).

[6] COWLING, T. G., "Solar Electrodynamics," Chapter 8 in *The Sun*, ed. by G. P. Kuiper (University of Chicago Press, 1958).

[7] SPITZER, L., Physics of Fully Ionized Gases (Interscience Publishers, Inc., New York, 1956).

[8] *Lectures on Physics of Ionized Gases*, Los Alamos Scientific Laboratory, Los Alamos, New Mexico, 1955.

II. THE BASIC EQUATIONS

§ 1. The general discussion of the Boltzmann equation will be found in ref. 4. The importance of the cumulative effect of distant encounters compared to the occasional close encounters for particles interacting according to the inverse square force law was first recognized by Jeans and is discussed in

[9] JEANS, J. H., Astronomy and Cosmogony (Cambridge; University Press, 1929), p. 318.

A comprehensive account of the Fokker-Planck equation based on general probability considerations will be found in

[10] CHANDRASEKHAR, S., *Revs. Modern Phys.* **15,** 1 (1943).

A derivation of the Fokker-Planck equation based on considerations of two body Coulomb interactions and for distribution functions isotropic in position and velocity space is due to

[11] LANDAU, L., *Physik Zeits. Sowjetunion* **10,** 154 (1936).

An extension of these considerations to the case when the distribution function is of the form $f^0 + \mu f^1$, where f^0 and f^1 are isotropic and μ is the direction cosine between the particle trajectory and some preferred direction in space, and f^1 is assumed to be small, will be found in

[12] COHEN, R. S., SPITZER, L., and ROUTLEY, R. M., *Phys. Rev.* **80,** 230 (1950).

The general case of arbitrary distribution functions has been considered by

[13] ROSENBLUTH, M. N., MAC DONALD, W. M., and JUDD, D. L., *Phys. Rev.* **107,** 1 (1957).

§ 2. A detailed discussion of the Chapman-Enskog method will be found in ref. 4. The application of the Chapman-Enskog method to ionized gases will be found in

[14] LANDSHOFF, R., *Phys. Rev.* **76,** 904 (1949).

[15] LANDSHOFF, R., *Phys. Rev.* **82,** 442 (1951).

A new approach to the problem of the transport phenomena in an ionized gas, based on the Fokker-Planck form for the collision term has been developed in ref. 12. See also

[16] SPITZER, L., and HÄRM, R., *Phys. Rev.* **89,** 977 (1953).

Plasma diffusion in a strong magnetic field has been discussed by

[17] LONGMIRE, C. L., and ROSENBLUTH, M. N., *Phys. Rev.* **103,** 507 (1956).

Material and thermal diffusion of a plasma in a strong magnetic field has been considered by

[18] ROSENBLUTH, M. N., and KAUFMAN, A. N., *Phys. Rev.* **109,** 1 (1958).

Transport co-efficients as discussed here are in the main taken from

[19] MARSHALL, W., *Report No. AERE T/R*, **2419**; Atomic Energy Research Establishment, Harwell, England.

A discussion of the Onsager relations will be found in

[20] DE GROOT, S. R., Thermodynamics of Irreversible Processes (Interscience Publishers, New York, 1951), Chap. VIII.

The following references may also be noted. Starting with the relativistic Boltzmann equation, relativistic magnetohydrodynamics for perfect and imperfect fluids has been discussed by

[21] GOTO, K., *Progr. Theoret. Phys. (Kyoto)* **20,** 1 (1958).

From a phenomenological viewpoint, relativistic hydromagnetics has been considered by

[22] HARRIS, E. G., *Phys. Rev.* **108,** 1357 (1957).

[23] ZUMINO, B., *Phys. Rev.* **108,** 1116 (1957).

§ 3. The equivalence of the Boltzmann equation in the absence of collisions and the particle orbit theory was first demonstrated by

[24] JEANS, J. H., Problems of Cosmogony and Stellar Dynamics (Cambridge: at the University Press, 1919).

The particle orbit theory is discussed in

[25] LONGMIRE, C. L., and ROSENBLUTH, M. N., *Ann. Phys.* **1,** 120 (1957).

A systematic discussion of the low temperature approximation will be found in

[26] OBERMAN, C. R., to be published.

The derivation of one-fluid hydromagnetic equations from the collisionless Boltzmann equation will be found in

[27] CHEW, G. F., GOLDBERGER, M. L., and LOW, F. E., *Proc. Roy. Soc. (London)* **A 236,** 112 (1956).

The general discussion of the collisionless Boltzmann equation for ionized gases of low density is given in

[28] WATSON, K. M., *Phys. Rev.* **102,** 12 (1956).

[29] WATSON, K. M., and BRUECKNER, K. A., *Phys. Rev.* **102,** 19 (1956).

[30] CHANDRASEKHAR, S., KAUFMAN, A. N., and WATSON, K. M., *Ann. Phys.* **2,** 435 (1957).

[31] CHANDRASEKHAR, S., KAUFMAN, A. N., WATSON, K. M., *Ann. Phys.* **5,** 1 (1958).

[32] ROSENBLUTH, M. N., and ROSTOKER, N., *Phys. Fluids* **2,** 23 (1959).

[33] ROSTOKER, N., and ROSENBLUTH, M. N., *Phys. Fluids* **3,** 1 (1960).

The Lagrangian formulation of the collisionless Boltzmann equation is discussed in

[34] LOW, F. E., *Proc. Roy. Soc. (London)* **A 248,** 282 (1958).

A relativistic formulation of the collisionless Boltzmann equation was first given by

[35] CLEMMOW, P. C. und WILSON, A. J., *Proc. Cambridge Phil. Soc.* **53,** 222 (1957)

III. WAVE PHENOMENA IN PLASMAS

§ 1. An excellent discussion of the normal mode analysis and the concept of stability will be found in

[36] CHANDRASEKHAR, S., *Daedalus (Proc. Am. Acad. Arts Sci.)* **86,** 323 (1957).

The energy principle for hydromagnetic stability problems is discussed in

[37] BERNSTEIN, I. B., FRIEMAN, E. A., KRUSKAL, M., and KULSRUD, R., *Proc. Roy. Soc. (London)* **A 244,** 17 (1958).

The boundary conditions in ideal hydromagnetics are also discussed in ref. 37.

§ 2. Plasma oscillations were discussed both experimentally and theoretically in connection with gaseous discharge in the classic paper by

[38] TONKS, L., and LANGMUIR, I., *Phys. Rev.* **33,** 195 (1929).

The effect of thermal motions on plasma oscillations was first discussed by

[39] THOMSON, J. J., and THOMSON, G. P., Conduction of Electricity through Gases (Cambridge: at the University Press, 1933), p. 353

and later independently by

[40] BAILEY, V. A., *Phys. Rev.* **78,** 428 (1950).

The following references may also be noted.

[41] GABOR, D., *Brit. J. Appl. Phys.* **2,** 209 (1951).
[42] BAILEY, V. A., et al, *Proc. Roy. Irish Acad.* **57,** 53 (1955).
[43] BAYET, M., *J. phys. radium* **13,** 579 (1952).
[44] BORGNIS, F., *Helv. Phys. Acta* **20,** 207 (1947).
[45] ALLIS, W. P., Proc. Symposium on Electronic Wave Guides (Polytechnic Press, Brooklyn, New York).
[46] VAN KAMPEN, N. G., *Physica* **23,** 641 (1957).

§ 3. Plasma oscillations in the presence of a magnetic field are considered in the following papers.

[47] AKHIEZER, A. I., and POLOVIN, R. V., *J. Tech. Phys.* (U.S.S.R.) **22,** 1794 (1952).
[48] AKHIEZER, A. I., LYUBARSKII, G., and POLOVIN, R. V., *Soviet Phys. — Tech. Phys.* **4,** 849 (1960).
[49] ALFVÉN, H., *Ark. Mat. Astr.* **29 B,** no. 2 (1942).
[50] ASTRÖM, E., *Arkiv Fysik* **2,** 443 (1950).
[51] AUER, P. L., HURWITZ, H., and MILLER, R. D., *Phys. Fluids* **1,** 501 (1958).
[52] BAÑOS, A., *Phys. Rev.* **97,** 1435 (1955).
[53] BAÑOS, A., *Proc. Roy. Soc. (London)* **A 233,** 350 (1955).
[54] BOHM, D., and GROSS, E. P., *Phys. Rev.* **75,** 1851 (1949).
[55] BOHM, D., and GROSS, E. P., *Phys. Rev.* **75,** 1864 (1949).
[56] COLE, G. H. A., *Phil. Mag.* Supplement **5,** 452 (1956).
[57] DUNGEY, J. W., *Nature* **167,** 1029 (1951).
[58] GERSHMAN, B. N., *Soviet Phys.—JETP* **4,** 582 (1957).
[59] OSTER, L., *Revs. Modern Phys.* **32,** 141 (1960).
[60] PIDDINGTON, J. H., *Phil. Mag.* **46,** 1037 (1955).
[61] SITENKO, A. G., and KIROCHKIW, Y. A., *Soviet Phys.— Tech. Phys.* **4,** 723 (1960).
[62] WALÉN, C., *Ark. Mat. Astr. Phys.* **30 A,** no. 15 (1944).

§ 4, 5. Instabilities in a plasma carrying current have been extensively discussed by the following.

[63] BAILEY, A. V., *Australian J. Sci. Research* **1,** 351 (1948).
[64] BAILEY, A. V., *Nature* **161,** 599 (1948).
[65] BAILEY, A. V., *J. Roy. Soc. (New South Wales)* **82,** 107 (1948).
[66] BAILEY, A. V., *Phys. Rev.* **78,** 428 (1950).
[67] BAILEY, A. V., *Phys. Rev.* **83,** 439 (1951).
[68] BUNEMAN, O., *Phys. Rev. Letters* **1,** 8 (1958).
[69] HAEFF, A. V., *Phys. Rev.* **75,** 1546 (1949).
[70] HAEFF, A. V., *Proc. Inst. Radio Engrs.* **37,** 4 (1949).
[71] HAEFF, A. V., *Phys. Rev.* **78,** 428 (1950).
[72] KAHN, F. D., *Revs. Modern Phys.* **30,** 1069 (1958).
[73] KAHN, F. D., *J. Fluid Mech.* **2,** 601 (1957).
[74] PARKER, E. N., *Phys. Rev.* **112,** 1429 (1958).
[75] PIDDINGTON, J. H., *Australian J. Phys.* **9,** 31 (1956).
[76] PIDDINGTON, J. H., *Phys. Rev.* **101,** 14 (1956).
[77] PIDDINGTON, J. H., *Phil. Mag.* **3,** 1241 (1958).
[78] PIERCE, J. R., *J. Appl. Phys.* **19,** 231 (1949).
[79] PIERCE, J. R., and HEBENSTREIT, W. B., *Bell System Techn. J.* **28,** 33 (1949).
[80] TWISS, R. Q., *Proc. Phys. Soc. (London)* **B 64,** 654 (1951).
[81] TWISS, R. Q., *Phys. Rev.* **88,** 1392 (1952).

The instability of transverse oscillations of interpenetrating streams in the presence of an external magnetic field was conjectured by T. Coor and the mathematical analysis was worked out by

[82] BERNSTEIN, I. B., and DAWSON, J., unpublished.

§ 7. Hydromagnetic waves from the Chew, Goldberger, and Low theory have been discussed by

[83] AKHIEZER, I. A., POLOVIN, R. V., and TSINTSADZE, N. L., *Soviet Phys.-JETP* **10,** 539 (1960).
[84] LÜST, R., Fortschritte der Physik (Akademie-Verlag, Berlin, 1959), Bd. VII, p. 503.

§ 8. The effect of finite pressure on hydromagnetic waves is discussed in

[85] GINSBURG, V. L., *J. Exptl. Theoret. Phys. (U.S.S.R.)* **21,** 788 (1951).
[86] GROSS, R. A., *J. Aero/space Sci.* **25,** 788 (1959).
[87] HERLOFSEN, N., *Nature* **165,** 1020 (1950).
[88] KONIUKOV, M. V., *Soviet Phys. - JETP* **5,** 429 (1957).
[89] LÜST, R., *Z. Astrophys.* **37,** 67 (1955).
[90] LARENZ, R. W., *Z. Naturforsch.* **10a,** 761 (1955).

The dissipative effects on hydromagnetic waves are considered in the following papers.

[91] DUNGEY, J. W., *J. Geophys. Research* **59,** 323 (1954).
[92] DE SOCIO, M., *Italian Acad. Sci. (Torino)* **92,** 243 (1957—58).
[93] KADOMSTEV, B. B., *Soviet Phys. - JETP* **4,** 926 (1957).
[94] ANDERSON, N. S., *J. Acoust. Soc. Am.* **25,** 529 (1953).
[95] GOLITSYN, G. S., and STANIUKOVICH, K. P., *Soviet-Phys. - JETP* **6,** 1090 (1958).
[96] PIDDINGTON, J. H., *M. Notices, Roy. Astr. Soc.* **114,** 638 (1954); **115,** 671 (1955); *Nature* **176,** 508 (1955).
[97] VAN DE HULST, H. C., *Problems of Cosmical Aerodynamics,* proc. of symposium published by U. S. Air Force (Dayton, Ohio, 1949).
[98] BAÑOS, A., I. A. U. Symposium No. 6 — Electromagnetic Phenomena in Cosmical Physics (Cambridge: University Press, 1958).

The discussion of the dissipative effects as given in § 8 is due to

[99] BERNSTEIN, I. B., and TREHAN, S. K.,

and is reported here for the first time.

IV. OSCILLATIONS OF BOUNDED AND NON-UNIFORM PLASMAS

§ 1. The oscillations of a cylindrical plasma have been considered by

[100] STIX, T., *Phys. Rev.* **106,** 1146 (1957).

The discussion of ion cyclotron waves is in the main taken from

[101] STIX, T., and PALLADINO, R. W., *Proc. of the 2nd International Conference on Peaceful Uses of Atomic Energy* **31,** 282 (1958).

The following references may also be noted.

[102] STIX, T., *Phys. Fluids* **1,** 308 (1958).
[103] STIX, T., and PALLADINO, R. W., *Phys. Fluids* **1,** 446 (1958).
[104] STIX, T., *Phys. Fluids* **3,** 19 (1960).

§ 2. Radiation by plasma oscillations has been considered by

[105] FIELD, G. B., *Astrophys. J.* **124,** 555 (1956).

[106] TIDMAN, D. A., *Phys. Rev.* **117,** 366 (1960).
[107] OBERMAN, C., and DAWSON, J., *Phys. Fluids* **2,** 103 (1959).

The discussion of radiation by plasma oscillations in a uniform sphere is due to

[108] OBERMAN, C., and DAWSON, J., to be published.

Vector spherical harmonics are discussed in

[109] MORSE, P. M., and FESHBACH, H., Methods of Theoretical Physics (McGraw-Hill Book Company, Inc., 1953), p. 1898.

§ 3. The discussion of the stability of inhomogeneous plasmas is due to

[110] BERNSTEIN, I. B., and TREHAN, S. K., to be published. The problem of radiation by oscillations in inhomogeneous plasmas will be discussed there also.

V. NON-LINEAR OSCILLATIONS

The treatment of non-linear plasma oscillations as presented here is in the main taken from

[111] DAWSON, J., *Phys. Rev.* **113,** 383 (1959).

The following references may also be noted.

[112] AKHIEZER, A. I., and LYUBARSKIZS, G. Ya., *Doklady Akad. Nauk S.S.S.R.* **80, 193** (1951).
[113] STURROCK, P., *Proc. Roy. Soc. (London)* **A242,** 277 (1957).
[114] DAVIS, L., LÜST, R., and SCHLÜTER, A., *Z. Naturforsch.* **13a,** 916 (1958).
[115] MONTGOMERY, D., *Phys. Fluids* **2,** 585 (1959).

The discussion on the breaking of large amplitude waves as given here is due to

[116] DAWSON, J., in press.

(Manuscript received on 6 June 1960)

Reprinted from Journal of Physics USSR Vol. X, No. 1 (1946), published by House of Academy of Science of the USSR.

ON THE VIBRATIONS OF THE ELECTRONIC PLASMA

By L. LANDAU

Institute for Physical Problems, Academy of Sciences of the USSR

(Received June 2, 1945)

The vibrations of the electronic plasma are considered, which arose as a result of an arbitrary initial non-equilibrium distribution in it. It is shown that the vibrations of the field in plasma are always damped, and the dependence of the frequency and of the damping decrement on the wave vector is determined for small and for large values of the latter.

The penetration of a periodical external electric field into the plasma is considered. The case of the frequency of the external field being almost at resonance with the proper frequency of plasma is considered separately.

The high frequency vibrations of the electronic plasma are described by comparatively simple equations. If the frequency is high enough, the collisions of the electrons with the ions and with each other are unessential, and in the kinetic equation the collision integral can be neglected. The distribution function of ions can be considered as invariable, and only the distribution of electrons vibrates. Let $F(\mathbf{v}, \mathbf{r}, t)$ be the electronic distribution function, if $f_0(v)$ is the equilibrium function (the Maxwell distribution), then

$$F = f_0(v) + f(\mathbf{v}, \mathbf{r}, t). \tag{1}$$

f being a quantity small as compared with f_0. The kinetic equation (without the collision integral) is

$$\frac{\partial f}{\partial t} + \mathbf{v}\nabla f - \frac{e}{m}\nabla\varphi\frac{\partial f_0}{\partial \mathbf{v}} = 0 \tag{2}$$

(φ — the electric field potential). The Poisson equation is

$$\Delta\varphi = -4\pi e\int f d\tau \quad (d\tau = dv_x dv_y dv_z) \tag{3}$$

(the equilibrium electronic charge $e\int f_0 d\tau$ is of course compensated by the positive charge of the ions). Equations (2), (3) form a complete set of equations.

These equations were used by A. A. Vlasov(1, 2) for investigation of the vibrations of plasma. However, most of his results turn out to be incorrect. Vlasov looked for the solutions of the form const $e^{-i\omega t + i\mathbf{kr}}$ and determined the dependence of the frequency ω on the wave vector $\mathbf{k}$. The equation, which he obtained for this dependence contains a divergent integral; this already indicates on mathematical incorrectness of his method. Vlasov(2) [and also Adirovich(3)] tries to escape from this difficulty by taking the principal value of the integral involved, however, without any foundation. Actually there exists no definite dependence of ω on $\mathbf{k}$ at all, and for a given value of $\mathbf{k}$ arbitrary values of ω are possible. The fact that the solutions of the form of $e^{-i\omega t + i\mathbf{kv}}$ are insufficient can be seen already by observing that they give only a ∞^3 multitude of solutions (according to three independent parameters k_x, k_y, k_z), whereas there must actually exist a ∞^6 multitude of solutions (the equations contain six independent variables x, y, z, v_x, v_y, v_z).

§ 1. The vibrations with a given initial distribution

In order to obtain a correct solution of equations (2), (3), it is necessary to consider the problem in concretely stated; we shall discuss here two of such problems.

Let us assume, that a definite (non-equilibrium) electronic distribution in plasma is given in the initial moment. The problem is to determine the resulting vibrations. As equations (2), (3) are linear and do not contain the coordinates explicitly, the function $f(\mathbf{r}, \mathbf{v}, t)$ can be expandet into a Fourier integral with respect to coordinates, and the equation can be written for every Fourier component separately. This means, that it is sufficient to consider the solutions of the form

$$f_{\mathbf{k}}(\mathbf{v}, t)\, e^{i\mathbf{kr}}.$$

Further we shall, for the sake of convenience, omit the index $\mathbf{k}$ in $f_{\mathbf{k}}$ so that $f(\mathbf{v}, t)$ will denote the Fourier component of the distribution function in question. By $g(\mathbf{v})$ we denote the Fourier component of the initial distribution $f(\mathbf{r}, \mathbf{v}, 0)$, we shall write shortly $g(\mathbf{v})$ for $g_{\mathbf{k}}(\mathbf{v})$. Finally, we choose the x axis along the direction of the considered value of the vector $\mathbf{k}$.

Taking the Fourier components of equations (2) and (3), we obtain

$$\frac{\partial f}{\partial t} + ikv_x f - ik\frac{e}{m}\varphi\frac{\partial f_0}{\partial v_x} = 0, \qquad (4)$$

$$k^2\varphi(t) = 4\pi e\int f\, d\tau, \qquad (5)$$

$\varphi(t)$ is the Fourier component of the potential $\varphi(\mathbf{r}, t)$. These equations can be solved by using the operational method. Following this method, we introduce the function $f_p(\mathbf{v})$ defined by means of

$$f_p(\mathbf{v}) = \int_0^\infty f(\mathbf{v}, t)\, e^{-pt}\, dt; \qquad (6)$$

then

$$f(\mathbf{v}, t) = \frac{1}{2\pi i}\int_{-i\infty+\sigma}^{+i\infty+\sigma} f_p(\mathbf{v})\, e^{pt}\, dp, \qquad (7)$$

the integration being performed here in the plane of the complex variable p along a straight line parallel to the imaginary axis and passing to the right of it ($\sigma > 0$).

We multiply both sides of equation (4) by e^{-pt} and integrate over dt. Noting that

$$\int_0^\infty \frac{\partial f}{\partial t} e^{-pt}\, dt = f e^{-pt}\Big|_0^\infty + p\int_0^\infty f e^{-pt}\, dt = pf_p - g$$

[we insert $f(\mathbf{v}, 0) \equiv g(\mathbf{v})$] we obtain

$$(p + ikv_x) f_p - ik\frac{e}{m}\varphi_p\frac{\partial f_0}{\partial v_x} = g.$$

In the same way (5) gives

$$k^2\varphi_p = 4\pi e\int f_p\, d\tau.$$

The first of these equations yields

$$f_p(\mathbf{v}) = \frac{1}{p + ikv_x}\left\{g(\mathbf{v}) + ik\frac{e}{m}\varphi_p\frac{\partial f_0(v)}{\partial v_x}\right\}, \qquad (8)$$

and inserting this into the second one, we obtain for φ_p:

$$\varphi_p = \frac{4\pi e}{k^2}\,\frac{\displaystyle\int \frac{g(\mathbf{v})}{p + ikv_x}\, d\tau}{1 - \displaystyle\frac{4\pi i e^2}{km}\int \frac{\partial f_0}{\partial v_x}\frac{d\tau}{(p + ikv_x)}}. \qquad (9)$$

These formulae solve, in principle, the problem considered. They determine the electronic distribution and the electric field for an arbitrarily given initial distribution.

Before proceeding to the investigation of the formulae obtained, we note that in (9) the integration over $dv_y dv_z$ can be performed directly. Introducing for the following the notation $v_x \equiv u$ and

$$g(u) = \int g(\mathbf{v})\, dv_y\, dv_z$$

we write

$$\varphi_p = \frac{4\pi e}{k^2}\,\frac{\displaystyle\int_{-\infty}^{+\infty} \frac{g(u)}{p + iku}\, du}{1 - \displaystyle\frac{4\pi i e^2}{km}\int_{-\infty}^{+\infty} \frac{df_0(u)}{du}\frac{du}{(p + iku)}} \qquad (10)$$

the equilibrium function being

$$f_0(u) = n\sqrt{\frac{m}{2\pi\varkappa T}}\, e^{-\frac{mu^2}{2\varkappa T}} \qquad (11)$$

($\varkappa$ — the Boltzmann constant, n — the equilibrium number of electrons per unit volume of the plasma).

An expression of the type of

$$\varphi_p = \int_0^\infty \varphi(t)\, e^{-pt} dt,$$

considered as a function of the complex variable p has a sense only in the right half-plane, *i. e.* for $\mathrm{Re}(p) > 0$. The same refers correspondingly to the expression (10). However, we can define φ_p on the left half-plane as the analytical continuation of expression (10). It is easy to see, that if $g(u)$ (considered as a function of the complex variable u) is an entire function of u (*i. e.* it has no singularities at finite u), then the integral

$$\int_{-\infty}^{+\infty} \frac{g(u)\,du}{p+iku},$$

continued analytically to the left half-plane of p also defines an entire function of p. Actually, to perform the analytical continuation of the function, defined by this integral, from the right half-plane to the left one, we displace the integration path in the complex plane of u far enough into the lower half-plane so, that the point $u = -p/ik$ would lie above it. In this way we shall obtain an analytical function, defined by the integral which for $\mathrm{Re}(p) > 0$, is taken along the real axis, and for $\mathrm{Re}(p) < 0$ along the path, which is drawn in Fig. 1 by a full line. This function has no singularities at finite values of p, *i. e.* it is an entire function.

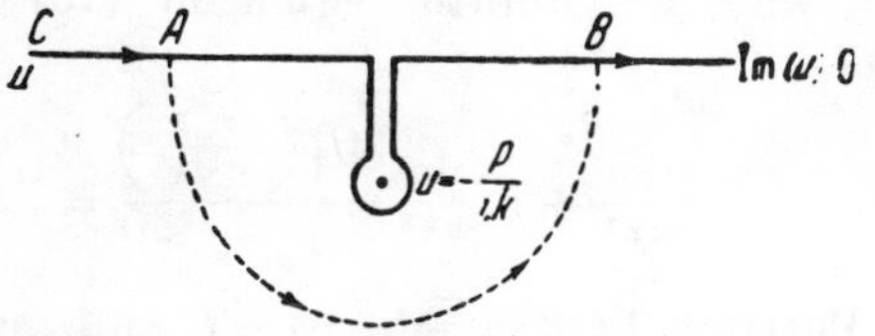

Fig. 1

The same refers also to the integral in the denominator of expression (10), for $df_0(u)/du$ is an entire function. Thus, an analytical, in the whole plane, function φ_p is (if $g(u)$ is entire) a ratio of two entire functions. Hence the only singularities (poles) of the function φ_p are the zeros of the denominator in (10); all of these poles lie in the left half-plane.

These considerations allow to determine the asymptotical form of the potential $\varphi(t)$ for large values of the time t. In the inversion formula

$$\varphi(t) = \frac{1}{2\pi i} \int_{-i\infty+\sigma}^{+i\infty+\sigma} \varphi_p e^{pt}\,dp \tag{12}$$

the integration is performed along a vertical line in the right half-plane. However, if φ_p is defined in the manner indicated above as a function which is analytical in the whole plane of p, we can displace the integration path into the left half-plane going around all the poles of φ_p it meets. Let p_k be that of the poles of φ_p, *i. e.* that of the roots of the equation

$$\frac{4\pi i e^2}{km} \int_C \frac{df_0}{du} \frac{du}{(p+iku)} = 1 \tag{13}$$

(integration along the path shown in Fig. 1), which has the least absolute value of its real part (*i. e.* which is the nearest to the imaginary axis). Let us perform the integration in (12) along the path, which is displaced far enough to the left and goes around the point $p = p_k$ in the manner shown in Fig. 2. Then in the integral (12) (with large values of t) only the residue relative to the pole p_k will be of importance. All other parts of the integral (among them the integral along the vertical line) will be exponentially small in comparison with the residue due to the presence of the factor e^{pt} in the integrated expression, which decreases rapidly with increasing $|\mathrm{Re}(p)|$.

Thus, for large values of t the potential of the field $\varphi(t)$ is proportional to $e^{p_k t}$. With complex p_k this factor splits into a periodical part and a decreasing ($\mathrm{Re}(p) < 0$) ones. We arrive, consequently, at an essential result, that the field is damped with time, the damping decrement being equal to $-\mathrm{Re}(p_k)$.

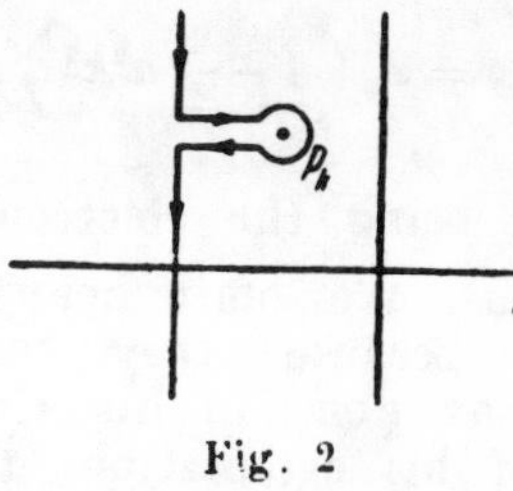

Fig. 2

Equation (13) determines p_k, *i. e.* the frequency and the damping decrement of the vibrations. It coincides formally with Vlasov's equations, the difference being that here the integration is performed along the path C, whilst Vlasov integrates simply along the real axis. This difference leads, as we shall see, to qualitatively new results, namely to the presence of damping.

Consider the limiting case of long waves, $k \to 0$. The point $u = -p/ik$ (Fig. 1) is displaced to very large $|u|$ and as the function $f_0(u)$ decreases rapidly with increasing $|u|$; we can integrate in (13), in the first approximation, only along the real axis. We expand the integrand in powers of k. The first term of the expansion disappears because

$$\int_{-\infty}^{+\infty} \frac{df_0}{du}\,du = f_0\Big|_{-\infty}^{+\infty} = 0.$$

The second term gives

$$\frac{4\pi e^2}{p^2 m}\int_{-\infty}^{+\infty} u\frac{df_0}{du}\,du = 1.$$

Taking into account that

$$\int_{-\infty}^{+\infty} u\frac{df_0}{du}\,du = uf_0\Big| - \int_{-\infty}^{+\infty} f_0\,du = -n_1 \quad (14)$$

we find

$$p_k = -i\omega, \quad \omega = \sqrt{\frac{4\pi ne^2}{m}} \equiv \omega_0 \quad (15)$$

(we have chosen here the sign, which corresponds to a wave, propagating in the positive direction of the x axis). This expression corresponds to the ordinary proper frequency of plasma; we denote it by ω_0. In the next approximation the calculation leads to the following dependence of the frequency on the wave vector:

$$\omega = \omega_0\left(1 + \frac{3}{2}a^2k^2\right). \quad (16)$$

$a = \sqrt{\frac{\varkappa T}{4\pi ne^2}}$ being the electronic Debye—Hückel radius. We omit here the detailed calculations because they coincide with that of Vlasov done in his first paper [1]. This part of his calculations turns out to be correct due to the fact, that in calculating the frequency for small values of k, we can approximately integrate in (13) only along the real axis.

However, the vibrations are actually damped, although the damping coefficient is small for small k. To calculate this decrement we start from an assumption (which is verified by the result), that for $k \to 0$ the real part of p_k tends to zero, the imaginary part remaining finite. Hence for small k the point $u = -p_k/ik$ (Fig. 1) is situated at a finite distance from the imaginary axis and very near to the real one (under the latter). Let

$$p_k = -i\omega - \gamma,$$

γ is the damping coefficient in question $(0 < \gamma \ll \omega)$. We choose a point A on the real axis (Fig. 1), situated not far of the point $u = -p_k/ik$, but so, that its distance from this point is still large as compared with $|\mathrm{Im}(u)|$. Then we draw a semicircle AB through this point (shown with a dotted line in Fig. 1) and use it instead of the corresponding part of the integration path C.

The integral along the straight parts of the integration path is real in the limiting case of $\mathrm{Re}(p) = 0$, in the approximation considered we can put it equal to $-4\pi ne^2/mp^2$. As to the integral along the semicircle, it equals the residue relative to the pole, multiplied by πi (a half of the total circle!). In this way we obtain equation (13) in the form

$$-\frac{4\pi ne^2}{mp^2} + i\frac{4\pi^2 e^2}{mk^2}\frac{df_0\left(-\frac{p}{ik}\right)}{du} = 1.$$

Putting here $p = -i\omega - \gamma$ and solving the equation by means of successive approximations, we get finally the following expression for the damping decrement:

$$\gamma = \omega_0\sqrt{\frac{\pi}{8}}\frac{1}{(ka)^3}e^{-1/2(ka)^2}. \quad (17)$$

Thus, the damping decrement decreases exponentially with decreasing k.

Formulae (15)—(17) are valid for $\gamma \ll \omega$. This condition leads to the inequality

$$ka \ll 1.$$

Consider now the opposite limiting case of large k. We put again $p = -i\omega - \gamma$. It will be verified by the result, that both ω and γ increase indefinitely with $k \to \infty$ but in such a way, that for large k $\omega \ll \gamma$ and the ratios ω/k, γ/k tend to zero and infinity respectively. Then the pole $u = -p/ik$ is situated relatively near to the imaginary, but far from the real axis [$\mathrm{Re}(u)$ is small, $\mathrm{Im}(u)$ is large]. As the function f_0 increases exponentially for large imaginary values of u, we can integrate in (13) only along the circle around the pole, neglecting the integral along the real axis. In this way we obtain from (13)

$$\frac{4\pi e^2}{mk^2} 2\pi i \frac{df_0\left(-\frac{p}{ik}\right)}{du} = 1$$

or, using expression (11), for $f_0(u)$

$$\sqrt{2\pi} \frac{p}{\omega_0 (ka)^3} e^{\frac{p^2}{2\omega_0^2 (ka)^2}} = 1. \qquad (18)$$

By taking the moduli of the expression on the both sides of the equation, and using the suggested inequality $\gamma \gg \omega$, we get

$$\xi e^{\xi^2/2} = \frac{1}{\sqrt{2\pi}} (ak)^2 \qquad (19)$$

with

$$\xi = \gamma/\omega_0 ka.$$

The phase factor of the expression in the left side of equation (18) is equal, in the same approximation, to

$$-\exp\left(\frac{i\gamma\omega}{\omega_0^2 a^2 k^2}\right).$$

As in the right of the equation stands a real positive quantity, this factor must be equal to $+1$. Hence we find:

$$\frac{\gamma\omega}{\omega_0^2 a^2 k^2} = \pi$$

[it can be shown, that by equating to 3π, 5π, we would get a root of the equation (13), which is not the nearest to the imaginary axis]. Together with the definition of the quantity ξ this gives

$$\omega = \pi \sqrt{\frac{\varkappa T}{m}} \frac{k}{\xi}, \quad \gamma = \sqrt{\frac{\varkappa T}{m}} k\xi. \qquad (20)$$

These formulae determine the frequency and the damping decrement of the vibrations, the function $\xi(k)$ being defined implicitly by equation (19). $\xi(k)$ is a slowly increasing function of k (it goes approximately as $\sqrt{\ln ka}$). The ratio γ/ω increases with k as ξ^2, *i. e.* approximately as $\ln ka$.

In the preceding calculations we supposed, that the given function $g(u)$ is an entire function. If this function has singularities, then φ_p will also possess singularities apart from the poles, which are zeros of the denominator in (10). The point p_k in Fig. 2, which determines the behaviour of the potential $\varphi(t)$ for large t, must be chosen as the nearest to the imaginary axis of all the roots of equation (13) and of the singularities, which arise from the singular points of $g(u)$.

In particular, if $g(u)$ is (on the real axis) a continuous function with a discontinuous derivative, then φ_p will have purely imaginary singular points $p = -iku_s$; u_s being the discontinuity points of $g(u)$. Thus, the behaviour of $\varphi(t)$ for large t will be determined by purely imaginary values of p_k, *i. e.* there will be no damping of the field. Hence it follows, that it is by no means possible to use a curve with angles (*e. g.* composed of straight pieces) for $g(u)$ instead of a smooth one in order to get an approximate solution of a given problem. Such a substitution will lead to a qualitatively incorrect picture with an undamped field vibrations.

Finally, it is necessary to discuss the electronic distribution function itself. For the distribution function, integrated over $dv_y dv_z$ we have, according to (8):

$$f_p(u) = \frac{1}{p + iku} \left\{ g(u) + \frac{ike}{m} \varphi_p \frac{df_0(u)}{du} \right\},$$

$$f(u, t) = \frac{1}{2\pi i} \int_{-i\infty+\sigma}^{+i\infty+\sigma} f_p(u) e^{pt} dt.$$

The behaviour of the function $f(u, t)$ for large t is determined by purely imaginary singular point $p = -iku$ of the function $f_p(u)$. Thus, the distribution function turns out to be proportional (for large t) to a periodical factor e^{-ikut}, *i. e.* it performs undamped vibrations with a frequency ku which depends on the velocity u.

§ 2. The vibrations of plasma in an external electric field

Suppose, plasma is placed into an external periodical electric field. The problem is to find the law of the penetration of the field inside the plasma. The external field can be expanded into a Fourier integral with respect to time; therefore, we can confine ourselves to consideration of a monochromatic field of a frequency ω. We suppose that the plasma is bounded by a plane wall; all the distribution is a function only of a one coordinate, say x, along the axis, perpendicular to the wall.

The electric field can be split into a longitudinal part, directed along the x axis, and a transversal part p which is parallel to the plane of the wall. It is no need to consider the transversal field, because the behaviour of a plasma in a transverse electromagnetic wave is described by well known formulae. Therefore, we confine ourselves to the case of a longitudinal field.

As in § 1, we use the distribution function, integrated over the unessential variables v_y, v_z. We can look for this function $f(u, x, t)$ in the form of $f(u, x)e^{-i\omega t}$ (u denotes, as above v_x).

The kinetic equation (2) becomes now

$$-i\omega f + u\frac{\partial f}{\partial x} + \frac{eE(x)}{m}\frac{df_0(u)}{du} = 0 \quad (21)$$

[we write the electric field in the form $E(x)e^{-i\omega t}$]. As a second equation it is convenient to use here [instead of the Poisson equation (3)] the equation, which expresses the absence of the sources for the total current (the real j current and the displacement current):

$$\operatorname{div}\left(\mathbf{j} - \frac{i\omega}{4\pi}\mathbf{E}\right) = \frac{d}{dx}\left(j - \frac{i\omega}{4\pi}E\right) = 0.$$

Hence we find that $4\pi j - i\omega E$ is a constant. Outside the plasma $j=0$; therefore, this constant equals $-i\omega E_0$ where $E_0 e^{-i\omega t}$ is the external field. Thus, we have an equation

$$-i\omega E(x) + 4\pi j(x) = -i\omega E_0. \quad (22)$$

The current density $j(x)$ can be expressed through the distribution function by means of

$$j = e\int_{-\infty}^{+\infty} uf(u, x)\,du. \quad (23)$$

At large distances from the wall the field E in the plasma is determined directly by the condition of the constancy of the longitudinal component of the induction $D=\varepsilon E$, the dielectric constant ε of the plasma being equal to the well-known expression

$$\varepsilon = 1 - \frac{4\pi ue^2}{m\omega^2}. \quad (24)$$

Outside the plasma $D=E_0$; hence the boundary condition at infinity is

$$E = \frac{E_0}{\varepsilon} \quad \text{for } x = +\infty \quad (25)$$

(the positive direction of the x axis is inwards the plasma).

As to the properties at the wall, we shall suppose (as it is usually done in analogous cases), that it has an ideal reflection power. This means that an electron, colliding with the wall, is reflected under the angle, equal to that of the incidence, and with the unchanged absolute value of its velocity (so that v_y, v_z remain unchanged, and $v_x=u$ changes its sign). Then the distribution function must satisfy on the wall ($x=0$) the boundary condition

$$f(u, 0) = f(-u, 0). \quad (26)$$

We integrate formally equation (21) and find:

$$f(u, x) = -e^{i\omega x/u}\int\frac{eE(x)}{mu}\frac{df_0}{du}e^{-i\omega x/u}\,dx.$$

In order to determine the integration constant, we proceed in the following way. Consider ω as a complex parameter with a small positive imaginary part (which we tend in the following to zero). Then the external field $E_0 e^{-i\omega t}$ increases with time, but as it is finite for every finite value of t, the distribution function must also be everywhere (for all $x=\infty$) finite.

If $u<0$ then the factor $e^{i\omega x/u}$ increases indefinitely with x, and in order that $f(u, \infty)$ remains finite we must write for $u<0$:

$$f(u, x) = e^{i\omega x/u}\int_x^{\infty}\frac{eE(\xi)}{mu}\frac{df_0(u)}{du}e^{-i\omega\xi/u}\,d\xi. \quad (27)$$

As to the function $f(u,x)$ for $u>0$ it must be written so, as to fulfil the condition (26). This gives for $u>0$:

$$f(u, x) = e^{i\omega x/u}\left[\int_0^{\infty}\frac{eE(\xi)}{mu}\frac{df_0(u)}{du}e^{i\omega\xi/u}\,d\xi - \int_0^{x}\frac{eE(\xi)}{mu}\frac{df_0}{du}e^{-i\omega\xi/u}\,d\xi\right] \quad (28)$$

(it is to be remembered, that $f_0(u)$ is an even function of u, hence df_0/du is an odd function).

Using the obtained expressions, we calculate the current density (23):

$$j = \frac{i\omega}{4\pi}\left\{\int_0^x E(\xi)K(x-\xi)\,d\xi + \int_x^\infty E(\xi)K(\xi-x)\,d\xi - \int_0^\infty E(\xi)K(x+\xi)\,d\xi\right\}, \tag{29}$$

where the function $K(\xi)$ is defined by means of

$$K(\xi) = \frac{4\pi i e^2}{m\omega}\int_{0}^{\infty}\frac{df_0}{du}e^{i\omega\xi/u}du, \quad \xi > 0 \tag{30}$$

[(29) contains $K(\xi)$ only for positive values of the argument].

In the following it is convenient to split $E(x)$ into two terms, separating the value of the field for $x \to +\infty$:

$$E(x) = \frac{E_0}{\varepsilon} + E_1(x). \tag{31}$$

According to (25), $E_1(x)$ satisfies the boundary contidion $E_1(\infty)=0$. Inserting (31) into (29), we obtain easily:

$$j = j_1(x) + \frac{i\omega}{2\pi\varepsilon}E_0\int_0^x K(\xi)\,d\xi. \tag{32}$$

$j_1(x)$ defined by (29) with $E_1(x)$ standing instead of $E(x)$.

Inserting (31), (32) into (22) and performing some elementary transformations, we obtain the following integral equation for the function $E_1(x)$

$$E_1(x) - \int_0^x K(x-\xi)E_1(\xi)\,d\xi - \int_x^\infty K(\xi-x)E_1(\xi)\,d\xi + \int_0^\infty K(\xi+x)E_1(\xi)\,d\xi = -\frac{2E_0}{\varepsilon}\int_0^\infty K(\xi)\,d\xi. \tag{33}$$

In calculations we used here expression (24) for ε and the expression for the integral $\int_0^\infty K(\xi)\,d\xi$ which can be obtained in the following way. Consider again ω as a complex parameter with $\mathrm{Im}(\omega) > 0$. Then $e^{i\omega\xi/u}$ is zero for $\xi=\infty$, and integrating over $d\xi$ under the sign of integral in (30), we get

$$\int_0^\infty K(\xi)\,d\xi = -\frac{4\pi e^2}{m\omega^2}\int_0^\infty u\frac{d_0}{du}du.$$

The integrand $u(df_0/du)$ is an even function of u hence this integral is a half of the integral (14). Finally,

$$\int_0^\infty K(\xi)\,d\xi = \frac{2\pi e^2 n}{m\omega^2}. \tag{34}$$

The integral equation (33) can be solved in the following way. The function $E_1(r)$ has a physical meaning only inside the plasma, *i. e.* for $x > 0$. We continue this function, and also the function $K(\xi)$ into the region of negative values of the argument by means of the definitions:

$$K(-\xi) = K(\xi), \quad E_1(-x) = -E_1(x) \tag{35}$$

[the function $E_1(x)$, thus defined, has a discontinuity at $x=0$]. Then equation (33) after a simple transformation is reduced to a simpler form:

$$E_1(x) - \int_{-\infty}^{+\infty} K(x-\xi)E_1(\xi)\,d\xi = \begin{cases} -\frac{2E_0}{\varepsilon}\int_x^\infty K(\xi)\,d\xi & \text{for } x > 0, \\ \frac{2E_0}{\varepsilon}\int_{-x}^\infty K(\xi)\,d\xi & \text{for } x < 0. \end{cases} \tag{36}$$

In this form it can be solved by using Fourier method. Multiplying both sides of the equation by e^{-ikx} and integrating over dx within the limits between $-\infty$ and $+\infty$, we obtain:

$$E_{1k}(1-K_k)=\frac{2iE_0}{\varepsilon}\frac{K_0-K_k}{k},$$

E_{1k}, K_k being the Fourier components:

$$E_{1k}=\int_{-\infty}^{+\infty}E_1(x)e^{-ikx}dx,\quad K_k=\int_{-\infty}^{+\infty}K(\xi)e^{-ik\xi}d\xi$$

(K_0 is the value of K_k for $k=0$). By means of the inverse transformation

$$E_1(x)=\frac{1}{2\pi}\int_{-\infty}^{+\infty}E_{1k}e^{ikx}dk$$

we get the function $E_1(x)$ in question in the form of an integral:

$$E_1(x)=\frac{iE_0}{\pi\varepsilon}\int_{-\infty}^{+\infty}\frac{K_0-K_k}{k(1-K_k)}e^{ikx}dk. \tag{37}$$

The function K_k can be presented in the following form:

$$K_k=\frac{4\pi e^2}{m\omega}\int_{-\infty}^{+\infty}\frac{u\frac{df_0}{du}}{ku-\omega}du \tag{38}$$

[we used the definitions (30), (35) and the integration over $d\xi$ is performed under the sign of the integral over du with ω considered again as complex with $\mathrm{Im}(\omega)>0$]. If this integral is taken simply along the real axis, it diverges at the point $u=\omega/k$. However, it is easy to see which must be actually the path of integration. In deducing (38) we assumed that $\mathrm{Im}(\omega)>0$ and the integral was taken along the real axis, *i. e.* along a path, passing below (if $k>0$), or above (if $k<0$) the singular point $u=\omega/k$. Therefore, after putting $\mathrm{Im}(\omega)$ equal to zero, the integral (38) must be taken (if $k>0$) along the path C_1 (Fig. 3), which proceeds along the real axis and goes around the singular point below it, or (if $k<0$) along the path C_2 which goes around the singular point above it.

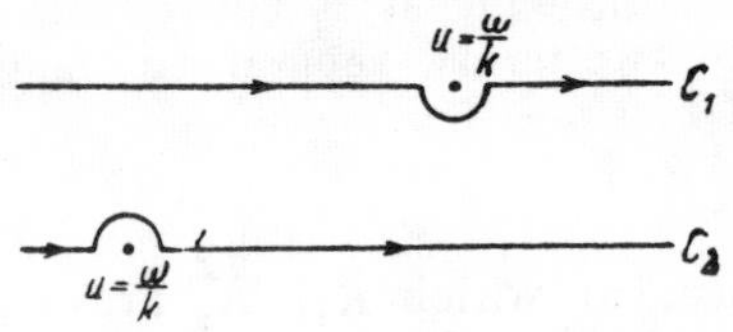

Fig. 3

We introduce the notations:

$$K_k=K_1(k)\text{ for }k>0;\ K_k=K_2(k)\text{ for }k<0. \tag{39}$$

The functions $K_1(k)$ and $K_2(k)$, defined formally by (38) with the integral taken along the path C_1 or C_2, are analytical functions in all the plane of the complex variable k.

Expression (37) is inconvenient for calculations. Introducing the functions K_1, K_2 we can represent it, after a simple transformation, in the form of

$$E_1(x)=\frac{iE_0}{\pi\varepsilon}\int_{-\infty}^{+\infty}\frac{K_0-K_2(k)}{k[1-K_2(k)]}e^{ikx}dk+\frac{iE_0}{\pi\varepsilon}\int_{-\infty}^{+\infty}\frac{K_2(k)-K_1(k)}{k[1-K_1(k)][1-K_2(k)]}e^{ikx}dk. \tag{40}$$

In transformation we used, that according to (24), (38), (14) we have

$$K_0=1-\varepsilon. \tag{41}$$

The difference $K_2(k)-K_1(k)$ is evidently expressed by the same formula (38), the integration being performed simply along a closed contour enclosing the pole (in the negative direction). According to the theorem of the residues, we have, consequently,

$$K_2(k)-K_1(k)=-\frac{4\pi e^2}{m\omega k}2\pi i\left(u\frac{df_0}{du}\right)_{u=\omega/k} \tag{42}$$

or

$$K_2(k)-K_1(k)=\frac{i\sqrt{2\pi}\,\omega\,e^{-\frac{\omega^2}{2\omega_0^2a^2k^2}}}{\omega_0a^3k^3}$$

It is easy to see, that the functions K_1, K_2 are connected with each other by means of the following relations:

$$[K_2(k)]^* = K_1(k^*),$$
$$K_1^*(-k^*) = K_1(k), \quad K_2^*(-k^*) = K_2(k). \qquad (43)$$

At infinity both functions K_1, K_2, vanish. An investigation which we omit here, shows, that the functions $K_1(k)$, $K_2(k)$ have in the whole plane of the complex variable k only one singular point — namely, an essential singularity at $k=0$. The quantity K_0 is the limit to which K_1, K_2 tend when k tends to zero along the real axis. It can also be shown, that $K_1(k)$ tends to the same limit K_0 when k tends to zero along an arbitrary path, passing outside a right-angled sector in the upper half-plane, bounded by two straight lines, which intersect at the coordinate origin and make an angle of 45° with the imaginary axis. The same holds for $K_2(k)$ outside an analogous sector in the lower half-plane.

In the integrals (40) those points are of importance, at which K_1, K_2 are equal to unity. It can be shown, that the equation $K_1(k)=1$ has an infinite number of roots in the upper half-plane, which converge to a condensation point at $k=0$. In the lower half-plane there are no roots at all if $\varepsilon > 0$ (*i. e.* if $K_0 < 1$), or there is one root on the imaginary axis if $\varepsilon < 0$ (*i. e.* if $K_0 > 1$). Analogous results for the function $K_2(k)$ follow directly from the relations (43): the equation $K_2(k)=1$ has an infinite number of roots in the lower half-plane, and has no roots at all (if $\varepsilon > 0$), or has one root on the imaginary axis (if $\varepsilon < 0$) in the upper one.

Consequently, if $\varepsilon > 0$ the integrand of the first integral in (40) has no poles in the upper half-plane and by pushing the path of integration to infinity in this half-plane, we find, that the integral vanishes. If, on the other hand, $\varepsilon < 0$, there is a pole in the upper half-plane and the integral is reduced to the residue relative to this pole. Its dependence on x is, consequently, given by an exponentially decreasing factor $e^{-\alpha x}$, $\alpha \geqslant 0$.

A complete evaluation of the integrals in (40) can be performed only numerically. It is, however, possible to obtain an asymptotical expression, which determines $E_1(x)$ for large values of x ($x \gg a$). We shall see, that in this region the second integral in (40) is larger as compared with the first one and we must calculate only it. We shall do it with the aid of the well-known "method of steepest descent". Inserting (42) into (40) we obtain in the integrand an exponential factor

$$\exp\left\{-\frac{1}{2}\left(\frac{\omega}{\omega_0 a k}\right)^2 + ikx\right\}.$$

Following the method of steepest descent we expand the exponent in powers of $\delta k = k - k_0$ where

$$k_0 = e\sqrt[3]{\frac{\omega^2}{\omega_0^2 a^2 x}}\; e^{i\pi/6}$$

is the extremum point of the exponent, and then integrate along the path of "the steepest descent". In the non-exponential factor we can put $k=k_0$ and take it out of the integration sign. In the denominator we can put $1-K_2(k_0) = 1-K_1(k_0) \cong 1-K_0 = \varepsilon$ (k_0 is small for large x). After a simple calculation we obtain the following final result

$$E_1(x) = \frac{2E_0}{\sqrt{3}\varepsilon^2}\left(\frac{\omega}{\omega_0}\right)^{4/3}\left(\frac{x}{a}\right)^{2/3} e^{-\frac{3}{4}\left(\frac{\omega x}{\omega_0 a}\right)^{2/3}} e^{i\left[\frac{3\sqrt{3}}{4}\left(\frac{\omega x}{\omega_0 a}\right)^{2/3}+\frac{2\pi}{3}\right]}. \qquad (44)$$

Thus, the field $E_1(x)$ decreases according to an exponential law with $x^{2/3}$ in the exponent [as to the first term in (40), we have seen that it decreases according to a stronger law $e^{-\alpha x}$ and is, consequently, insignificant for large x]. Expression (44) contains also a periodical factor.

The case of the frequency ω, being nearly at resonance with the proper frequency of the plasma, needs a separate consideration. The dielectric constant is here small, $|\varepsilon| \ll 1$ (and is connected with the frequency by means of a simple relation $\varepsilon = 2\frac{\omega-\omega_0}{\omega_0}$). The calculations proceed differently for $\varepsilon < 0$ and for $\varepsilon > 0$.

Suppose first that ε is small and negative. We have seen, that for $\varepsilon < 0$ the first term in (40) decreases as $e^{-\alpha x}$, *i. e.* faster than the second one. But with $|\varepsilon| \ll 1$ the coefficient α turns out to be small, and therefore, the second term becomes predominant only for very large x; for smaller values of x the first term prevails.

We shall see, that the integrand of the first term has (for small $|\varepsilon|$) a pole, lying on the imaginary axis near to the coordinate origin [we are speaking of the only root of the equation $K_2(k)=1$ in the upper half-plane]. To calculate this root we can, therefore, expand $K_2(k)$ in powers of k. As to the path of integration C_2 in the integral (38), which defines $K_2(k)$, it is reduced simply to the whole real axis — this path passes above the singular point $u=\omega/k$ (which lies now on the negative half of the imaginary axis). A simple calculation gives in the second approximation

$$K_2(k)=1-\varepsilon+3(ka)^2.$$

Hence we find for the root of the equation $K_2(k)=1$:

$$k=\frac{i}{a}\sqrt{\frac{|\varepsilon|}{3}}.$$

Evaluating the first integral (40) as the residue relative to this pole, we find, finally, the following expression for the total field $E(x)$

$$E(x)=\frac{E_0}{\varepsilon}\left(1-e^{-\frac{x}{a}\sqrt{\frac{|\varepsilon|}{3}}}\right). \qquad (45)$$

Thus, if ε is small and negative, the field increases monotonically, according to a simple exponential law, tending to the limit E_0/ε. For $x=0$ (45) gives $E(x)=0$ instead of the correct value E_0, this is connected with the fact that in the adopted approximation the quantities of the order of ε are neglected.

Consider, finally, the case of small positive values of ε. For $\varepsilon>0$ the first term in (40) vanishes. However, the second integral contains, except the expression (44), also a term, which decreases according to a law $e^{-\lambda x}$. For very small ε this term becomes predominant for all values of x, except the largest. This term is due to the residue relative to the integrand, which lies in the upper halt-plane near the real axis. It turns out, that among the infinite number of the roots of the equation $K_1(k)=1$ in the upper half-plane there exists one, which lies (for small ε) very near to the real axis. Expanding the function $K_1(k)$ in powers of k, it is easy to obtain the following expression for the root in question:

$$k=\frac{1}{a}\left[\sqrt{\frac{\varepsilon}{3}}+i\frac{3}{2\varepsilon^2}\sqrt{\frac{\pi}{2}}e^{-3/2\varepsilon}\right].$$

Calculating the residue relative to this pole, we obtain, finally, the following expression for the field:

$$E(x)=\frac{E_0}{\varepsilon}\left[1-\exp\left\{\frac{i}{a}\sqrt{\frac{\varepsilon}{3}}x-\frac{3}{2a}\sqrt{\frac{\pi}{2\varepsilon}}e^{-3x/2\varepsilon}\right\}\right]. \qquad (46)$$

Thus, in this case we find that the amplitude of the field increases, first, from zero (actually from E_0) up to $2E_0/\varepsilon$, and then it performs damped oscillations (with a very small damping decrement) around the value E_0/ε to which it tends on large distances.

Translated by E. Lifshitz.

REFERENCES

[1] А. Власов, Журн. экспер. и теор. физ. (A. Vlasov, Journ. Exper. a. Theor. Phys.), 8, 291 (1938).

[2] A. Vlasov, Journ. of Phys., 9, 25 (1945).

[3] E. Adirovich, C. R. Acad. Sci. URSS, 48, No. 8. (1045).

Reprinted from Plasma Physics and Controlled Nuclear Fusion Research Vol. 1 Conference Proceeding, Culham, September 6-10, 1965, published by International Atomic Energy Agency, Kärntner Ring, Vienna 1, Austria, by Permission.

LANDAU DAMPING OF ELECTRON PLASMA WAVES

J.H. MALMBERG. C.B. WHARTON AND W.E. DRUMMOND
GENERAL ATOMIC DIVISION, GENERAL DYNAMICS CORPORATION,
SAN DIEGO, CALIF., UNITED STATES OF AMERICA

Abstract — Résumé — Аннотация — Resumen

LANDAU DAMPING OF ELECTRON PLASMA WAVES. It has been predicted by Landau that longitudinal electron waves in a plasma of finite temperature are damped, even in the absence of collisions. The validity of the theory has been challenged on various grounds. Experimental verification is desirable both because the damping is an important phenomena and because the method of calculation has been widely used for related problems. We have measured the damping of electron plasma waves propagating along a cylindrical plasma column immersed in a magnetic field. The plasma matches the assumptions of the theory, namely, collisions are so rare as to produce negligible damping; the number of particles in a Debye sphere is large, the plasma radius is large compared to the Debye length, and the electron velocity distribution function is Maxwellian. The frequency, wavelength and damping length of the waves are measured. The electron velocity distribution function is measured for electron velocities corresponding to the range of wave phase velocities. We observe heavy exponential damping of the waves in a density range where collisional damping is negligible. The magnitude of the observed damping and its dependence on phase velocity are predicted accurately, without any normalizations, by the theory of Landau. The plasma boundary conditions may be adjusted to remove electrons exceeding a given velocity from the plasma. When the velocity at which the distribution function is truncated is reduced to the phase velocity of the wave, the wave damping decreases dramatically. By making this measurement as a function of wave phase velocity, we establish that the damping is caused by a very few electrons travelling in the direction of and at the phase velocity of the wave, as expected from theory.

AMORTISSEMENT DE LANDAU DES ONDES DE PLASMA ELECTRONIQUE. Landau avait prévu que les ondes électroniques longitudinales dans un plasma de température finie sont amorties, même en l'absence de collisions. On a contesté, pour diverses raisons, la validité de cette théorie. Il est souhaitable d'en faire la vérification expérimentale à la fois parce que l'amortissement est un phénomène important et parce que la méthode de calcul a été largement utilisée pour des problèmes connexes. Les auteurs ont mesuré l'amortissement d'ondes de plasma électronique se propageant le long d'une colonne de plasma cylindrique plongée dans un champ magnétique. Le plasma se comporte comme prévu, c'est-à-dire que les collisions sont si rares qu'elles ne produisent qu'un amortissement négligeable, le nombre de particules dans une sphère de Debye est important, le rayon de plasma est grand par rapport à la longueur de Debye, et la fonction de distribution des vitesses électroniques est maxwellienne. Les auteurs ont mesuré la fréquence, la longueur d'onde et la longueur d'amortissement des ondes. Ils ont mesuré la fonction de distribution des vitesses électroniques pour des vitesses d'électrons correspondant à la gamme des vitesses de phase des ondes. Ils ont observé un fort amortissement exponentiel des ondes dans un intervalle de densités où l'amortissement par collisions est négligeable. La théorie de Landau permet de prévoir de façon exacte, sans aucune normalisation, la grandeur de l'amortissement observé et sa dépendance à l'égard de la vitesse de phase. On peut ajuster les conditions aux limites du plasma pour écarter du plasma les électrons dont la vitese dépasse une valeur donnée. Lorsque la vitesse à laquelle la fonction de distribution est tronquée est réduite à la vitesse de phase de l'onde, l'amortissement de l'onde décroît fortement. En procédant à cette mesure en fonction de la vitesse de phase de l'onde, les auteurs ont établi que l'amortissement est causé par quelques rares électrons se déplaçant dans la direction de l'onde et à la vitesse de phase de cette onde, comme prévu d'après la théorie.

ЛАНДАУСКОЕ ЗАТУХАНИЕ ЭЛЕКТРОННЫХ ПЛАЗМЕННЫХ ВОЛН. Ландау предсказал затухание продольных электронных волн в плазме конечной температуры даже при отсутствии столкновений. Правильность этой теории подверглась сомнению по различным причинам. Экспериментальное подтверждение желательно как из-за того, что затухание представляет собой важное явление, так и потому, что метод расчетов широко использовался для решения родственных проблем. Мы измерили затухание электронных плазменных волн, распространяющихся по цилиндрическому плазменному столбу, помещенному в магнитное поле. Плазма соответствует предположениям теории; а именно, столкновения столь редки, что возникает лишь незначительное затухание; число частиц в сфере Дебая велико, радиус плазмы по сравнению с длиной Дебая является большим, а функция распределения электронов по скоростям – максвелловским. Измерялась частота, длина волны и длина затухания волн. Для скоростей электронов, соответствующих диапазону фазовых скоростей волны, измерена функция распределения скоростей электронов. Мы наблюдаем сильное экспоненциальное затухание волн в диапазоне плотности, где столкновительное затухание является незначительным. Теория Ландау точно, без всяких нормализаций, предсказывает величину наблюдаемого затухания и ее зависимость от фазовой скорости. Граничные условия плазмы могут быть подобраны так, чтобы удалить из плазмы электроны, превышающие данную скорость. Когда скорость, при которой функция распределения обрезается, уменьшается до фазовой скорости волны, затухание волн резко уменьшается. Производя это измерение как функции фазовой скорости волны, мы устанавливаем, что затухание вызывается очень небольшим количеством электронов, двигающихся в направлении волны и имеющих фазовую скорость волны, как и следовало ожидать из теории.

AMORTIGUAMIENTO DE LANDAU DE LAS ONDAS DE PLASMA ELECTRONICO. Según la teoría de Landau, las ondas electrónicas longitudinales en un plasma de temperatura finita están amortiguadas aun en ausencia de colisiones. Por diversos motivos, se ha puesto en tela de juicio la validez de esta teoría. La verificación experimental es deseable, tanto porque el amortiguamiento es un fenómeno importante cuanto porque el método de cálculo se ha aplicado extensamente a problemas conexos. Los autores midieron el amortiguamiento de ondas de plasma electrónico que se propagaban a lo largo de una columna de plasma situada en un campo magnético. El plasma satisface los supuestos teóricos: las colisiones son tan raras que el amortiguamiento debido a ellas es despreciable; el número de partículas contenidas en una esfera de Debye es elevado; el radio del plasma es grande comparado con la longitud de Debye; la función correspondiente a la distribución de las velocidades de los electrones es maxwelliana. Los autores midieron la frecuencia, la longitud de onda y la longitud de amortiguamiento de las ondas. Determinaron también la distribución de velocidades de los electrones para valores correspondientes al intervalo de velocidad de fase de la onda. Observaron un marcado amortiguamiento exponencial de las ondas en un intervalo de densidades en el cual puede despreciarse el amortiguamiento por colisiones. La teoría de Landau predice con exactitud, sin normalizaciones de ninguna índole, la magnitud del amortiguamiento observado y su relación con la velocidad de fase. Las condiciones de contorno del plasma pueden ajustarse para extraer del mismo los electrones cuya velocidad supere un determinado valor. Cuando la velocidad a la cual queda truncada la función de distribución se reduce a la velocidad de fase de la onda, el amortiguamiento de esta última decrece en forma muy acentuada. Efectuando esta medición en función de la velocidad de fase de la onda, los autores establecieron que el amortiguamiento es causado por unos pocos electrones que se desplazan en la dirección de la onda y a la velocidad de fase de la misma, como cabía esperar según la teoría.

I. INTRODUCTION

It has been predicted by Landau [1] that electrostatic electron waves in a plasma of finite temperature will be damped, even in the absence of collisions. The theory has been challenged on various grounds [2] and a number of experiments designed to detect the effect for electrostatic electron waves or ion acoustic waves have been reported [3]. The existence of the damping is of interest not only for its own sake, but because the method of calculation has been widely used for related problems. We report here measurements of the damping of electron waves propagating along a cylindrical column immersed in a magnetic field. The experimental results agree in detail with the theory of Landau.

II. THEORY

The theory of spatial Landau damping in an infinite homogeneous medium [1] can be generalized, in the limit of large magnetic field, to the case of a plasma which is inhomogeneous in the direction perpendicular to the magnetic field [4]. The result is

$$\nabla_{\perp}^{2}\phi = - k_{\perp}^{2}\phi = \epsilon k_{\parallel}^{2}\phi \qquad (1)$$

where $k_\parallel$ is the (complex) eigenvalue for a given frequency, ω, and

$$\epsilon = 1 - \frac{4\pi e^2}{mk_\parallel} \int_{-\infty}^{\infty} dv_\parallel \frac{\frac{\partial f_0(v_\parallel, v_\perp)}{\partial v_\parallel}}{\omega - k_\parallel v_\parallel} \tag{2}$$

For a Maxwellian plasma with mean thermal speed $\bar{v} = KT/m$, and plasma frequency, ω_p, ϵ is approximately given by

$$\epsilon = \epsilon_r + i\Gamma \tag{3}$$

where

$$\epsilon_r \cong 1 - \left(\frac{\omega_p}{\omega}\right)^2 \left[1 + \frac{3}{x^2} + \frac{5}{x^4} + \dots\right] \tag{3a}$$

$$\Gamma = \sqrt{\frac{\pi}{2}} \left(\frac{\omega_p}{\omega}\right)^2 x e^{-x^2/2} \tag{3b}$$

and we have defined

$$x = \frac{\omega}{k_\parallel \bar{v}} \tag{4}$$

The function $(\nabla_\perp^2 \phi)/k_\parallel^2 \phi$ depends only on $k_\parallel a$ and is generally a decreasing function of the mean radius of the plasma, a; that is, $(k_\perp/k_\parallel)^2 = f(k_\parallel a)$ and $f' < 0$, where f is different for different radial distributions. For example in a cylindrical plasma of uniform density with radius a, and $k_\parallel a \gg 1$

$$\left(\frac{k_\perp}{k_\parallel}\right)^2 = \left(\frac{P_{n\nu}}{k_\parallel a}\right)^2, \qquad n = 0, 1, 2 \dots \tag{5}$$

where $P_{n\nu}$ is the νth zero of the nth order Bessel function. For a slab plasma with a density variation in the y direction of the form $n = n_0/\cosh^2(y/a)$

$$\left(\frac{k_\perp}{k_\parallel}\right)^2 = \frac{n(n+1)}{(k_\parallel a)^2} + \frac{(2n+1)}{k_\parallel a}, \qquad n = 0, 1, 2 \dots \tag{6}$$

However, it is not necessary to measure the radial density distribution to calculate the damping if the group velocity is measured, as we will now show.

The dispersion relation can be written as

$$(\epsilon_r + f) + i\Gamma = 0 \tag{7}$$

Letting $k_i = \text{Im}(k_\parallel)$, $k_r = \text{Re}(k_\parallel)$, and assuming $k_i \ll k_r$, k_r and k_i can be found by expanding $(\epsilon_r + f)$ around $k_\parallel = k_r$ to give

$$(\epsilon_r + f) = 0 \tag{8a}$$

$$ik_i \left.\frac{\partial(\epsilon_r + f)}{\partial k}\right]_{k_r} + i\text{Re}\Gamma = 0 \tag{8b}$$

where we have neglected $\text{Im}\Gamma$.

From Eq. (8a) we have

$$\frac{\partial(\epsilon_r+f)}{\partial k} = -\frac{\partial(\epsilon_r+f)}{\partial\omega}\left(\frac{d\omega}{dk}\right) = -\frac{\partial\epsilon_r}{\partial\omega}v_g \qquad (9)$$

since f is not a function of ω and $d\omega/dk = v_g$, the group velocity. From Eq. (3a),

$$\frac{\partial\epsilon_r}{\partial\omega} = +\frac{2}{\omega}\left(\frac{\omega_p}{\omega}\right)^2\left(1+\frac{6}{x^2}+\frac{15}{x^4}+\ldots\right) \qquad (10)$$

and using Eq. (9)

$$\frac{\partial(\epsilon_r+f)}{\partial k} = -\frac{2}{\omega}v_g\left(\frac{\omega_p}{\omega}\right)^2\left(1+\frac{6}{x^2}+\frac{15}{x^4}+\ldots\right) \qquad (11)$$

Inserting this in Eq. (8b) and using Eq. (3b) for the real part of Γ we obtain

$$\frac{k_i}{k_r} = \sqrt{\frac{\pi}{8}}\left(\frac{\bar{v}}{v_g}\right)\frac{x^4 e^{-x^2/2}}{\left(1+\frac{6}{x^2}+\frac{15}{x^4}+\ldots\right)} \qquad (12)$$

In Eq. (12), $x = \omega/k_\parallel\bar{v}$ can be replaced by $x_r = (\omega/k_r\bar{v})$ without loss of accuracy except in the exponent, where we have

$$x^2 = x_r^2\left(1 - 2i\frac{k_i}{k_r}\right).$$

Our final result is thus

$$\frac{k_i}{k} = \frac{\sqrt{\frac{\pi}{8}}\left(\frac{\bar{v}}{v_g}\right)x_r^4 e^{-x_r^2/2}\cos\left(x_r^2\frac{k_i}{k_r}\right)}{\left(1+\frac{6}{x_r^2}+\frac{15}{x_r^4}+\ldots\right)} \qquad (13)$$

It can be shown the corrections to Eq. (13) for the effect of finite magnetic field are less than 1% for the present experiment ($\Omega/\omega_p \simeq 3$). The purpose of the present experiment is to test Eq. (13). All quantities appearing in the equation are measured. Note that the radial density distribution does not appear explicitly.

III. DESCRIPTION OF THE PLASMA

A schematic diagram of the machine which produces the plasma [5] is given in Fig. 1. The plasma is produced in a duoplasmatron arc source and drifts from it into a long uniform magnetic field of a few hundred gauss. Since the duoplasmatron has a magnetic field of approximately 3 kilogauss at its orifice, there is a strong magnetic mirror at its end of the machine. At the other end, the ions are attracted to the negatively charged end plate and die, but the electrons are reflected by the electrostatic field and return to the magnetic mirror. Some electrons are scattered out of the loss cone by the time they return to the mirror, and are captured in the plasma. Thus, the electrons are contained at one end by a magnetic mirror and at the other end by an electrostatic field. The ions are not contained; they simply flow through the machine, providing a background of positive charge. The entire machine is steady-state. The suppressor grid is held 15 volts negative with respect to the end plate to prevent the secondary electrons due to ions striking the end plate from being injected into the plasma. It is important to note that electrons whose velocity along the magnetic field is several times the mean thermal velocity are preferentially in the loss cone. These electrons are not contained. Since they are in the loss

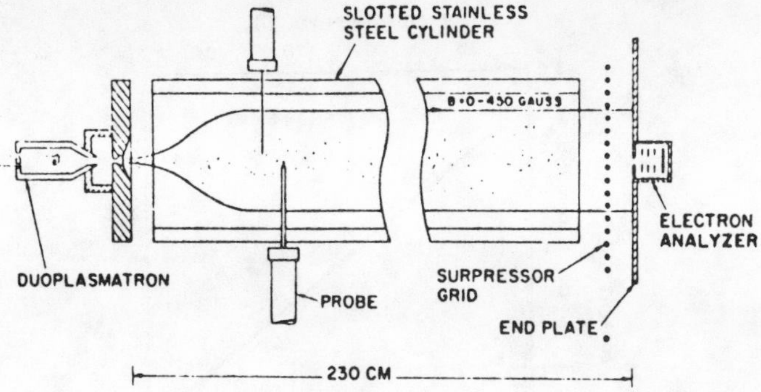

FIG. 1. Schematic diagram of the machine.

cone they enter the collision dominated region at the orifice of the duoplasmatron and die after one transit to the end plate and back. If the end plate is not sufficiently negative to reverse the motion of these electrons, they are lost to the end plate of the machine. In this situation, the electron velocity distribution function in the machine is normal in the downstream direction (from duoplasmatron to end plate) but truncated at a velocity determined by the end plate potential in the upstream direction. This circumstance enables us to remove a few electrons from the velocity distribution; in fact, just those electrons which cause Landau damping for waves propagating toward the duoplasmatron. The damping of waves propagating in the other direction is not affected.

An electron velocity analyzer is mounted behind a 1 mm diameter hole in the end plate. Electrons in line with the hole and with enough energy to reach the end plate pass into the analyzer. By means of a series of grids the analyzer rejects any ions which enter it, and measures current of electrons with energy greater than a given adjustable value. Thus we obtain the part of the electron velocity distribution function of interest for damping experiments by direct measurement. A typical result is shown in Fig. 2. The ordinate is the logarithm of electron current. The abscissa is electron energy measured in electron volts and on a separate scale, in units of the mean thermal energy. This is a plot of $\int_{E_0}^{\infty} F(E)dE$. The straight curve on this semi-log plot proves that the distribution function is decreasing exponentially with energy for this range of electron energies, i.e., it is Maxwellian. The temperature of the plasma may be obtained directly from the slope of the curve to an accuracy of about 5%. We have differentiated such data electronically as the analyzer voltage is swept, obtaining the distribution function itself, and obtained the same conclusion. The range of electron energies shown in Fig. 2 corresponds to the relevant velocities for the associated damping data. The distribution function is measured at various radii by varying the position of the plasma with magnetic correction coils and the plasma temperature is not a function of radius.

For a given gas in the arc (usually H_2), the plasma temperature is determined almost entirely by the relationship of pressure in the duoplasmatron to arc current. At a fixed current the temperature rises as the pressure is reduced, at first very slowly and then rapidly, until a point is reached at which the arc goes out. Temperatures range from 5 to 20 ev. The radial distribution of plasma density as measured by ion saturation current to a Langmuir probe is given in Fig. 3. The radial size is influenced by the adjustments of the machine, especially by the magnitude of the magnetic field. The central density is typically 10^8 - 10^9 electrons/cm^3. In the pressure range where the temperature is not very sensitive to arc current, the density of the plasma is almost directly proportional to arc current. The density is also a function of longitudinal position, since the ions diffuse radially as they drift down the machine. This diffusion process is much too fast to be the result of two-body collisions. It is not understood

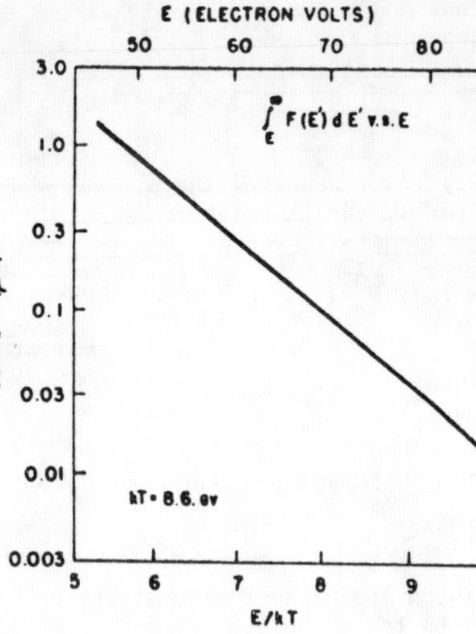

FIG. 2. $\int_E^\infty F(E')dE'$ versus E.

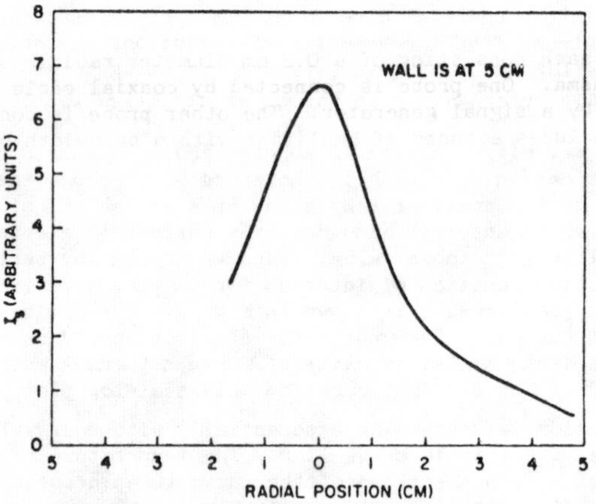

FIG. 3. Radial density distribution.

at this time. Typically the central density decreases a factor of two from one end of the machine to the other.

The machine is pumped by two 10" diameter oil diffusion pumps with liquid nitrogen cooled baffles to remove neutrals escaping from the source and neutralized ions which have hit the end plate. The background pressure is typically 1.7 × 10^{-5} torr (mostly hydrogen). The electron mean free path for electron-ion collisions is of the order of 1000 meters and for electron-neutral collisions is about 40 meters. Thus the damping length due to collisions is of the order of 40 meters. Since the measured damping lengths are in the range 2 to 50 cm, collisional damping is completely negligible. Debye length is typically 1 mm, and the number of particles in a Debye sphere about 10^6. The machine thus provides us with a plasma which matches all the assumptions of the theory and whose electron velocity distribution function is known.

The density of ions and electrons in the plasma must be approximately equal, both in the main part of the machine and in the collision dominated orifice of the duoplasmatron. The ions acquire a much larger Larmor radius than the electrons at the point of injection, and some electrons are contained while the ions are not. Both effects tend to increase the relative electron density. To maintain quasi-neutrality, the center of the plasma charges negatively with respect to the duoplasmatron anode by roughly 3 KT. When the duoplasmatron anode is grounded, the center of the plasma is about 3 KT negative with respect to the grounded stainless steel cylinder bounding the plasma, and a radial electric field of a few volts per centimeter is established. This radial field crossed into the longitudinal magnetic field produces an E × B rotation of the plasma and an associated instability. This rotation is readily observed with probes. The rotation may be prevented by removing the radial electric field. As the potential of the duoplasmatron anode is varied from ground to positive values, the rotation slows, stops, and then begins again in the opposite direction. For the experiments reported here, the anode potential was adjusted to prevent the rotation. This phenomenon will be reported in more detail elsewhere. The fluctuations in ion saturation current to a Langmuir probe are less than 1% when the anode potential is adjusted so the plasma does not rotate. The strongest component of the fluctuations is 360 cycle ripple which directly reflects the ripple in the arc current supply. The remaining noise is less than 1% and contains frequencies from almost zero to many megacycles. Some of this noise is due to sheath noise at the probe; some of it represents actual fluctuations of the plasma.

IV. WAVE MEASUREMENTS

The dispersion and damping measurements, which have previously been the subject of a preliminary report [6], are made in the following manner:

Two probes, each consisting of a 0.2 mm diameter radial tungsten wire are placed in the plasma. One probe is connected by coaxial cable to a chopped amplifier driven by a signal generator. The other probe is connected to a receiver which includes a tuned rf amplifier with a bandwidth of about 2 megacycles, a string of broad-band amplifiers, an rf detector, a video amplifier, and a coherent detector operated at the transmitter chopping frequency.

For some measurements we use a sharp rf filter in the receiver to obtain a band-width of about 200 kilocycles. Provision is made to add a reference signal from the transmitter to the receiver rf signal with a balanced mixer, i.e., we may use the system as an interferometer. The reference signal, which is not chopped, is orders of magnitude larger than the received signal, so the chopped part of the interferometer output is linear with the received rf signal for at least 30 db. The contribution of the unchopped reference signal to the detected signal is steady state and rejected by both the video amplifier and the coherent detector.

The transmitter is set at a series of fixed frequencies, and at each, the receiving probe is moved longitudinally. The position of the receiving probe, which is transduced, is applied to the x axis of an x-y recorder, and the interferometer output, its logarithm, or the logarithm of the received power is applied to the y axis.

Typical raw data are given in Fig. 4. The slope of the power curve is the e-folding length for power damping of the wave. In the case shown this is accurately exponential for two orders of magnitude, and in fact more, since the range is limited by the range of the logging circuit. The wave power in the plasma is of the order of 1 $\mu W/cm^2$. A 30 db reduction in transmitter power does not change the damping length. The signal decreases smoothly as the probe is retracted radially with a half-maximum diameter about equal to that of the density profile. The distance between maxima on the interferometer curve is the wavelength, which can be determined to 2% over most of the range of the experiment. (Since the wave is damped, the distance between maxima is slightly less than one wavelength. The correction, which can be accurately determined from the damping data, is too small to be important in most cases.)

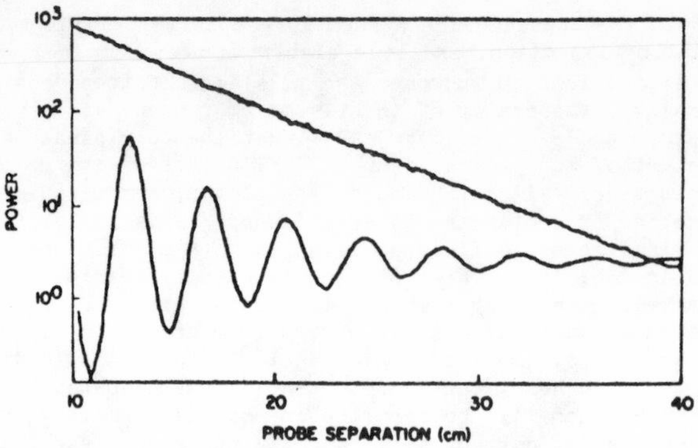

FIG. 4. Raw data. Upper curve is the logarithm of received power. Lower curve is interferometer output. Abscissa is probe separation.

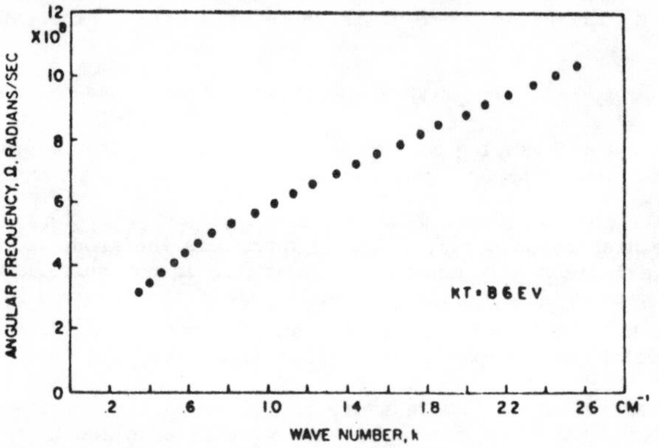

FIG. 5. Dispersion curve.

From data such as Fig. 4 we determine, as a function of frequency the real and imaginary parts of the parallel wave number, ($k_r = 2\pi/\lambda$, $k_i = 1/2\lambda$). A typical measured dispersion relation for the waves is plotted in Fig. 5. These data have not been analyzed in detail, but the absolute magnitude and shape of the curve are approximately as expected for longitudinal electron oscillations in a strong magnetic field when the radial density distribution and finite temperature are included in the theory. The dispersion is dominated by the radial density distribution, and to obtain an exact fit to the dispersion curve, the actual density profile would have to be put into the theory, presumably numerically.

In Fig. 6, we compare the measured damping with the theory. The ordinate is the ratio of the imaginary to the real part of longitudinal wave number and the abscissa is the square of the ratio of the phase velocity to the mean thermal velocity. The ratio k_i/k_r and the phase velocity of the wave (the product of the wave length and frequency) are obtained directly from data like Fig. 4. Since we have shown previously that the electron velocity distribution is a Maxwellian and measured its temperature, the mean thermal velocity is also known experimentally.

The experimental points are from two separate sets of data taken with different plasma parameters, especially a temperature difference by about 50%. The magnitude of the damping at any given phase velocity for these two sets of data is different by an order of magnitude. However, when the phase velocity is

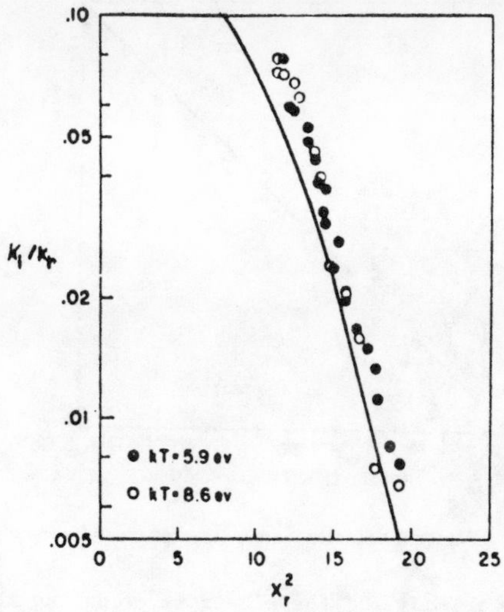

FIG. 6. k_i/k_r versus x_r^2.

normalized to the mean thermal velocity agreement is obtained. To compute the theory, we require the ratio of the mean thermal velocity to the group velocity. The slope of the dispersion curve, (Fig. 5), $d\omega/dk$, is the group velocity, so this quantity too is experimentally measured. The ratio is not sufficiently different between the two sets of data to significantly affect the theoretical curve. Thus the theoretical curve is a not subject to any normalization. The experimental data have also not been normalized in any manner. We have not attempted to assign errors to the data but some idea may be obtained from the scatter of the points, which is typical of several similar sets of data. The most important systematic error in Fig. 6 is due to the uncertainty of about 5% in the temperature measurement, which is sufficient to completely account for the small horizontal shift between the theoretical curve and the experimental points.

Figure 6 demonstrates that the magnitude of the damping, its dependence on phase velocity, and its dependence on plasma temperature, are as predicted by Landau. The damping lengths observed range from 2 cm to 50 cm while the electron mean free path, which is roughly the collisional damping length, is of the order of 40 m. Damping due to currents in the boundary shield, wave scattering from irregularities in the plasma, and from wave-wave scattering from noise in the plasma have been estimated and also appear to be orders of magnitude too small to explain the result. And none of these effects are expected to give a damping with such a strong dependence on phase velocity.

The damping observed for wave propagation in the upstream and downstream directions agrees within the random errors when plotted against x_r^2, provided that the end plate is sufficiently negative to contain all the electrons. To test the effect of end plate potential on the damping, we have observed the power transmission between two fixed probes as a function of end plate voltage. This is a very sensitive way to observe small changes in damping length since the received power depends exponentially on damping length. For downstream propagation the signal is almost independent of end plate potential. For propagation in the upstream direction, the signal is almost independent of the end plate potential until a particular voltage is reached, and then switches to a much larger value. This voltage corresponds to the "escape energy" of the electrons producing the damping, and allowing for the plasma potential, may be converted to the velocity of these electrons in the plasma. Only one electron in 10^3 to 10^4 is escaping the plasma when the abrupt change in damping occurs. By repeating the measurement at a variety of frequencies (and thus various phase

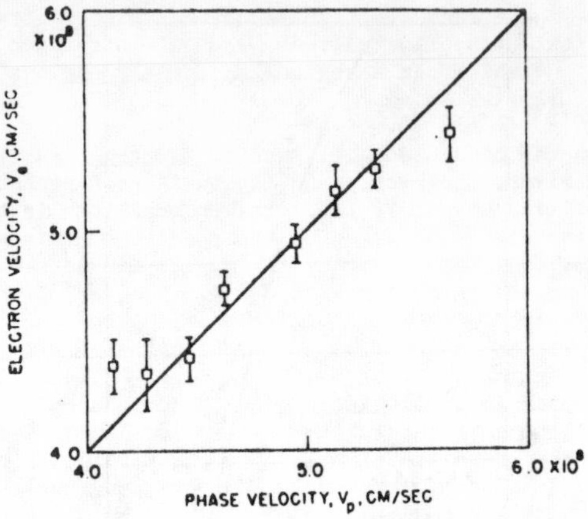

FIG. 7. Electron velocity versus wave phase velocity.

velocities) we obtain the velocity of the electrons producing the damping as a function of wave phase velocity. The result, shown in Fig. 7, demonstrates that the damping is caused by electrons traveling at the phase velocity of the wave, as expected from theory.

The stainless steel cylinder bounding the plasma at 5 cm acts as a wave guide beyond cutoff to suppress direct capacitive coupling between the probes. The limit for the short wavelength measurements is reached when the damping length for the waves becomes approximately equal to the attenuation length of the much stronger direct capacitive signal. The phase of the direct capacitive signal changes very slowly as a function of position along the wave guide (in an idealized system, not at all), and thus the phase of the reference signal in the interferometer may be adjusted to reject this component of the received signal. We are able to discriminate against the direct signal by 20-30 db by this method. The damping is then obtained by measuring the amplitude of successive maxima on the interferometer curve. Since only signals which remain in phase during the final averaging time of the system contribute to these peaks, the bandwidth of this sort of receiver is about one cycle per second.

Extra care must be taken with the measurement of very long damping lengths because of the longitudinal plasma density variation mentioned previously. Very slight changes in plasma density change the dispersion relation and thus the phase velocity at a given frequency. However, a slight change in phase velocity causes a large change in the damping length, which depends exponentially on the square of the phase velocity. For long damping lengths, it is observed that the phase velocity and damping length are functions of longitudinal position. However, as long as both are measured at the same point in the machine, the expected damping is obtained. When the damping length becomes very long, strong standing waves are generated for the whole length of the machine.

The receiver bandwidth can be made sufficiently narrow that plasma noise picked up by the probe is reduced to a completely negligible level, especially when the interferometer with a relative bandwidth of about 10^{-8} is used. However, the influence of plasma noise on the dynamics of wave propagation must be considered. Especially since the damping depends on a very few electrons on the tail of the distribution function, and their density may be fluctuating more than that of the bulk of the plasma. Large noisy fluctuations in the phase and amplitude of the received signal are observed. That this modulation is introduced in part by the sheath around the probes may be proved in the following manner: A wave is launched in the plasma and then detected by two separate identical probes placed in the plasma and separated by a distance short compared to the wavelength, but long compared to the Debye length. The probes are connected to two separate receivers. It is observed that the fluctuations in the phase and amplitude of the received signals are not highly correlated with each other. This means that these fluctuations were not introduced in transmission through the plasma, but rather in a region immediately surrounding the probes which is a few Debye lengths thick.

Fluctuations in the phase and amplitude of the received signal are averaged over time by the receiver. However, such fluctuations represent frequency modulation of the transmitted wave. If the receiver bandwidth is too narrow, they remove energy from the signal accepted by the receiver. This effect is not important for fluctuations introduced by the sheath around the probe since the power loss is not changed as the probe is moved. However, fluctuations introduced during transmission through the plasma became larger as the probes are separated and result in an apparent damping. At phase velocities for which the Landau damping is large, this effect is negligible. At phase velocities for which the Landau damping is small, this produces an apparent residual damping. This effect can be distinguished experimentally from Landau damping by showing it is not caused by electrons traveling at the phase velocity of the wave, and by investigating the details of the damping curves as a function of receiver bandwidth. This apparent residual damping provides a limit on the longest damping lengths which can be measured. The data reported here were taken with a bandwidth of two megacycles and terminated at the point where a bandwidth 200 kc gave a materially different result. There are other systematic differences in the damping observed with various bandwidth receivers which are not completely understood, but these effects are too small to be important for the present experiment.

V. CONCLUSIONS

The experiment demonstrates that longitudinal electron waves exhibit heavy exponential damping under conditions where collisional damping is negligible. The damping is caused by electrons traveling at the phase velocity of the wave, and the magnitude of the damping, its dependence on phase velocity, and its dependence on plasma temperature are accurately predicted by the theory of Landau.

ACKNOWLEDGMENTS

We wish to thank Mr. Charles D. Moore for his contributions to the experimental work.

This project was sponsored by the Advanced Research Projects Agency, Department of Defense, as part of Project DEFENDER, and the Defense Atomic Support Agency, monitored by Air Force Weapons Laboratory, Kirtland Air Force Base, New Mexico, Research and Technology Division, Air Force Systems Command, United States Air Force, under Contract No. AF29(601)-6366.

REFERENCES

[1] LANDAU, L., J. Phys. 10, 45 (1946).

[2] WEITZNER, H., Phys. Fluids 6, 1123 (1963); ECKER, G. and HOLLING, J., Phys. Fluids 6, 70 (1963).

[3] KOFOID, M. J., to be published; CAULTON, M., HERSHENOV, B., and PASCHKE, F., J. Appl. Phys. 33, 800 (1962); STOVER, H. L., and KINO, G. S., Bull. Am. Phys. Soc. 9, 336 (1964); HIRSHFIELD, J. L., and DENNIS, Jr., R. N., Proceedings of the Sixth International Conference on Ionization Phenomena in Gases, Paris, 1963, edited by P. Hubert (S.E.R.M.A., Paris, 1964); DOLGAPOLOV, V. V. et al, Zh. Eksperim. i Teor. Fiz. 45, 1260 (1963) [translation: Soviet Phys.--JETP 18, 866 (1964)]; WONG, A. Y., MOTLEY, R. W., and D'ANGELO, N., Phys. Rev. 133, A436 (1964).

[4] DRUMMOND, W. E., Phys. Fluids 7, 816 (1964).

[5] MALMBERG, J. H., et al, Proceedings of the Sixth International Conference on Ionization Phenomena in Gases, Paris, 1963, edited by P. Hubert (S.E.R.M.A. Paris, 1964).

[6] MALMBERG, J. H., and WHARTON, C. B., Phys. Rev. Letters 6, 184 (1964).

DISCUSSION

H. MOTZ: In your paper in Physical Review Letters, [6], you stated that the received power varies by as much as 100% owing to changes in the tail of the electron distribution function. The detector averages out fluctuations, but does the choice of filters not change the attenuation curves significantly?

J.H. MALMBERG: For receiver bandwidths which are too small, yes. We terminated the series of measurements at the point where 200-kc/s and 2-Mc/s bandwidths gave different results. A detailed study of attenuation curves as a function of bandwidth showed that this procedure was the proper one.

H. MOTZ: An exact calculation by Wu and Klevans on the basis of the Lenard-Guernsey-Balescu equations shows that the ratio of non-collisional and collisional damping changes varies sharply with k. You might be more certain of evidence for non-collisional damping if you could go to somewhat higher values of k. Would this be possible?

J.H. MALMBERG: The damping is caused by a very few electrons travelling at the phase velocity of the wave, about 1 in 10^3 or 10^4 of the total. This seems to be conclusive evidence that we are not seeing collisional damping. In addition, the electron mean free path is about 10^3 times the damping lengths observed. Finally, the parameter dependence of the damping agrees with the prediction of Landau but is completely wrong for collisional damping, especially the observed spectacular dependence on phase velocity.

M.N. ROSENBLUTH (Chairman): I believe that under the conditions described by Dr. Malmberg the collisional effects are negligible.

H. MOTZ: Can you identify the mode of propagation in your plasma column by comparison with the curve of k_r versus ω? I have made a very approximate comparison and find the (02) mode fits better than the lowest mode.

J.H. MALMBERG: I believe your calculation is for a uniform radial distribution of density terminated by a wall; our density distribution is strongly non-uniform, and this circumstance dominates the dispersion curve. We believe this is an m=0 mode because all higher modes at a given frequency have somewhat lower phase velocity and, as a result, should exhibit much more violent damping.

J.B. TAYLOR: In quasi-linear theory of instability arising from inverse Landau damping, the waves interact with the particle distribution in such a way as to change the growth rate and so limit the instability. Should one not similarly expect that in your experiment the waves would also modify the particle distribution function and so affect the damping rate? This would perhaps lead to a non-linear damping.

J.H. MALMBERG: The effect should occur, but at much larger wave powers than we use. The wave power is chosen so that the effect, which can be calculated, is negligible. In addition, we have reduced the power by a factor of 1000 and no change in damping length is observed.

S.J. BUCHSBAUM: Did you vary the radius of the plasma column?

J.H. MALMBERG: The data exhibited are typical of results using various magnetic fields which control the radius of the plasma. It should be noted that, except for a weak dependence on the group velocity (which is experimentally measured), the theory is independent of the radial distribution of the density.

R.M. KULSRUD: Is any correction to exponential space damping of the wave observed or predicted?

J.H. MALMBERG: W.E. Drummond did the work by the theory of Landau, therefore no such correction was considered. For weakly damped waves, and hence long distances, the density, dispersion and, consequently, the damping of the wave are a function of position.

The only precaution required in this case is that phase velocity and damping be measured in the same region.

S. YOSHIKAWA: Is k_i essentially zero when there is no wave damping by Landau damping (that is to say, if the electron collector is sufficiently biased)?

J.H. MALMBERG: Within our experimental accuracy, which is limited by fluctuation effects, it is.

Reprinted from Physics of Fluids 5, No. 4, April 1962 by Permission

One-Dimensional Plasma Model

JOHN DAWSON
Plasma Physics Laboratory, Princeton University, Princeton, New Jersey
(Received June 27, 1961; revised manuscript received December 27, 1961)

A one-dimensional plasma model consisting of a large number of identical charge sheets embedded in a uniform fixed neutralizing background is investigated by following the sheet motions on a high-speed computer. The thermalizing properties and ergodic behavior of the system are examined and found to be in agreement with the assumption that one is equally likely to find the system in equal volumes of the available phase space. The velocity distribution, Debye shielding, drag on fast and slow sheets, diffusion in velocity space, the Landau damping of the Fourier modes, the amplitude distribution function for the Fourier modes, and the distribution of electric fields felt by the sheets were obtained for the plasma in thermal equilibrium and compared with theoretically predicted values. In every case, except one, the drag on a slow sheet, the numerical results agreed with theory to within the statistical accuracy of the results. The numerical results for the drag on a slow sheet were about a factor of 2 lower than the theory predicated indicating that the approximations made in the theory are not entirely valid. An understanding of the cause of the discrepancy might lead to a better understanding of collisional processes in plasmas.

INTRODUCTION

It often occurs in physics that one can obtain an insight into the behavior of a complicated system by investigating simple models which exhibit some of the properties of the system of interest. It is the purpose of this paper to describe such a model for a plasma, and to give examples of some of the things which can be done with it.

The model is that of a one-dimensional plasma. In essence, it is a system composed of a large number of identical charge sheets embedded in a uniform fixed neutralizing background. The sheets are constrained to be perpendicular to the x axis and to move only in the x direction. They are allowed to pass freely through one another. The sheets may be viewed as point charges in one dimension and thus this model is a one-dimensional plasma.

This model exhibits a number of real-plasma properties. The forces between sheets are long range, and because of this the model exhibits collective motions as well as individual particle (sheet) motions. Each of the sheets surrounds itself with a Debye-shielding cloud; the Fourier modes exhibit Landau damping.

The model is sufficiently simple so that the motions of systems containing more than 1000 sheets can be followed in detail on a high-speed computing machine. Statistical mechanics may be applied to systems of this size. We may thus obtain statistical theories for the behavior of the system. The predictions of such theories may be compared with the machine results, and we may thus check such theories and the assumptions which go into them. Further, we have complete control of the initial state of the plasma and we can obtain as complete information as we desire about the motion of the system. The theoretical predictions may thus be checked in more complete detail than is possible with a real plasma.

Other authors have used electronic computers to solve problems in statistical mechanics. Many of these calculations have been involved with equilibrium properties.[1-4] However, some nonequilibrium calculations have been made on systems composed of particles which interact through short-range forces.[5]

MODEL

There are three equivalent versions of the one-dimensional plasma model. Two of these have been given elsewhere.[6] However, for completeness they will also be described here. The first of these has already been mentioned and is illustrated in Fig. 1. It consists of a number of identical charge sheets embedded in a fixed neutralizing background. We let the charge and mass per unit area be $-en_0\,\delta$ and $mn_0\,\delta$, where $-e$ and m are the electron charge and mass, and δ is the intersheet spacing. The background charge density is n_0e. If we wish to make a

[1] A. W. Rosenbluth, M. N. Rosenbluth, A. H. Teller, and E. Teller, J. Chem. Phys. **21**, 1087 (1953).
[2] M. N. Rosenbluth and A. W. Rosenbluth, J. Chem. Phys. **22**, 881 (1954).
[3] W. W. Wood and F. R. Parker, J. Chem. Phys. **27**, 720 (1957).
[4] B. J. Alder, S. P. Frankel, and V. A. Lewinson, J. Chem. Phys. **23**, 417 (1955).
[5] Work by B. J. Alder and T. Wainwright described in C. Kittel, *Elementary Statistical Physics* (John Wiley & Sons, Inc., New York, 1958).
[6] J. M. Dawson, Project Matterhorn Rept. MATT-31 (1960).

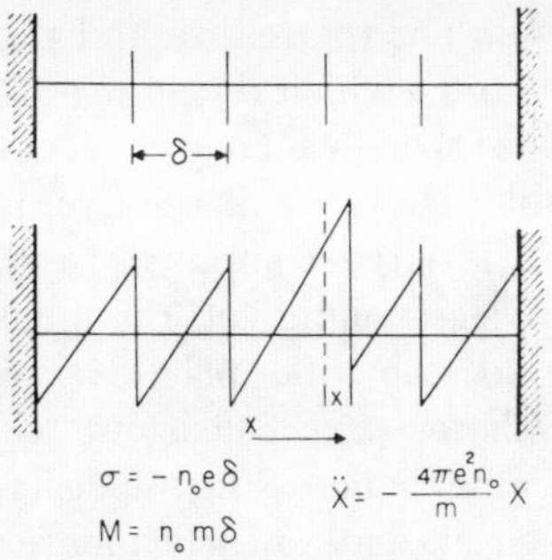

FIG. 1. One-dimensional plasma model.

correspondence between this plasma and a real plasma we must take n_0 to be the number density of the electrons.

When the system is in its equilibrium state the sheets are at rest and equally spaced. The electric field then has the sawtoothed shape shown in Fig. 1. At each sheet it jumps by $-4\pi e n_0 \delta$. In between sheets it varies linearly with distance due to the background charge.

When a sheet is in its equilibrium position the average electric field which it sees is zero. If it is displaced a distance X from its equilibrium position it passes over an amount of positive charge equal to en_0X. Let us take X positive for the sake of argument. Then if the sheet does not cross any other sheet it will see a net positive charge per unit area equal to en_0X on its negative side and a net charge $-en_0X$ per unit area on its positive side. Gauss' law then gives for the electric field which it feels

$$E = 4\pi e n_0 X. \tag{1}$$

The equation of motion of the sheet is thus given by

$$n_0 m\ \delta \ddot{X} = -4\pi e^2 n_0\ \delta X,$$

or

$$\ddot{X} = -\omega_p^2 X, \tag{2}$$

with

$$\omega_p^2 = 4\pi e^2 n_0/m.$$

For small noncrossing displacements each sheet performs simple harmonic motion about its equilibrium position, independent of what all the other sheets are doing. For noncrossing situation the system is equivalent to the system of noninteracting oscillators considered by Goldstein and Lepkin,[7] and hence exhibits the same collective modes they found.

When a sheet crosses other sheets the situation is no longer so simple. Nevertheless, we may obtain an expression similar to (2) which determines its motion. We observed that under small displacements each sheet behaved like a harmonic oscillator bound to its equilibrium position. There is one equilibrium position per sheet. Now when two sheets cross we may view them as exchanging equilibrium positions or centers of attraction. Thus the equation of motion for a sheet is the following:

$$\ddot{x} = -\omega_p^2 X. \tag{3}$$

Here x is the actual position of the sheet and X is the displacement from its instantaneous equilibrium position.

It is now possible to construct a second one-dimensional plasma model. Suppose that instead of having sheets which pass freely through one another we had perfectly elastic sheets. Now it is a property of perfectly elastic collisions between identical particles in one dimension that the particles simply exchange velocities. This leads to the same situation that results from the particles passing through each other. The only difference between the end results is the names of the particles.

It is possible to build a mechanical model of the one-dimensional plasma. It consists of a number of identical pendulums which are lined up and constrained to oscillate only along this line of centers.

One can illustrate a number of properties of the one-dimensional plasma with this model. For example, if the first pendulum is pulled aside and released so as to strike the second it will give its velocity to the second, the second in turn gives its velocity to the third and so on. A pulse thus moves through the pendulums. When a pendulum strikes its neighbor it gives up its velocity, but not its displacement. Thus the pulse leaves the pendulum behind it in a displaced state and they start to oscillate. This is equivalent to the excitation of a plasma oscillation by a fast sheet moving through a plasma.

The third model is based on the second. Suppose we have a system containing N pendulums. Consider now an N-dimensional space in which the displacement of the ith pendulum is represented by the value of the ith coordinate. The N pendulums are equivalent to an N-dimensional oscillator in this space. Now the pendulums are constrained by the conditions that the ith cannot cross the $(i + 1)$st. Thus the system satisfies conditions

$$X_i \le X_{i+1} + \delta, \qquad X_1 \ge -\delta, \qquad X_N \le \delta, \tag{4}$$

where δ is the spacing between pendulums, and the last two conditions are imposed by the ends. The

[7] S. Goldstein and H. J. Lepkin, Ann. Phys. (N. Y.) **6**, 301 (1959).

equal signs give a set of surfaces [$(N - 1)$-dimensional hyperplanes] which the system cannot cross. These walls form a closed polyhedron in N dimensions inside of which the N-dimensional oscillator is constrained to move. When two pendulums strike each other the oscillator strikes one of the walls of the polyhedrons. It rebounds elastically, i.e., its velocity perpendicular to the wall is reversed.

It is convenient to introduce the Fourier modes at this point. To do this consider the linear transformations

$$A_j = \left(\frac{2}{N+1}\right)^{\frac{1}{2}} \sum_{i=0}^{N+1} X_i \sin\left(\frac{\pi j i\ \delta}{L}\right), \tag{5}$$

$$X_i = \left(\frac{2}{N+1}\right)^{\frac{1}{2}} \sum_{j=0}^{N+1} A_j \sin\left(\frac{\pi j i\ \delta}{L}\right). \tag{6}$$

Here i refers to the ith pendulum and j to the jth Fourier mode. The walls, particles 0 and $N + 1$, are considered part of the system but are held fixed. Equation (5) is an orthogonal transformation from the X_i's to the A_j's. The A_j's are in fact the same as the normal coordinate for the problem of N identical mass points connected by identical massless springs.[8] Since Eqs. (5) and (6) are the equations for an orthogonal transformation they represent a rotation of the coordinate axis.

The A_j's do not quite correspond to the usual Fourier modes. The quantity $i\delta$ is the equilibrium position of the ith pendulum. Thus these are the Fourier modes of the system in terms of Lagrangian coordinates. The usual Fourier modes are expressed in terms of Eulerian coordinates or actual positions. As long as the displacements are small compared to the wavelength of the mode ($\lambda = 2L/j$) the two are almost the same.

THERMALIZATION, ERGODIC BEHAVIOR, AND RECURRENCE TIME

The first problem that is of interest is whether or not one can apply statistical mechanics to this model; that is, whether or not this model behaves roughly ergodically. For motions with small amplitudes where crossing does not take place, the system clearly does not thermalize. On the other hand, when crossing does take place there is an exchange of energy between sheets and we may expect thermalization.

If the average energy per sheet is kept constant and the number of sheets in the system becomes very large, then we can always find motions of the system which do not exhibit crossing. These are motions in which neighboring sheets perform similar motions. These motions do not thermalize and they cannot be reached from states which do show crossing. Thus a region of phase space which is consistent with energy is unavailable. However, if the average displacement of a sheet is large compared to the intersheet spacing then the volume of the phase space in which crossing does not take place is small compared to the total phase space consistent with the energy. This is because noncrossing modes require that neighboring sheets have nearly identical motions.

We can estimate the ratio of the volumes available to crossing modes and noncrossing modes in the following way. Let us consider only the velocity space and assume the potential energy is negligible. The space available to the crossing modes is essentially all the velocity space which is consistent with the energy. This is the surface of the N-dimensional sphere with radius v,

$$v = (2\mathcal{E}_{\text{tot}}/m), \tag{7}$$

where $\mathcal{E}_{\text{tot}}$ is the total energy of the system. This volume τ_T is given by

$$\begin{aligned} \tau_T &= \frac{2(\pi)^{\frac{1}{2}N}}{\Gamma(\frac{1}{2}N)} \left(\frac{2\mathcal{E}_{\text{tot}}}{m}\right)^{\frac{1}{2}(N-2)} \\ &\cong 2(2e\pi)^{\frac{1}{2}(N-2)}(\langle V^2\rangle)^{\frac{1}{2}(N-2)}. \end{aligned} \tag{8}$$

Here $\langle V^2\rangle$ is the average square velocity of a particle.

To obtain the volume available to noncrossing modes consider the $N - 1$ variables ξ_i given by

$$\xi_i = X_i - X_{i-1}. \tag{9}$$

From (2) we see that the ξ_i's satisfy oscillator equations for noncrossing motions.

$$\ddot{\xi}_i = -\omega_p^2 \xi_i. \tag{10}$$

It follows directly that the quantity Q is a constant of the motion.

$$Q_i = \dot{\xi}_i^2 + \omega_p^2 \xi_i^2. \tag{11}$$

Now ξ_i must be less than δ (the intersheet spacing) for all time if crossing is not to take place. This is true only if Q_i satisfies (12), and this means $\dot{\xi}_i$ must satisfy (13).

$$Q_i < (\omega_p\ \delta)^2, \tag{12}$$

$$|\dot{\xi}| < (\omega_p\ \delta). \tag{13}$$

The volume τ_{nc} in velocity space available to noncrossing modes is thus of the order of the volume of an $(N - 1)$-dimensional cube with dimension given by (13). Its volume τ_{nc} is

$$\tau_{nc} \simeq (2\ \delta\omega_p)^{(N-1)}. \tag{14}$$

[8] J. W. S. Rayleigh, *The Theory of Sound* (Dover Publications, Inc., New York, 1945), Vol. 1, pp. 172–176.

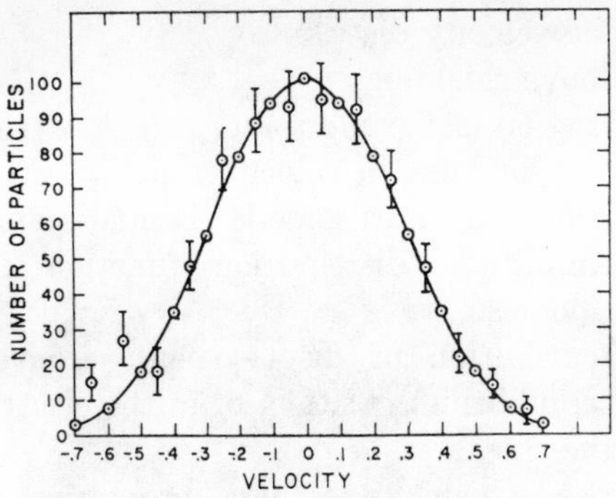

FIG. 2. Average velocity distribution function for a 9-sheet system.

Taking the ratio of τ_{nc} to τ_T gives

$$\frac{\tau_{nc}}{\tau_T} = 2\left(\frac{2}{e\pi}\right)^{\frac{1}{2}(N-2)}\left(\left\langle\frac{\omega_p^2\,\delta^2}{V^2}\right\rangle\right)^{\frac{1}{2}(N-2)} \propto \left(\frac{\delta}{D}\right)^N, \quad (15)$$

where D is the Debye length,

$$D = (kT/4\pi e^2 n_0)^{\frac{1}{2}} = (\langle V^2\rangle/\omega_p^2)^{\frac{1}{2}}, \quad (16)$$

if the plasma is in thermal equilibrium. If the Debye length is several intersheet spacings and N is of the order of hundreds this ratio is indeed small and τ_{nc} can be neglected provided there is crossing.

While this argument shows that the phase space available to noncrossing modes is negligible it does not show that the system will thermalize. In order to investigate thermalization and recurrence times, systems containing five and nine sheets were followed for 60 oscillations times ($120\pi/\omega_p$). Both systems were started out with all the energy in the first Fourier mode. The amplitude was taken sufficiently large so that crossing took place. The state of the system was printed out 120 times or twice per oscillation.

We may estimate the portion of the time these systems should spend in a state in which the first Fourier modes has more than 95% of the energy (the 95% state). Again consider only the velocity. Let the total kinetic energy of the system at time t be KE(t). The velocity spaces available to the systems are the surfaces of 5- and 9-dimensional spheres with radii ρ_v,

$$\rho_v = [2\mathrm{KE}(t)/m]^{\frac{1}{2}}. \quad (17)$$

If the first mode has all the kinetic energy then

$$A_1 = \pm\rho_v, \qquad A_j = 0, \qquad j \neq 1.$$

If we require that the kinetic energy of the first mode be 95% or more of the total kinetic energy, then we are restricted to small regions of the energy surfaces about these points. These regions can be approximated by small 4- and 8-dimensional spheres with radii Δv,

$$\Delta v = [2\mathrm{KE}(t)/20m]^{\frac{1}{2}}. \quad (18)$$

The ratio r of their volume to the surface area of the total spheres are given by

$$r_5 = \frac{6}{16}\left(\frac{1}{20}\right)^2 \simeq 10^{-3}, \quad 5 \text{ sheets},$$
$$r_9 = \frac{105}{768}\left(\frac{1}{20}\right)^4 \simeq 10^{-6}, \quad 9 \text{ sheets}. \quad (19)$$

If we assume the potential is negligible and that the motion is ergodic then (19) gives the portion of the time for which the mode has more than 95% of the energy. The potential energy is not quite negligible. It averaged about 20% of the total energy for the 5-sheet case and about 13% for the 9-sheet case. However, the maximum amplitude allowed the jth Fourier mode by the constraints (4) is proportional to $[\sin(j\pi/2N)]^{-1}$. Thus the first Fourier mode is allowed the largest amplitude, and most of the potential energy is in this mode. Because of this we can expect that the potential will not greatly influence the estimates given by (19) and it is possible it will even increase the portion of the time the system spends in the 95% state.

Out of the 120 samplings, the 5-sheet system was found to return to the 95% state once. This occurred after about 45 oscillation times. At that time the potential and kinetic energies of the first mode were 38 and 57%, respectively, of the total energy. This is somewhat more often than we might expect, but is not impossible in view of the crudeness of the theory and the smallness of the sample.

The 9-sheet system never returned to the 95% state during the time it was followed, and in fact the first mode never got more than 50% of the energy after the initial transients. This is in agreement with the statistical arguments.

Figures 2 and 3 show much stronger evidence of the accuracy of the statistical approximation. Figure 2 shows the time summed velocity distribution for the 9-sheet case. With so few sheets, we could not hope to obtain a smooth velocity distribution function at any one time. However, we can expect that the sum of the velocity distributions at a great many times will be accurate. The curve shown in Fig. 2 is the theoretical curve obtained if we assume that the energy available for kinetic energy is equal to the total energy minus the average potential energy. It is proportional to the area on the energy sphere one obtains if a given particle has velocity between v and $v + dv$. Its formula is

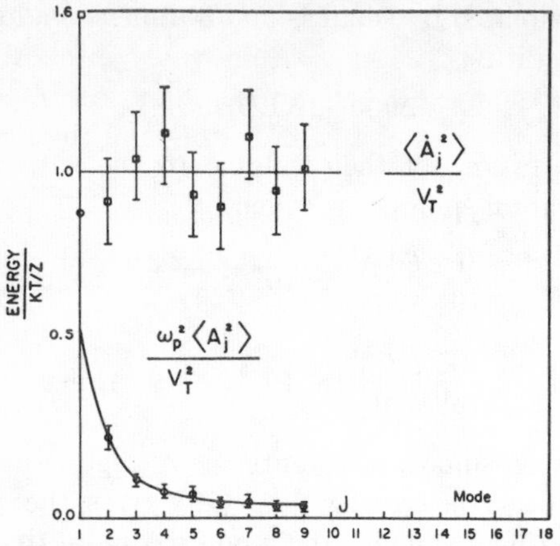

FIG. 3. Average kinetic and potential energies in the Fourier modes for a 9-sheet system.

$$F(v) \propto [1 - mv^2/2(\mathcal{E}_{tot} - \langle\phi\rangle)]^3, \qquad (20)$$

where $\mathcal{E}_{tot}$ is the total energy and $\langle\phi\rangle$ is the average potential energy. Since the average potential energy amounts to only 13% of the total energy it is almost negligible and the above approximation is not bad. Similar agreement is obtained for the 5-sheet case.

Figure 3 shows the average potential and kinetic energies of the Fourier modes for the 9-sheet case. The straight line through the kinetic-energy points is the average kinetic energy ($\frac{1}{2}KT$), while the curve through the potential-energy points is a theoretical curve whose derivations will be given later. It will be observed that all the points fall near their predicted values except for the first mode. It has about 1.5 times the predicted average kinetic and potential energies. There are several possible causes of this. The most probable one is that the system was started out with all the energy in the first mode and the finite relaxation time for the plasma resulted in the mode having a higher than average energy.

On the whole these results indicate that statistical arguments can be applied to this model. We can expect the agreement to be even better for systems containing a larger number of particles. In the next section the theoretically predicted properties of large systems are compared with the calculated properties. The excellent agreement found there is further justification for the application of statistical mechanics to the model.

PROPERTIES OF THE ONE-DIMENSIONAL PLASMA IN THERMAL EQUILIBRIUM

We may now investigate the properties of the one-dimensional plasma near thermal equilibrium. Some properties which are of interest and which will be investigated here are the following:

(1) The velocity distribution;

(2) Debye shielding;

(3) Drag on fast (supersonic) and slow (subsonic) sheets, and diffusion in velocity space;

(4) Drag on a Fourier mode (Landau damping);

(5) Amplitude distribution function for the Fourier modes;

(6) Distribution of displacements from instantaneous equilibrium position, or of the electric fields felt by the sheets.

Theories which give these properties can be developed. This section is devoted to the comparison of such theories with the machine results. It will be divided into subsections each of which deals with one of the properties. The theory of each property will be given when it is not standard.

The numerical results used for comparison were obtained by starting the system off in essentially thermal equilibrium. Because the system contained only a finite number of sheets it was impossible to start with an exact Maxwell distribution. Therefore, the particles were distributed among 16 uniformly spaced velocity groups; the number of particles in a group was proportional to exp $(-V^2/2V_T^2)$, where V was the velocity of the group. The velocity of a particle i was chosen randomly in the following way. The velocities of all the particles were put on IBM cards which were thoroughly shuffled. The resultant deck was used to give the initial velocities of the sheets. All sheets were started at their equilibrium positions.

A. Velocity Distribution

The velocity distribution of the sheets should be Maxwellian. Figure 4 shows the time summed velocity distribution for a system of 1000 sheets with a mean square velocity of 26.67 $\delta^2\omega_p^2$. This velocity gives a Debye length of 5.16 δ, $[(\langle V_T^2\rangle/\omega_p^2)^{\frac{1}{2}}]$, or a little over five intersheet spacings. The smooth curve is the theoretical Maxwell distribution obtained by assuming the energy available for velocity was equal to the total energy minus the average potential energy. Since the total potential energy should fluctuate only slightly, this should be a good approximation. Further the average potential amounted to only 8% of the total energy, so that this correction was small in any case.

The agreement between the numerical results and the theoretical curve is good. However, it is not as good as would be expected if the samples taken at different times were statistically independent. The error in this case would be of the order of $[N(V)\,\Delta V]^{\frac{1}{2}}$ and is indicated by the error bars. In these calcu-

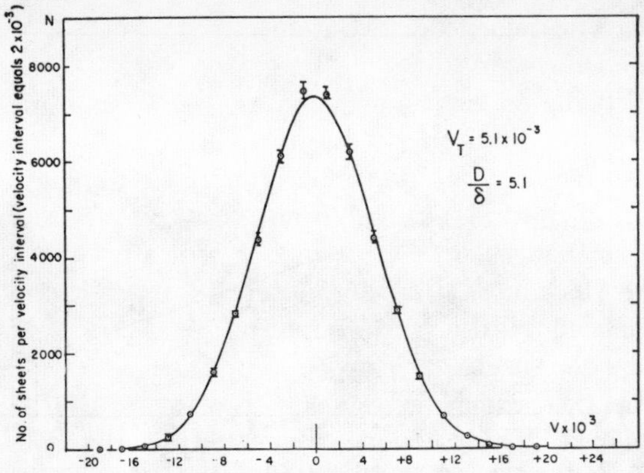

FIG. 4. Average velocity distribution function for a 1000-sheet system.

lations the system was sampled three times per plasma period $2\pi/\omega_p$. The relaxation time (the time required for a Maxwell distribution to be re-established after a small perturbation) is of the order of $[(2\pi)^{\frac{1}{2}}D/\delta\omega_p]$ as will be discussed in the section on the relaxation time. Two samples must be separated in time by more than a relaxation time if they are to be statistically independent. The system was sampled roughly six times during a relaxation time and thus the expected deviations should be of order $[6N(V)\ \Delta V]^{\frac{1}{2}}$ rather than $[N(V)\ \Delta V]^{\frac{1}{2}}$. In another calculation (1000 sheets, $D = 10.5$) for which the relaxation time was longer and in which the samples were taken more frequently (six times per oscillation), the deviations from theory were found to be even larger. However, when they were corrected for the finite relaxation time they also agreed within the expected accuracy.

Other quantities which mirrored the distribution function such as the Debye shielding cloud also showed spuriously large fluctuations about the theoretical curves when the system was sampled many times during a relaxation time. In every case, these fluctuations decreased to the expected statistical fluctuations when the sampling time became comparable with the relaxation time.

These results show that the system was constantly fluctuating about its thermal equilibrium state and that agreement with theory is not simply due to the fact that the system was started out with roughly a Maxwell distribution.

B. Debye Shielding

The Debye shielding for a 1000-sheet system with a Debye length of 5.16 intersheet spacings is shown in Fig. 5. The points are the average number of particles between 0 and 1, 1 and 2, etc., intersheet spacings from a test sheet. To obtain these averages the number of sheets within each interval was counted for every tenth sheet. This was repeated at a large number of different times and the average of the whole group found.

The smooth curve is the theoretical curve obtained from the linearized Debye theory. It is the solution of the linearized form of

$$\frac{d^2\phi}{dx^2} = -4\pi e n_0\left[\exp\left(-\frac{e\phi}{kT}\right) - 1\right]$$

$$\simeq \frac{4\pi e^2 n_0 \phi}{kT} = \frac{\omega_p^2}{\langle V_T^2\rangle}\phi, \tag{21}$$

$$n(x) = n_0 \exp(-e\phi/kT) \simeq n_0(1 - e\phi/kT).$$

When the boundary conditions

$$E_\pm(0) = (d\phi/dx) = \mp 2\pi n_0 e\delta, \qquad x = 0,$$

$$\lim_{x\to\pm\infty} E = \frac{d\phi}{dx} = 0, \tag{22}$$

are imposed, the linearized solution (23) is obtained.

$$n(x) = n_0[1 - (1/2\ D)\exp(-|x|/D)],$$

$$E = \mp 2\pi e n_0\ \delta \exp(-|x|/D), \qquad \begin{matrix}-\text{for } x > 0\\ +\text{for } x < 0\end{matrix}$$

$$\phi = 2\pi e n_0\ \delta\ D \exp(-|x|/D). \tag{23}$$

Here D is the Debye length,

$$(kT/4\pi e^2 n_0)^{\frac{1}{2}} = \langle V_T^2\rangle/\omega_p^2, \tag{24}$$

which in this case is 5.16 δ.

It turned out that the Debye shielding was one of the more difficult quantities to obtain from the machine calculations. This was due to the fact that the statistical error in the density was of the order of $N^{\frac{1}{2}}$, where N is the number of test charges averaged over. Thus, for the above case where the maximum depression of the density is 10% we require 100 cases before the depression equals the fluctuations.

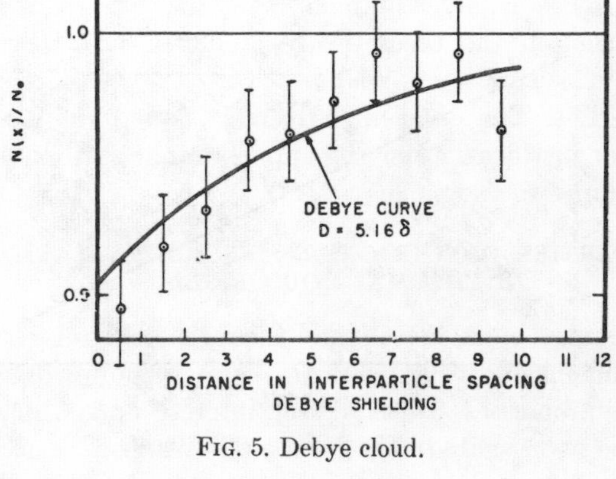

FIG. 5. Debye cloud.

To obtain the density depression of 10 percent accuracy requires 10^4 samples.

C. Drag on a Sheet and Diffusion in Velocity Space

1. *Drag on a Fast Sheet*

Let us first consider the drag on a very fast or supersonic sheet. We will take the velocity of the sheet to be positive for the sake of argument.

The plasma ahead of such a sheet cannot know of its approach. Thus, there can be no disturbance and hence no electric field ahead of the sheet. However, in going from the negative to the positive side of the sheet the electric field must jump by $-4\pi e n_0\ \delta$. Thus, the electric field behind the sheet is $4\pi e n_0\ \delta$.

The average electric field E felt by the sheet is $E = 2\pi e n_0\ \delta$, and its acceleration is given by

$$\frac{dV}{dt} = -\frac{n_0 e\ \delta E}{n_0 m\ \delta} = -\frac{\omega_p^2\ \delta}{2}. \tag{25}$$

The drag is thus independent of the velocity. It is due to the excitation of a plasma oscillation by the sheet.

Figure 6 shows a plot of the average absolute velocity as a function of time for two groups of fast particles. The initial velocity for the group represented by the circles was 2.35 V_T, while that for the triangles was $-2.35\ V_T$. These groups were obtained by looking for particles whose velocities lay in small velocity intervals about $\pm 2.35\ V_T$. These particles were then followed in time and the average velocities of the two groups (as functions of time) were found. The results shown are for a system of 1000 sheets with a Debye length of 10 δ. The straight line shown in Fig. 6 is the curve predicted by (25).

If the system (and hence the code) is time reversible, the drag in the negative time direction should be the same as in the forward time direction. This was found to be the case. Figure 7 shows a similar plot to 6. The data was from a 200-sheet system with a Debye length equal to 4.5 intersheet spacing. The points were obtained by looking for particles with velocities in the vicinity of 4×10^{-2}. The thermal velocity was 2.2×10^{-2}. The points show the average velocity of the group as a function of $|t - t_0|$ (t_0 was the time when we started to follow a particle). The circles are for $t - t_0$ positive while the squares are for $t - t_0$ negative. Thus the squares show the average velocity prior to the time they had velocity 4×10^{-2}.

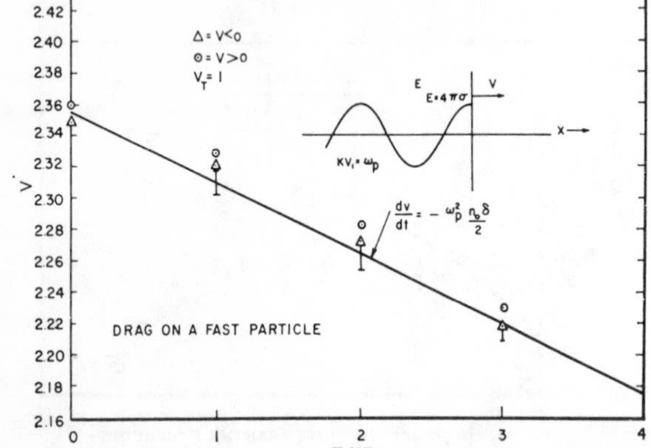

FIG. 6. The drag on a fast sheet.

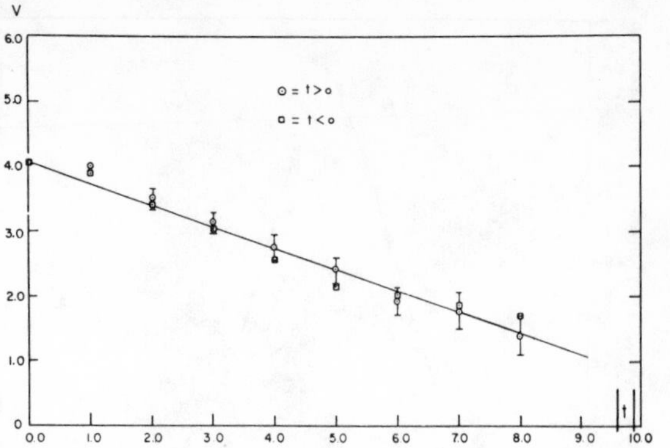

FIG. 7. The average velocity of a fast sheet as a function of the absolute time.

2. *Drag on a Slow Sheet*

Consider a sheet (test sheet) moving slowly through the plasma. Let its velocity be V. Due to its motion its Debye cloud will be distorted. It will encounter more sheets in its front than in its rear. Some of the bombarding sheets are reflected by the field surrounding it. Since more will be reflected from its front than from its rear, a slight negative charge builds up in front and a slight positive charge accumulates in its rear. The resultant field tends to slow down the sheet.

Figure 8 illustrates the distortion. The electric field will not be symmetric with respect to the sheet. Thus, if we take the potential to be zero at plus ∞ it will not be zero at $-\infty$. We will let the potential be ϕ_0 at the sheet and $\phi_{-\infty}$ at $-\infty$. We will work in the rest frame of the sheet.

The rate of change of momentum of a little element of the positive ion background is

$$n_0 e E\ \Delta x, \tag{26}$$

where Δx is the size of the element and E is the electric field which it feels.

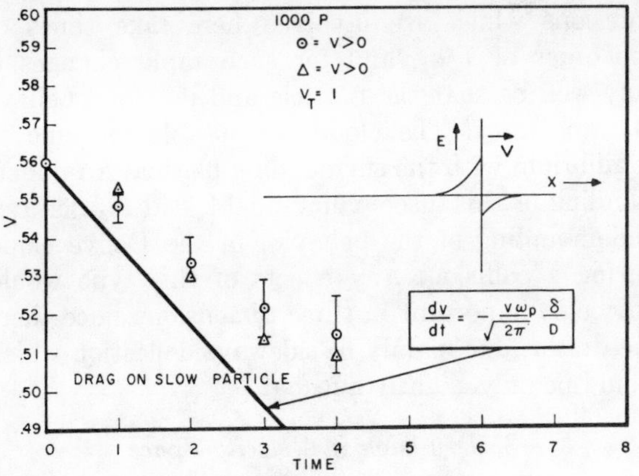

FIG. 8. The drag on a slow sheet.

Its total change in momentum in going past the sheet is

$$\delta P_i = \int n_0 e\, \Delta x E\, dt = -\int_{\infty}^{-\infty} n_0 e\, \Delta x E(x) \frac{dx}{-V}. \quad (27)$$

Here $-V$ is the velocity of the ions relative to the sheet. Due to the infinite mass of the ions V is constant and (27) is simply $n_0 e\, \Delta x \phi_{-\infty}/V$. In a unit time the length of column of positive ions which pass the sheet is V so that the total rate of change of the ion momentum is

$$dP_i/dt = en_0\phi_{-\infty}. \quad (28)$$

We must now find the change in momentum of the electrons (sheets). For the electrons passing through the sheet we have (29) from conservation of energy

$$v_{-\infty}^2 = v_{+\infty}^2 - (2e\phi_{-\infty}/m). \quad (29)$$

$v_{+\infty}$ and $v_{-\infty}$ are the velocities of the electron, relative to the test sheet at $\pm\infty$. For small velocities of the test sheet, $\phi_{-\infty}$ will be small; in fact it is proportional to V. Thus, for all electrons which can cross the sheet, $\phi_{-\infty}$ will be small compared to $\frac{1}{2}mv^2$. We thus find that $v_{+\infty} - v_{-\infty}$ is approximately

$$v_{+\infty} - v_{-\infty} = \Delta v = e\phi_{-\infty}/mv_{\infty+}. \quad (30)$$

From (30) we find the change in momentum of those sheets which pass over the potential barrier is given by

$$-e\phi_{-\infty}\left\{\int_{-\infty}^{\infty} f(v+V)\,dv - \int_{-(-2e\phi_0/m)^{\frac{1}{2}}}^{[-2e(\phi_0-\phi_{-\infty})/m]^{\frac{1}{2}}} f(v+V)\,dv\right\}. \quad (31)$$

The function f is the distribution function in the rest frame of the ions, and is Maxwellian. If we assume $[-2e\phi_0/m]^{\frac{1}{2}}$ is small, then we can expand f in a Taylor's series in the second integral of (31). We find that to first order in $\phi_{-\infty}$ (also V) (31) is equal to

$$-en_0\phi_{-\infty} + 2e\phi_{-\infty}f(0)[-2e\phi_0/m]^{\frac{1}{2}}. \quad (32)$$

Finally we must find the change in momentum for those sheets that are reflected by the Debye cloud. These sheets change their velocity by $-2v$ and thus their change in momentum is given by

$$m\left\{\int_{-(-2e\phi_0/m)^{\frac{1}{2}}}^{0} 2v^2 f(v+V)\,dv - \int_0^{[-2e(\phi_0-\phi_{-\infty})/m]^{\frac{1}{2}}} 2v^2 f(v+V)\,dv\right\}. \quad (33)$$

Making the same approximations as in (31) we find (33) is equal to (34) to first order in V or $\phi_{-\infty}$.

$$-2e\phi_{-\infty}f(0)(-2e\phi_0/m)^{\frac{1}{2}} - (-2e\phi_0/m)^2 f'(V). \quad (34)$$

Adding up (28), (32), and (34), the total change in momentum of the ions plus electrons and equating it to the negative of the rate of change of momentum of the test sheet gives

$$\frac{dP}{dt} = \frac{m\,dV}{dt} = m\left(\frac{-2e\phi_0}{m}\right)^2 f'(V) = mv_c^4 f'(V). \quad (35)$$

The quantity v_c is the minimum velocity a particle must have before it can cross the Debye cloud. If ϕ_0 is approximated by its value for V equal to zero we have

$$\phi_0 = -2\pi e n_0\,\delta D, \qquad D = V_T/\omega_p,$$

$$v_c^2 = 4\pi e n_0\,\delta D/m,$$

$$f = \frac{1}{(2\pi)^{\frac{1}{2}}V_T}\exp\left(\frac{-V^2}{2V_T^2}\right), \quad \frac{dV}{dt} = -\frac{\omega_p\,\delta}{(2\pi)^{\frac{1}{2}}D}V. \quad (36)$$

It is interesting to note that one obtains the same formula by the clothed particle approximation of Rostoker.[9] In this approximation the system is treated as one composed of particles whose interaction is given by their shielded fields. In this approximation the force per unit area on a sheet, say 1 by another, say 2 is given by

$$F = \mp 2\pi e^2 n_0^2\,\delta^2 \exp\left(\frac{|x_2 - x_1|}{D}\right), \quad \begin{matrix} - \text{ for } x_2 > x_1 \\ + \text{ for } x_2 < x_1 \end{matrix}. \quad (37)$$

The only sheets which impart a net momentum to the test sheet are those which are reflected from

[9] N. Rostoker, Nuclear Fusion 1, 101 (1961).

its Debye cloud. If one calculates from this model the drag on a test sheet pulled at constraint velocity through the plasma it is exactly given by (35) or (36).

Figure 8 shows the average drag on a group of particles whose initial velocity was 0.56 times the thermal velocity. The graph was obtained in a similar manner to Fig. 6 described previously. The straight line is the theoretical curve predicted by (36). As can be seen the observed drag is less by about a factor of 0.5 to 0.7. One might argue that $0.56V_T$ is not a small velocity and the difference is due to this. However, the velocity diffusion calculation that will be presented shortly gives the drag at zero velocity and it shows that the discrepancy is not due to this.

In the above calculation a number of approximations were made. First, the drag was computed as if the test sheet had an infinite mass. In reality it has the same mass as the sheets with which it is colliding. If we adopt the clothed sheet model of Rosktoker we can compute the drag for sheets of equal mass. There turns out to be two effects. First, due to the recoil of the test sheet the change in velocity of the colliding sheets is $-v$ rather than $-2v$. (v is the relative velocity of the two sheets.) Second, due to the recoil the relative velocity of a sheet with respect to the test sheet must be 2 times larger before it can cross the potential barrier. The first effect will decrease the drag by a factor of 2. However, the second effect increases the drag by a factor of 4 since it increases v_c by the factor 2 [see (35)]. Thus one would expect a net increase of a factor of 2. The numerical results, however, indicate that the drag predicted by (36) is already too large.

A number of other effects were neglected in the derivation of (36). For one, the effective mass of the sheet was assumed to be its actual mass. In reality, it would be slightly different, but this effect appears to be small (of the order of 10% for the case shown in Fig. 8).

There appears to be one possible effect which might account for the discrepancy. If one assumes that a sheet plus its Debye cloud constitute an entity and that one should add to the force on the particle the force on its Debye cloud one finds that the net force is reduced and that v_c is smaller by a factor of 2. This would correct for both the finite mass effect and the fact that (36) is already too large. Almost perfect agreement would be obtained if this were done. If two sheets are held at a fixed distance apart then (37) does indeed give the external force required to hold them there. However, the collisions which are involved here take times of the order of $1/\omega_p$, and for such rapid changes it may well be that the particle and its cloud behave like an entity. The cloud is not able to come to equilibrium with the surrounding plasma. An understanding of this discrepancy might lead to a clearer understanding of the behavior of the Debye cloud during a collision. Any effects of this type would not be so important in three dimensions since there the drag is due mainly to sideways deflection which would be only slightly affected.[9a]

3. *Diffusion in Velocity Space*

A quantity which is closely related to the drag on a sheet is the rate of diffusion in velocity space. For a system where collisions are weak these two quantities are related by the Fokker-Planck equation[10]

$$\frac{\partial f}{\partial t} + \frac{\partial}{\partial v} A(v)f(v) - \frac{1}{2}\frac{\partial^2}{\partial v^2} B(v)f(v) = 0. \tag{38}$$

Here $A(v)$ and $B(v)$ are the rate of slowing down and rate of spreading in velocity space for particles with velocity v. They are given by

$$A(v) = \lim_{\Delta t \to 0} \frac{1}{\Delta t} \int dv' \, (v' - v) P(v \mid v', \Delta t), \tag{39}$$

$$B(v) = \lim_{\Delta t \to 0} \frac{1}{\Delta t} \int dv' \, (v' - v)^2 P(v \mid v', \Delta t), \tag{40}$$

where $P(v \mid v', \Delta t)$ in the probability that a particle which has velocity v at $t = 0$ will have velocity v' at $t = \Delta t$. When the system is in equilibrium $\partial f/\partial t$ must equal zero. Thus if f is a Maxwell distribution, we obtain Eq. (41) relating $A(v)$ and $B(v)$.

$$A(v) \exp\left(\frac{-v^2}{2V_T^2}\right) - \frac{1}{2}\frac{\partial}{\partial v} B(v) \exp\left(-\frac{v^2}{2V_T^2}\right) = 0. \tag{41}$$

$B(v)$ must be a symmetric function of v so that its derivative must be zero for v equal to zero. Thus, for velocities near zero we have

$$(2V_T^2/v)A(v) = -B. \tag{42}$$

From the drag formula (36) and Eq. (42) we find that for v equal to zero B is given by

$$B(0) = [2\,\delta V_T/(2\pi)^{\frac{1}{2}}]\omega_p^2. \tag{43}$$

[9a] *Note added in proof.* In a private communication M. Feix and O. Eldridge of General Atomic Corporation have informed the author that if one calculates the drag on a test sheet from the linearized Vlasov equations using the method of Landau[11] one obtains the correct drag for a slow sheet. The author has checked this. Where the argument given in this paper is wrong is not known.

[10] N. Wax, editor, *Selected Papers on Noise and Stochastic Processes* (Dover Publications, Inc., 1954), p. 33.

TABLE I.

V_T	δ	B_c	B_{theoret}	B_c/B_T
10.5×10^{-3}	10^{-3}	$(5.0 \pm 0.5) \times 10^{-6}$	8.4×10^{-6}	0.60
5.25×10^{-3}	10^{-3}	$(2.1 \pm 0.2) \times 10^{-6}$	4.2×10^{-6}	0.50
22.6×10^{-3}	5×10^{-3}	$(45.0 \pm 5) \times 10^{-6}$	90.4×10^{-6}	0.50

For low velocities it is much easier to measure B than A because A goes to zero with v while B does not.

Table I shows a comparison of the values found for $B(0)$ at three different temperatures with the values predicted by (43). The numerical values are 40% to 50% lower than those predicted by (43). They are in agreement with the drag found for particles with velocity $0.56V_T$.

4. *Relaxation Time*

For small departures from a Maxwell distribution the system will relax to equilibrium in a time roughly equal to the time it takes a slow particle to be stopped, or the length of time it takes a group of particles with a definite velocity to spread out into a Maxwell distribution. From (36) or (43) we find that this time is of the order of τ,

$$\tau \simeq (2\pi)^{\frac{1}{2}} D/\omega_p \delta. \tag{44}$$

There is, of course, no true relaxation time. The drag on fast particles is proportionately less than on slow particles and thus they take longer to stop. Nevertheless, (44) gives roughly the length of time a fluctuation will last or the time required for the plasma to forget the state it is in. If we want two measurements of the velocity distribution to be statistically independent, we should make them at times separated by an interval greater than τ.

D. Drag on a Fourier Mode (Landau Damping)

We may ask the question, what is the drag on a Fourier mode? Landau[11] in his treatment of plasma oscillations was the first to compute such a drag or damping for a plasma in which long-range forces dominate (short-range collisions negligible). His method and results can be applied directly to the one-dimensional plasma. For waves with phase velocities high compared to the thermal velocity the frequency ω and damping γ are given by

$$\omega^2 = \omega_p^2 + 3k^2 V_T^2, \tag{45}$$

$$\gamma = \frac{\pi}{2} \frac{\omega_p^2}{k^2} \omega \left(1 - \frac{k}{\omega} \frac{d\omega}{dk}\right) f'\left(\frac{\omega}{k}\right), \tag{46}$$

with the electric field going like

$$E = E(x) e^{(i\omega - \gamma t)}$$

To check (45) and (46) for the one-dimensional plasma we must obtain averages similar to those used in finding the drag on a particle. However, the Fourier modes differ from the particles in that the modes behave like oscillators rather than like free particles. Their orbits in their phase planes (the A_k, $\dot{A}_k$ plane, where A_k is the amplitude of mode k) will be roughly circular. To obtain the appropriate average we proceed as follows. We mark out a small region of the phase plane and look for times (t_0's) when the mode is in this desired region. Every time we find the mode in this region we follow it forward in time for awhile. We then take averages of many such observations to obtain the average motion as a function of $t - t_0$.

One modification was made on this procedure. If we let ρ and θ be polar coordinates in the plane then it was assumed that the average orbit was a function of $\theta - \theta_0$, ρ, $t - t_0$, where θ_0 is the θ coordinate of the small region of phase space which was marked out. Thus, it was assumed that orbits starting out with different θ_0 will be similar and differ only by the phase θ_0. The average motion was found as a function of $\theta - \theta_0$ and was averaged over all θ_0 as well as t_0. Thus a ring was used for the small element of phase space. This was necessary to obtain enough samples for good statistics.

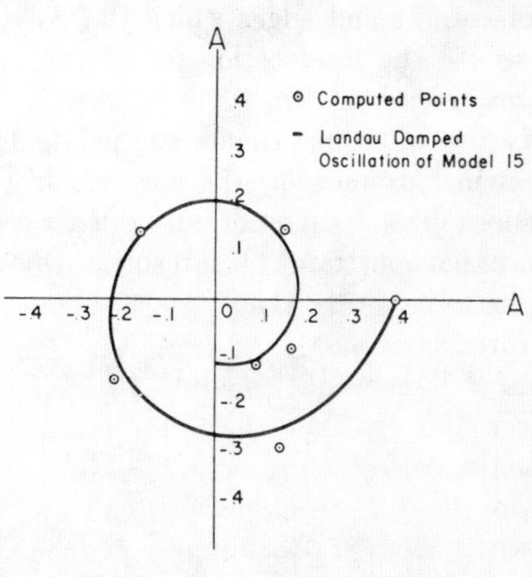

FIG. 9. The Landau damping of Fourier mode.

[11] L. Landau, J. Phys. (U. S. S. R.) **10**, 25 (1946).

Figure 9 shows the average motion of mode 15 for a 1000-sheet system with a Debye length of 10.5 intersheet spacings. The smooth curve is that predicted by the Landau theory. While the average orbit spiraled into the organ, the group spread out to fill Maxwell distribution about the organ.

The agreement is quite good and is within the statistical accuracy of the points. The orbit in the phase plane shows that not only the damping, but also the frequency is given correctly by the theory.

The wavelength for this mode was 133, ($2 \times 1000/15$), intersheet spacings, its frequency ω was $1.29\omega_p$, its phase velocity was 2.6 times the thermal velocity and its damping time was $6.7/\omega_p$.

E. Amplitude Distribution Function for the Fourier Modes

If we wish to find the amplitude distribution function for mode j for thermal equilibrium, we must evaluate the following expression:

$$P(A_j) = \frac{\int \cdots \int \exp\left(-\frac{m\omega_p^2 A_j^2}{2KT}\right) \prod_{\substack{l=1 \\ l\neq j}}^{N} dA_l \exp\left(-\frac{m\omega_p^2 A_l^2}{2KT}\right)}{\int \cdots \int \prod_{l=1}^{N} dA_l \exp\left(-\frac{m\omega_p^2 A_l^2}{2KT}\right)}. \tag{47}$$

The integration is to be carried out over the interior of the N-dimensional polyhedron bounded by the surfaces

$$X_i = X_{i+1} - \delta \tag{48}$$

(see the section on the model). We can write conditions (48) in terms of the Fourier modes by making use of Eq. (6). The constraints written in this manner are given by

$$\left(\frac{2}{N+1}\right)^{\frac{1}{2}} \sum_j A_j \left\{ \sin\left[\frac{(i+1)j\pi\ \delta}{L}\right] - \sin\left(\frac{ij\pi\ \delta}{L}\right)\right\} = \left(\frac{2}{N+1}\right)^{\frac{1}{2}} \cdot \sum_j 2A_j \sin\left(\frac{j\pi\ \delta}{2L}\right) \cos\left[\frac{(i+\frac{1}{2})j\pi\ \delta}{L}\right] = \delta. \tag{49}$$

The constraints (49) give the limits of integration for (47). They are very complicated and it is not possible to work with them directly. The complication comes about because of the large number of corners and edges which the polyhedron has. These are the intersection of two or more of the surfaces given by (49).

We may try and approximate the polyhedron by a surface which rounds off the corners. If the set of equations (49) are squared and added we obtain such an average constraint. The result of this operation leads to

$$\frac{2}{N+1} \sum_{j,l,i} 4A_j A_l \sin\left(\frac{j\pi\ \delta}{2L}\right) \sin\left(\frac{l\pi\ \delta}{2L}\right) \cdot \cos\left[\frac{(i+\frac{1}{2})j\pi\ \delta}{L}\right] \cos\left[\frac{(i+\frac{1}{2})l\pi\ \delta}{L}\right] = \sum_j 4A_j^2 \sin^2\left(\frac{j\pi\ \delta}{2L}\right) = N\delta^2 = \frac{L^2}{N}. \tag{50}$$

The first equality comes from summing on i and making use of the following orthogonality relation:

$$\sum_i \cos\left[\frac{(i+\frac{1}{2})j\pi\ \delta}{L}\right] \cos\left[\frac{(i+\frac{1}{2})l\pi\ \delta}{L}\right] = \frac{N\ \delta_{jl}}{2}.$$

Here δ_{jl} is the Kronecker δ. Equation (50) is the equation for an ellipsoid. The coordinate axis A_j lies along the axis of the ellipsoid.

We can make some comparisons of the ellipsoid with the polyhedron. First the volume of the ellipsoid V_e is given by

$$V_e = \frac{L^N(\pi/4N)^{N/2}}{\Gamma[\frac{1}{2}(N+2)]} \prod_{j=1}^{N} \left[\sin\left(\frac{j\pi\ \delta}{2L}\right)\right]^{-1}. \tag{51}$$

If we take the log of (51) and approximate the sum which appears by an integral and use Sterling's approximation for the gamma function, then we find that V_e is closely approximated by (52).

$$\ln V_e = N\left(\ln L - \ln N + \frac{1}{2}\ln\frac{e\pi}{4}\right) - \frac{2N}{\pi}\int_0^{\frac{1}{2}\pi} \ln(\sin x)\, dx = N\left(\ln\frac{L}{N} + \frac{1}{2}\ln\frac{e\pi}{4} + \ln 2\right), \tag{52}$$

$$V_e = (e\pi)^{\frac{1}{2}N}(L/N)^N.$$

The volume of the polyhedron V_p is given by Eq. (53):

$$V_p = \int_{-\delta}^{x_2+\delta} dx_1 \int_{-2\delta}^{x_3+\delta} dx_2 \cdots \int_{-n\delta}^{x_{n+1}+\delta} dx_n \cdots \int_{-N\delta=-L}^{\delta} dx_n. \tag{53}$$

Carrying out the integration we find

$$V_p = L^N/N! \simeq (eL/N)^N. \quad (54)$$

The ratio of the volume of the ellipsoid to the volume of the polyhedron is

$$V_e/V_p = (\pi/e)^{\frac{1}{2}N}. \quad (55)$$

If all the dimensions of the ellipsoid were shrunk by the factor $(\pi/e)^{\frac{1}{2}} = 1.075$ the ellipsoid would have the same volume as the polyhedron. Shortly, we will use the ellipsoid to compute the amplitude distribution functions for the Fourier modes. The agreement that is obtained with the computed distribution function indicates that no such correction is needed.

Another comparison we can make between the ellipsoid and the polyhedron is the distances between the origin and the points of intersection of the Fourier mode axis with the two surfaces. For the ellipsoid these distances can be obtaimed directly from (50) and are given by

$$d_j = \frac{L}{2N^{\frac{1}{2}} \sin (j\pi\ \delta/2L)}. \quad (56)$$

To find these distances for the polyhedron, we must find the minimum value of A_j which will satisfy the constraint conditions (49) when all other A's are zero. A close approximation to this is obtained by setting $\cos [(i + \frac{1}{2})j\pi\delta/L]$ equal to 1. We thus find

$$d_j = \left(\frac{N+1}{2}\right)^{\frac{1}{2}} \frac{\delta}{2 \sin (j\pi\ \delta/2L)}$$

$$\cong \frac{L}{(2N)^{\frac{1}{2}} 2 \sin (j\pi\ \delta/2L)}. \quad (57)$$

The two quantities are the same function of j and differ only by a factor $\sqrt{2}$.

Turning again to the problem of finding $P(A_j)$ we substitute the ellipsoidal boundary given by (50) for the polyhedron surface given by (49). We will make one further approximation; that the potential energy in all modes except the jth is small compared to KT, i.e.,

$$m\omega_p^2 A_l^2/2KT \ll 1.$$

When the Debye length is large compared to the intersheet spacing this assumption will be found to be valid for almost all modes. With these two approximations the integrals appearing in the numerator of (47) simply give the volume of the $(N-1)$-dimensional ellipsoid whose equation (58) is obtained directly from (50).

$$\sum_{l \neq j} 4A_l^2 \sin^2 \left(\frac{l\pi\ \delta}{2L}\right) = \frac{L^2}{N} - 4A_j^2 \sin^2 \left(\frac{j\pi\ \delta}{2L}\right). \quad (58)$$

The volume of this ellipsoid is given by

$$V = \left(\frac{\pi}{N-1}\right)^{\frac{1}{2}(N-1)} \frac{[L^2/N - 4A_j^2 \sin^2 (j\pi\ \delta/2L)]^{\frac{1}{2}N}}{\Gamma(\frac{1}{2}N)} \cdot \prod_{l \neq j} \left[2 \sin\left(\frac{l\pi\ \delta}{L}\right)\right]^{-1}$$

$$= C \exp [-A_j^2(2N^2/L^2) \sin^2 (j\pi\ \delta/2L)]. \quad (59)$$

The constant C depends on N but has no A_j dependence. With this value for the integral we find upon substituting in (47) that $P(A_j)$ is proportional to (60).

$$P(A_j) \propto \exp \left[-A_j^2\left(\frac{m\omega_p^2}{2KT} + \frac{2N^2}{L^2} \sin^2 \frac{j\pi\ \delta}{2L}\right)\right]. \quad (60)$$

In the limit of small j and large L, (61) takes the form

$$P(A_j) \propto \exp \{-A_j^2[(m\omega_p^2/2KT) + \tfrac{1}{2}k^2]\}, \quad (61)$$

where $k = j\pi/L$. One also obtains (61) if one takes $P(A_j)$ to be given by

$$P(A_j) \propto e^{-\psi(A_j)/KT}, \quad (62)$$

where ψ is the potential of average force required to create the wave. It is the work done against the electrostatic and the pressure force; the pressure being given by the isothermal pressure law, P equals nKT. This approach is equivalent to that given by Bohm and Pines.[12]

The energy density due to a displacement X in this approximation is given by

$$\psi = \tfrac{1}{2}n_0 m\omega_p^2 X^2 + \tfrac{1}{2}n_0 KT(\partial X/\partial x)^2, \quad (63)$$

where the first term is the work done against the electric field and the second term is the work done against the pressure. Taking X to be equal to $(2/N)^{\frac{1}{2}}A_k \sin kx$ and integrating (64) from 0 to L gives (64) for the potential of the average force.

$$\psi = A_k^2[(n_0 m\omega_p^2 L/2N) + (k^2 n_0 KTL/2N)]$$

$$= A_k^2(\tfrac{1}{2}m\omega_p^2 + \tfrac{1}{2}k^2 KT). \quad (64)$$

Substitution of (64) in (62) also gives (61) for $P(A_j)$.

The potential energy of the jth mode $[\int (E^2/8\pi)\, dx]$ is equal to $\frac{1}{2}m\omega_p^2 A_j^2$. The average value of this quantity $\langle\phi_j\rangle$ obtained from (60) is given by

$$\langle\phi_j\rangle = \left[\frac{2}{KT} + \frac{8N^2}{m\omega_p^2 L^2} \sin^2\left(\frac{j\pi\ \delta}{2L}\right)\right]^{-1}. \quad (65)$$

Figures 10 and 11 show a comparison of formula (65) with machine results. Figure 10 shows a plot of $(2\langle\phi_j\rangle/KT)^{\frac{1}{2}}$ vs j for a 1000-sheet system with

[12] D. Pines and D. Bohm, Phys. Rev. 85, 338 (1952).

a Debye length of 10.5 intersheet spacings. The smooth curve is the curve predicted by (65). The agreement is good for all modes beyond the tenth. The explanation of the deviation for the low modes is the following. The initial state of the plasma was such that on the average a mode has an energy of $\frac{1}{2}KT$. The low modes behave like oscillators so that if they did not couple to the rest of the plasma their average potential energy would be $\frac{1}{4}KT$. These modes couple weakly to the rest of the plasma since their phase velocity is much larger than the thermal velocity (small Landau damping). Thus the modes below 10 did not have time to come to equilibrium during the calculations.

Figure 11 shows a similar plot for large j's for a 200-sheet system with a Debye length of 4.5 intersheet spacings. The curve is that predicted by (65).

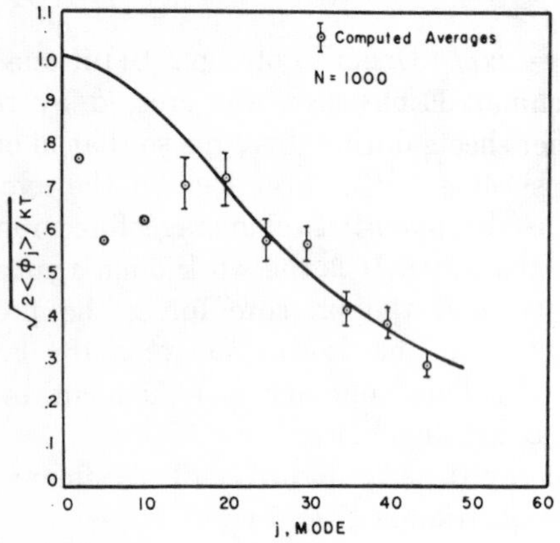

FIG. 10. The root mean square amplitude vs Fourier-mode number.

The agreement is good all the way out to the 200th mode.

For large j Eq. (60) is approximately given by

$$P(A_j) \propto \exp\{-A_j^2[(2N^2/L^2)\sin^2(j\pi/2N)]\}. \qquad (66)$$

For j between $\frac{1}{2}N$ and N the width of this Gaussian varies only slightly (by the factor $\sqrt{2}$). Because of this all these modes have nearly the same probability distributions for A_j and so we can take the average amplitude distribution for these modes. Since the Fourier modes, unlike the sheets, are not identical, this rough equivalent of the high modes is important in obtaining good statistics.

Figure 12 shows the average amplitude distribution function for modes 100 to 200 for the 200-sheet system mentioned above. The smooth curve is the average Gaussian for this group. Again the agreement is very good confirming the accuracy of (60).

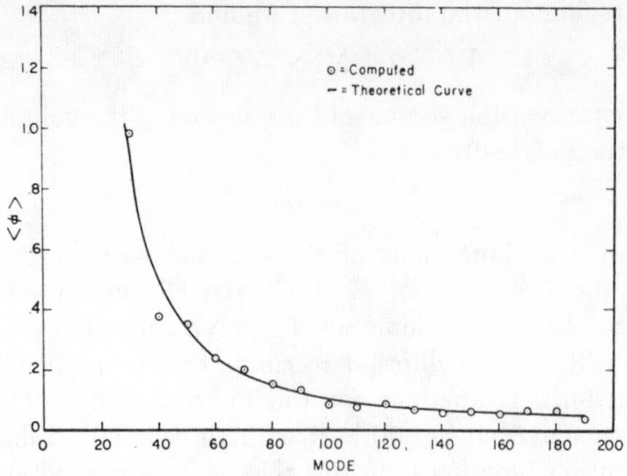

FIG. 11. Average potential energy vs Fourier-mode number.

F. Distribution of Displacements from Instantaneous Equilibrium Position or of the Electric Fields Felt by the Sheets

Let us investigate the distribution of displacements from instantaneous equilibrium position. By Eq. (1) this is equivalent to finding the probability that a sheet feels an electric field $E = 4\pi e n_0 X$. This problem is most easily attacked by picking out one sheet, a test sheet, and treating it like an oscillator (see the section on the model) while the other sheets are treated as a gas of freely interpenetrating sheets which, however, cannot pass through the test sheet. We will compute the potential of the average force.

Let the test sheet be displaced a distance X from its equilibrium position. By Eq. (1) the electric field at the sheet is equal to $4\pi e n_0 X$. The rest of

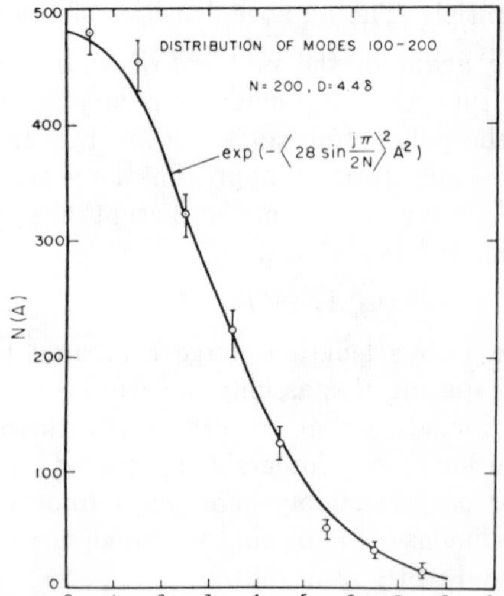

FIG. 12. Average amplitude distribution function for large J modes.

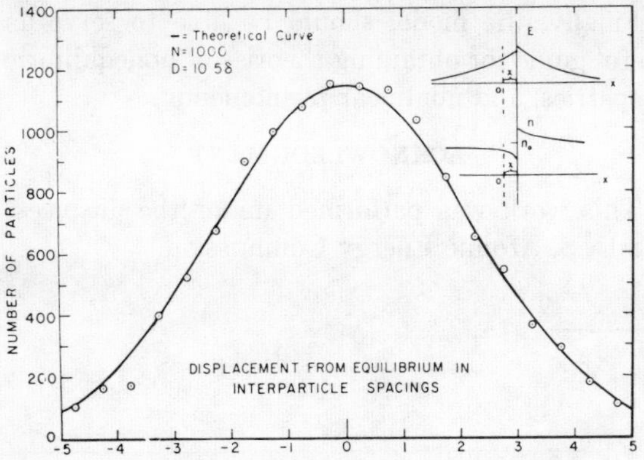

FIG. 13. Distribution of displacements from equilibrium position.

the plasma will shield itself from this electric field and the E field will die out exponentially with distance from the sheet. Taking the sheet's position (not its displacement from equilibrium) as zero, the electric field is given by

$$E = 4en_0Xe^{-|x|/D}. \tag{67}$$

Here X is the displacement from equilibrium and the field due to the sheet itself is neglected. The potential on the positive side of the sheet with respect to $+\infty$ is given by (68), while the potential on the negative side with respect to $-\infty$ is given by (69).

$$\phi_+ = +4\pi en_0X\, De^{-x/D}, \tag{68}$$

$$\phi_- = -4\pi en_0X\, De^{+x/D}. \tag{69}$$

Since there is no direct contact between the gas on both sides of the sheet we can work with these two potentials. The number densities of the gas on the positive and negative sides are

$$n_\pm = n_0 \exp\left(-\frac{e\phi_\pm}{KT}\right) \simeq n_0\left(1 - \frac{e\phi_\pm}{KT}\right). \tag{70}$$

By (68), (69), and (70) there is a jump in density across the test sheet which is equal to Δn,

$$\Delta n = n_+(0) - n_-(0) = 8n_0^2e^2X\, D/KT. \tag{71}$$

As a result there is a pressure difference across the sheet given by (72).

$$P_+ - P_- = KT(n_+ - n_-) = 2n_0\omega_p^2 m\, XD. \tag{72}$$

The average force F per unit area on the sheet produced by both the electric field and the pressure jump is given by

$$F = -m\omega_p^2X(1 + 2n_0\, D), \tag{73}$$

while the potential of the average force is given by

$$\psi = \tfrac{1}{2}m\omega_p^2X^2(1 + 2n_0\, D). \tag{74}$$

The distribution of displacements from instantaneous equilibrium positions is proportional to $\exp(-\psi/KT)$ and is equal to

$$P(x) \propto \exp\left[-(\omega_p^2X^2/2V_T^2)(1 + 2n_0\, D)\right]. \tag{75}$$

Figure 13 shows a plot of $P(x)$ vs X for a system of 1000 sheets with Debye length of 10.5 δ. The smooth curve is that predicted by (75) and the agreement is within the accuracy of the numerical results.

CHECKS ON THE CALCULATIONS

A number of checks were made on the calculations. First, the conservation of energy was checked. It was found that the energy had a tendency to drift down. For the 1000-sheet system with a Debye length of 10.5 the system lost 7 parts in 1000 of its energy during 18 oscillations (2200 time steps on the machine). Each sheet was crossed by roughly 2000 other sheets during this time so that in crossing another sheet a given sheet lost on the average 3 parts in 10^6 of its energy. It was possible to increase the accuracy at the expense of speed by shortening the time step. However, this did not seem worthwhile.

Second, the motion of a 9-sheet system was reversed and found to retrace its path within an accuracy of one part in 10^3 (all orbits were this accurate) over a period of 6 oscillations.

Third, a case was run (9 sheets) when no crossing took place. These were checked against exact analytic results and found to be accurate to a few parts in 10^8 over a period of one oscillation.

Fourth, the drag on the particle was the same in the negative and positive time directions. Thus, even though the calculations had a definite direction, foward in time, the results were symmetric in time. This indicates that computational errors were small.

CONCLUSIONS

The results of these calculations and their agreement with theoretical predictions show that it is possible to check statistical theories and any approximations and assumptions which go into them by following the motion of sufficiently simple models in detail on a high-speed computer.

The good agreement between theory and computation leads to a considerable confidence in the theory. Since the theory that has been used and approximations that have been made are on the whole those which are often employed in plasma physics, the results strongly support their validity. The only result that deviated from the theoretical prediction was that for the drag on a slow sheet. Here the deviation amounts to about 50%. It appears that the theoretical result may depend on the detailed behavior of the Debye clouds for two colliding particles.

Finally, the model should be able to serve as a useful guide for obtaining theories of nonequilibrium properties, and nonlinear phenomenon.

ACKNOWLEDGMENT

This work was performed under the auspices of the U. S. Atomic Energy Commission.